New Writing from the Philippines

LEONARD CASPER is professor of creative writing and contemporary American literature at Boston College. He holds three degrees from the University of Wisconsin, and has taught at Wisconsin, Cornell, Northwestern, and Rhode Island. In 1962/63, he was Fulbright lecturer at Ateneo de Manila, as well as at the University of the Philippines, on whose faculty he had previously served from 1953 to 1956. He has been both a Stanford Fellow in Creative Writing and a Bread Loaf Scholar, as a result of extensive publication of his poetry, fiction, and non-fiction. His articles on Philippine culture have appeared in such periodicals as *Saturday Review*, *Journal of Asian Studies*, and *South Atlantic Quarterly*. He is the author of *Robert Penn Warren: The Dark and Bloody Ground*, editor of *Modern Philippine Short Stories*, and coeditor with T. Gullason of *The World of Short Fiction*. Two volumes of his Philippine literary studies have appeared in Manila since *Six Filipino Poets* (1955). His wife, a Filipina, is both a novelist and a member of the Philippine bar.

New Writing from the Philippines

A CRITIQUE
AND ANTHOLOGY

LEONARD CASPER

Syracuse University Press

Sa aking minamahal,
Linda at Pipit

Preface

New Writing from the Philippines must have had its quiet inception during 1951/52, while I was a Fellow in Creative Writing at Stanford. Wallace Stegner had just returned from a series of traveling interviews with authors in Asia and, in a Saturday Review article, "Renaissance in Many Tongues," had written with special feeling of the Philippine writer's response to incredible conditions. One of those writers, Amador Daguio, lived in the dorm-room across from mine. His personal struggle to prove that he had not died during the war came to epitomize, for me, the effort of his countrymen—and of anyman—to be counted among history's survivors.

Urged by these experiences and by motives more subjective, I went to Quezon City in 1953, to teach and to learn. In most instances, I met authors first, their publications later. My curiosity was drawn to works-in-progress, simply because I could at least comprehend problems of craft even while I remained ignorant of the intricate demands of the writers' situation. Gradually I found myself drifting into formal literary criticism —without having perceived the magnitude of the local need for it, and without fully realizing how closely the critic's travail must resemble the fiction-maker's harrowing effort to achieve, at once, both an intimacy and an objectivity.

Even more gradually, as naivete or stubborn preconception diminished, did textual reading begin to benefit from a knowledge of social contexts. That development was stimulated, to some extent, by research into southern agrarian ideals and rural actualities which found Philippine analogues, while I was revising my Robert Penn Warren: The Dark and Bloody Ground (Seattle: University of Washington Press, 1960); but, to a larger extent, by puzzlement over the behavior of persons long

since pigeonholed and by speculation on the meaning of surprises still in them.

New Writing from the Philippines is one of the consequences of those fifteen years spent as witness and agent to a
literature in formation and a people in search of completion.
By design, it is expected to have an "intimate objectivity" and
"ordered surprises" of its own: for example, a rationale discernible but not so rigid as to stifle the inventive reader's re-
combinations. It is natural, and proper, that each person will
discover his own Philippines; for every country is a mode of encounter: and this fact of experience *New Writing from the
Philippines* tries to reproduce in a number of ways.

The two chapters which constitute the critical text are intended to provide access to Philippine literature in English,
whose personages and themes are exemplified, in part, by the
anthology to which it is attached; and, otherwise, by the checklist of Philippine stories, poems, and plays published in the
United States since 1930, as well as by the bibliography of publications in the Philippines. In turn, these critical chapters
proceed from the initial chapter on the writer's milieu: those
socioeconomic conditions which, historically, have both provoked and prevented the search for cultural continuity; and,
more especially, the climate of the Philippine imagination itself,
including the unremitting reputation of Jose Rizal's nineteenth-
century novels. Appropriately, the placement of the critical
text emphasizes its role as intermediary in the courtship of
literature and society.

The focus of the first critical chapter is on the uneasy coexistence of traditional folk patterns and the impulse toward
social mobility. Most Philippine writers occupy themselves with
the deprivations and consolations of the *provinciano*, the common *tao*, wherever he may reside: on the frontier wilderness or
lonely reaches of tenant farms (Arguilla, Gonzalez, Rotor,
Alfon); or, only partially transported, in metropolitan slums
and suburban eddies (Arcellana, Dizon, Cruz, Aprieto, Florentino). In most cases, a deceptively simple style accompanies this

concern with folk values. Finally, the provincial image is sub-sectioned and studied as "the comic primitive" (Bulosan, Roces, Carunungan) and "the guerrilla warrior" (Laya, Edilberto Tiempo, Javellana). As the *provinciano* finds authority in the role of white-collar professional in the *barrio* or moves into the lower middle class, his moral discomfiture is defined and his follies exposed (Rivera, Edith Tiempo, Guerrero, Cordero-Fernando). But the severest incrimination is reserved for the new *ilustrado*, the ambitious and corruptible bourgeoisie thrusting itself into positions of economic and social management (Jose, Polotan).

The second critical chapter attends to contours and dimensions beyond class distinction, as the Filipino tries to synthesize conflicting allegiances impressed on him by a multiplicity of traditions and a complex of personal roles. Recoiling from the extremist emphasis given either hermetic self (Villa) or society reduced to abstraction (Lopez, da Costa), writers have experimented with epic structures that permit reconciliation of public and private, ancient and present selves (Demetillo, Hufana). A similiar sense of ingathering, of community profoundly reconstructed, is given sometimes a geographical dimension (Santos: the exile's inevitable return), sometimes a historical dimension (Ty-Casper: absorption of all pasts, native and imported). Finally, the search for national identity has occasionally been seen as a counterpart of cosmic alienation and the universal solicitude after spiritual wholeness (Joaquin, Brillantes).

The principle employed in selecting authors to be discussed in detail depended, initially, on their having published at least one book, in English. Admittedly, there are major as well as more-than-promising writers who, for reasons of scruple or the hazards of publication, have not yet released their books: for several years, devotees have awaited Virginia Moreno's "13 Poems" and Wilfrido Nolledo's collection of stories, "Don't Sing Love Songs, You'll Wake My Mother." Out of respect for such caution and in recognition of the difficulty of evaluating works scattered, meanwhile, throughout a nation's periodicals, final judgment has been withheld on these and other authors. Nevertheless, since to ignore them would be equally unfair, they have been represented in the anthology, along with poems which Edith Tiempo reportedly is assembling for the Swallow Press under the working title of "Green Hearts and Other Poems." To these the anthology joins Daguio's "Off the Aleutians," which suggests something of the Filipino's homing instinct; Viray's description of an analogous dis-ease among Manila's minorities; and Torres' two poems which, together, convey the Filipino's fear that some final thunderclap may sound even before past glory and glory of *having* a past (think of the Sung vase, for example, as a relic from the Kalatagan diggings southeast of Manila) are fully recovered. Such poems are variations on themes noticed in novels which, themselves, cannot be reproduced here.

Another principle of selection—literary worth—clearly had to be employed in the rationing of critical comment. The best-selling, but less-than-minor, verses of Rolando Carbonell, *Beyond Forgetting* and *Echoes of the Heart* (which fail even their apparent model, Walter Benton's *This Is My Beloved*), as well as less handsomely packaged volumes by Francisco Tonogbanua and others have been excluded. Inferior writers have been admitted only for instructive purposes; otherwise, the very real "conspiracy of mediocrity," which obtains in the Philippines just as it does elsewhere, has been ignored.

Absences of a very different sort may be noticed by old Manila hands: Maximo Kalaw, Francisco Icasiano, Alfred E. Litiatco, Zoilo Galang, and the like. So dispersed now are the prewar writings of these men and, especially, so fragmentary the contextures from which their associations—human and verbal— took meaning, that any casual report would be impressionistic and incompetent. I leave them to another time or, preferably, to another critic. "New" in this volume's title describes the fact that the literature of less than three decades falls within its scope—just as the volume accepts the limitation of commenting only on Philippine literature reproduced in the original English, without judgment of the growing literature in several vernaculars or in translation.

Taken together, these principles of selection correctly imply that *New Writing from the Philippines* represents, rather than exhausts, the range of contemporary literature. Since a single volume can hardly contain a whole culture, the intention of this collection is to complete, rather than to compete with, whatever Philippine writing has already appeared in the United States. For example, although the anthology is of a quality that any author might envy, virtually none of it duplicates previous American publications. Furthermore, a cardinal reason for constructing the checklist has been to direct congenial readers to their libraries, book dealers, and publishing houses, where more Filipiniana is available.

One last opportunity to open little windows on the ways of Filipinos has been found in the index. There, every word of special acculturation is listed—and glossed in a fashion that, hopefully, will contribute to an understanding beyond textual illumination.

Leonard Casper

Saxonville, Massachusetts
January 1966

Contents

CRITIQUE

ANTHOLOGY

Critique

Stability and Change: The Philippine Experience

FOR BOTH Philippine society and Philippine literature, social realities are as multiple and divergent as ought to be expected of a people with a long, discontinuous, and pluralistic past. Since to be perpetually undefined or only artificially identified is intolerable for man, there is an abiding compulsion in the Filipino to sift through these intricacies, these neglected legacies, for personal and public self-knowledge. There is a radical impulse to take a less limited part in the processes of history. In this collective venture, the writer is an ordinary citizen with an extraordinary facility for sorting out image from mirage, thereby sustaining the dream of human worth.

The Filipino has reason to be an enigma to himself. Thirty million inhabitants are concentrated in relatively few and scattered areas, on islands whose mountain ranges often make direct communication between coasts difficult. In one sense, to be most Filipino is to be regionalistic. This physical separation is reinforced by multiple language barriers. English entered the country by accident and remained chiefly as a practical means of mass education, under monolingual American administrators, but also as a device for linguistic liaison among the dispersed island peoples. Because English as the language of government and education was intended to be no more permanent than American rule itself, an Institute of National Language was created in 1935 to contrive a single, unifying language (now called Pilipino) from nine major vernaculars but chiefly from Tagalog, the language of Manila and its environs. Since independence, for every nationalist denouncing the presence of English there has been a regionalist denouncing Pilipino as Tagalog disguised and nationalized. Loudest outcries come from Visayan Filipinos who inhabit the central and adjacent southern islands and constitute roughly half the Christian Filipino population.[1]

Above all, the Philippines historically has been a crossroads for diverse Malayan, Mediterranean, and American influences. As a result, its performance as Christian and democratic model for Asia is sometimes anomalous. Occasionally the culture betrays an uneasy coexistence between pagan and Christian practices and attitudes. In 1964, over 86 per cent of the people were registered as Catholics (5 per cent are Aglipayan schismatics dating from the Revolution; 4 per cent Protestant; and 4 per cent Moslem): but there is only one priest for every 6,320 Catholics, and only 317 of 2,184 priests in religious orders are Filipinos.[2] Similarly, political democracy has had to adapt to a society built on interpersonalism, nepotism, and hierarchies of dependence. Although provincial governors are elected, their administrative department heads are appointed by their Manila counterparts. In half the chartered cities, mayors are appointed by the president. Governors and mayors may be replaced for cause by Malacañang. As for the villages, until 1957 barrio lieutenants were appointed by municipal councilors.[3]

After the Philippines' separation from other insular Southeast Asians was forcibly caused by conquest, its progress toward self-identification has had to adapt to roles conceived for the Filipino by a variety of colonial temperaments and occupation policies during nearly four centuries of suppression. At a USIS-sponsored symposium on literature and society held in suburban

[1] A fair representation of positions argued for several decades can be found in the "Babel of Tongues" issue of the *Philippines Free Press*, Jan. 12, 1963. See also the remarks of James F. Donelan, S.J., on the effect of improper English on the Philippine novelist's forcefulness: "The Future of the Filipino Novel," in *Literature at the Crossroads* (Manila: Florentino, 1965), pp. 42–50.

[2] Jaime Bulatao, S.J., "A Social-Psychological View of the Philippine Church," in appendix to Jose Vicente Braganza, S.V.D., *The Encounter* (Cebu City: University of San Carlos, 1965), p. 201.

[3] David Wurfel, "The Philippines," in *Governments and Politics of Southeast Asia*, 2nd ed., ed. George McTurnan Kahin (Ithaca: Cornell University Press, 1964), pp. 738–39.

Manila early in 1964, a prediction was made that the Philippine experience, when finally documented, would display unity without uniformity. Horacio de la Costa, S.J., one of the foremost Philippine historians, counseled his countrymen that "we must steel ourselves against the shock of finding somewhere in this vast area an Asian nation of Malay stock, socially structured on a basically Indonesian pattern, containing a large infusion of Chinese blood and attitudes, but with a cultural heritage in part Spanish, in part Anglo-Saxon." [4] He, and others, understand only too well the resentment of the Filipino against dependence on strangers for his cultural description; and his consequent tendency to define himself just as oversimply, but with reverse emphasis.

The average American—if, influenced by the general silence of U.S. mass media, he thinks of the Filipino at all—is likely to picture him as someone rescued in 1898 from deprivation and perhaps from depravities both indigenous and induced; and nourished sacrificially ever since, until he has become indistinguishable from the creditor whose goods he imports so lavishly. In self-defense and under the influence of postwar partisan nationalism, a Filipino may feel compelled to assert so vehemently that he is not American that, at times, he may be considered anti-American. Yet he is gradually forced to realize that, though he may properly reject histories written for him by others, he cannot escape history itself. He cannot refrain from choosing among actualities which of his many inherited tracks of experience he will follow.

Especially from his literature there emerges a constant, if often unself-conscious, image of the Filipino as a stranger in his own country and to much of his own past; and this recurring image compels an urgency in him to account for what he is, rather than for what he is not. The increasingly clear impulse among Philippine writers is to struggle toward a national self-

[4] [Alberto Florentino, ed.], *Literature and Society: A Symposium on the Relation of Literature to Social Change* (Manila: Florentino, 1964), p. 103.

knowledge which is positive without being false; and which, through its art, is particularized and humanized enough to avoid being fantasy or formula.[5]

The Philippines is the oldest, and one of the most stable, postwar republics; but an independent identity less than half a century old may seem too recent to be secured against artificiality; and because dreaming forward too far has its own dangers, Filipinos have tried to stretch the period of their republic's existence back to the end-of-the-century revolutions. Since 1962, June 12 has been celebrated as Philippine Independence Day, in commemoration of the 1898 proclamation of a provisional government by Emilio Aguinaldo, who commanded Philippine forces in rebellion against Spain, and in proud repudiation of inferences drawn from having borrowed America's Independence Day since 1946. Whatever his identity, the Filipino knows that it was earned, and not donated.

Sometimes, in his more desperate moments, he has been tempted to reject all American and Spanish influences as alien and to pursue his essence, instead, in the image of the non-Christian tribesmen from the massive *cordillera* of northern Luzon, or the never-wholly-conquered Moros (now more respectfully referred to as Moslems) from the Sulu Archipelago, or perhaps even the pygmy Negritos. The instinct to take pride in the indigenous peoples is not without some precedent: in 1890, Jose Rizal, propagandist for equal rights, published in Paris an extensively annotated version of Antonio de Morga's *Sucesos de las Islas Filipinas* (1609). From his personal investigations at the British Museum, Rizal verified the high level of pre-Spanish culture recorded by de Morga.[6]

Furthermore, since traditionally the pagan mountaineer and the Moro have been considered outsiders by society at large, their

[5] In *Identity and Change: Towards a National Definition* (Manila: Solidaridad, 1965), his first published book in the Philippines, Carlos P. Romulo comments on typical considerations being weighed by his countrymen today.

[6] The first Philippine edition was made available in Manila in 1958. A subsequent edition appeared in 1962, under the imprint of the Jose Rizal National Centennial Commission.

partial recovery is a sign of national maturation. The ethnohistorical studies made by Barton, Vanoverbergh, Lambrecht, and Garvan [7] during the first half of this century have influenced the scrupulous method and lack of condescension in such recent research as Maceda's into the Mindanao Negritos and the Institute of Philippine Culture's into the art and mores of Sulu.[8] One can foresee the day when fact-gathering will provide some reliable measurement of cultural continuity among all the ethnic groups as well as, through vestiges still intact, between ancient and modern times. In the interim, however, the Philippine intellectual candidly admits that the motive for his own nonprofessional interest in his non-Christian brothers is a romantic one: they are the image of his inviolable self. He would be the first to resent any foreign stereotype of himself as a primitive in G-strings, standing tarsier-eyed at the jungle's edge. With Rizal, he understandably chooses to emphasize the more civilized customs of his ancestors and their replicas.

If identification with the proto-Malay or Stone and Bronze Age Indonesian is difficult and unfulfilling, the Filipino is equally reluctant to deprive himself of the most recent four centuries of his existence. His proper compensation, therefore, lies in becoming his own chronicler of these years of foreign domination. For example, *A Short History of the Filipino People* (Quezon City: University of the Philippines, 1960), by Teodoro Agoncillo and Oscar Alfonso, considers pre-1872 history largely lost to Filipinos, because the documents before that date concern the colonials too exclusively: "The mere fact, for instance,

[7] R. F. Barton, *The Half-Way Sun: Life Among the Headhunters of the Philippines* (N.Y.: Brewer and Warren, 1930), *The Kalingas: Their Institutions and Custom Law* (Chicago: University of Chicago Press, 1949), *The Mythology of the Ifugaos* (Philadelphia: American Folklore Society, 1955), *Autobiographies of Three Pagans*, 2nd ed. (New Hyde Park: University Books, 1963); studies made of the Isnegs by Morice Vanoverbergh, C.I.C.M. and of the Mayawyaws by Francis Lambrecht, C.I.C.M., for the Catholic Anthropological Conference in Washington (III and IV, respectively; 1932–41); John M. Garvan, *The Negritos of the Philippines* (Horn, Vienna: Berger, 1964).

[8] Marcelino N. Maceda, *The Culture of the Mamanua* (Cebu City: University of San Carlos, 1964); *Sulu's People and Their Art*, ed. Frank Lynch, S.J. (Quezon City: Ateneo de Manila University, 1963).

that Filipinos were employed as rowers and fighters in Spanish galleons sent to the Moluccas, the Carolines, and elsewhere, is no excuse for discussing those events as if the fate of the Filipinos hinged on them." [9] Instead, attention is diverted to Philippine attempts to repossess their lands and their destinies; and to create a protective solidarity—a nation not by fiat but by need —against their oppressors.

According to such typical reconsiderations, the pioneer inhabitants of the archipelago were fiercely independent of one another, at the time of Magellan's arrival in 1521.[10] Befriended by several, Magellan was slain in battle off Cebu by Chief Lapulapu, who refused to pay tribute to Spain. Partially, however, because the one ship of Magellan's that completed circumnavigation of the globe was so richly laden with spices, the Spanish continued to send expeditions until the centers of population were adequately subjugated.[11] The islands became involved in the galleon trade and were administered from Mexico until 1821. Local rule was managed, in the absence of large numbers of troops, by friars—often acting in a civil capacity—and select men of property to whom tax-collecting was farmed out. Representation of the Philippines in the Spanish Cortes was erratic and never included an *indio*; it ceased altogether in 1837. Before 1863, there was no public school system; and, afterward, a nominal system only. In response to such conditions, major uprisings

[9] Horacio de la Costa, S.J., however, argues in *Literature and Society*, p. 5, that although "much of the material is written by Spaniards for Spaniards, the native population was of vital concern to them." To examples cited in his speech or evident in his detailed *The Jesuits in the Philippines, 1581–1768* (Cambridge: Harvard University Press, 1961) could be added Felix Keesing's *Ethnohistory of Northern Luzon* (Stanford: Stanford University Press, 1962), an amazing accumulation of data on the mountain people, from Spanish sources.

[10] David Wurfel remarks in *Governments and Politics of Southeast Asia*, p. 679, that the Philippines "is the only nation in Southeast Asia which became subject to Western colonialism before it had developed a centralized governmental structure ruling over a large territory or an advanced elite culture that customarily grew up around a royal court. The consequence of this are far-reaching."

[11] In honor of permanent Spanish influence, which began with the arrival of the Legazpi expedition in 1565, the fourth centennial of Christianity in the Philippines was celebrated in 1965. See the *Philippines Free Press* special issue, May 1, 1965.

occurred in every century (the large island of Bohol, for example, was kept from Spanish hands for over eighty years). However, because most of the revolts were only locally organized, few were long-lived.

Reflecting disturbances in the homeland itself, sixty-one changes of governor general occurred in the islands between 1806 and 1898. Civil war (1868) in the Spanish peninsula had some liberalizing effect on the rights of Spanish subjects but not on the Overseas Ministry. Nevertheless, encouraged by this fact as they had been previously by the granting of Mexican independence in 1822, and confirmed in cosmopolitan concepts as a result of the newspaper's introduction to Manila in 1822, the Suez Canal's opening in 1869, and their own occasional opulence which permitted study in Europe, Philippine *ilustrados* began to campaign for reforms. In Madrid, a number of Propagandists (including Rizal, Lopez Jaena, Marcelo del Pilar, and others) contributed to *La Solidaridad*, the reform newspaper, from 1889 to 1895. Rizal's novels, *Noli Me Tangere* (1887) and *El Filibusterismo* (1891), advocated not separation but assimilation of *indios* as first-class citizens.

In retaliation, the Spanish exiled Rizal to Mindanao, in 1892, where he rejected as premature attempts by Andres Bonifacio, self-educated *Supremo* of the Katipunan underground, to solicit his aid in managing an immediate uprising. Instead, Rizal removed himself from complicity by enlisting as a doctor to serve Spanish troops in Cuba. However, when Bonifacio's men set fire to the outskirts of Manila, Rizal's ship was stopped at Barcelona, and he was arrested and returned to the Philippines for summary trial and execution in December of 1896. Early in 1897, Bonifacio clashed with Emilio Aguinaldo over the question of leadership; he was found guilty of treason and, with his brother, was executed in May. Within months, the Spanish sued for peace; and Aguinaldo went into exile in Hong Kong, in return for an indemnity of 400,000 pesos which he safeguarded against the next opportunity for revolt.

Then it became America's turn to underestimate the Filipinos. At the outbreak of Spanish-American hostilities early in 1898, the U.S. consul at Singapore invited Aguinaldo to cooperate with Commodore George Dewey. After Dewey's fleet destroyed the Spanish in Manila Bay during a one-day engagement, May 1, the American campaign stalled for lack of policy. Too late the Department of State sent word not to enter into unauthorized negotiations with Aguinaldo because Congress, urged at first by Theodore Roosevelt and Henry Cabot Lodge and later by lobbyists from the chambers of commerce, was considering an all-out invasion. Few Americans involved knew more about the Philippines than that it presented an opportunity for a Pacific coaling station en route to an opening China. Dewey wrote Washington, in surprise, that "these people are superior in intelligence and more capable of self-government than the natives of Cuba," [12] whose independence had already been guaranteed by the United States.

By the time American troops arrived in July, Aguinaldo's forces were already laying successful siege to Manila and, north at Malolos, had proclaimed the republic's independence and ratified an exemplary constitution based on those of Belgium, France, Mexico, and several South American countries. General Thomas Anderson was quick to assure the Filipinos that "in 122 years we have established no colonies." [13] However, Philippine troops had to abandon their trenches to the Americans and were not allowed to enter Manila when it capitulated. Nor were Aguinaldo's emissaries permitted to be present at the Treaty of Paris, in December.

Expansionism clearly had been rationalized by the sanctimonious decision to "civilize and Christianize" the Philippine people before recognizing their independence. The Anti-Imperi-

[12] Quoted in Leon Wolff, *Little Brown Brother: How the United States Purchased and Pacified the Philippine Islands at the Century's Turn* (Garden City, N.Y.: Doubleday, 1961), p. 73.
[13] Quoted in *Ibid.*, p. 101.

alist League of Boston could not prevent annexation. General Elwell Otis, who became commander of the expeditionary forces, increased friction between the two nationalities by falsifying statements of official attitudes. The inevitable armed incident between sentries occurred February 4, 1899. Even then, Aguinaldo offered an armistice; but it was brushed aside, just as the Spanish offer to negotiate, after the *Maine* was sunk, had been ignored. General Arthur MacArthur advanced without hesitation: the Philippine-American War had begun.[14] For the next three years the "insurrectos," fighting largely as guerrilla units, proved themselves to be, in General Henry W. Lawton's words, "the bravest men I have ever seen." [15] American gains were infinitesimal, local, temporary.

Despite the continued assurances of General Otis to Congress that only the Tagalogs, out of several "tribes," were rebelling, Filipinos throughout the archipelago proved remarkably consolidated. Occasionally rivalry split the guerrillas, most notably when General Antonio Luna, a clever tactician but a hotheaded authoritarian, was assassinated by Aguinaldo's elite guards, whose behavior was never punished or even investigated. Portions of the *ilustrado* class collaborated openly; and treacherous natives sometimes betrayed Aguinaldo and his men: an Igorot led to the entrapment and death of twenty-four-year-old General Gregorio del Pilar, fighting a rear-guard action at Tirad Pass; and Macabebe scouts brought Americans into the mountain hideout where Aguinaldo was captured. Still, such acts failed to end the war, just as before them the desperate use of water torture, dumdums, and civilian executions had failed. Despite President William McKinley's proclamation of "benevolent

[14] General Douglas MacArthur, in *Reminiscences* (N.Y.: McGraw-Hill, 1964), p. 19, records that "originally, there was little thought of long occupation; our one desire was to help those seeking independence." Yet shortly, careless of the possible contradiction, he refers to "the insurgent army around Manila" and the "brigands" and "desperadoes" on Iloilo. Officially, in American histories, the struggle for independence is still referred to as the Philippine Insurrection.

[15] Quoted in Wolff, *Little Brown Brother*, p. 290.

assimilation, substituting the mild sway of justice and right for arbitrary rule," [16] it is estimated that over 200,000 Philippine casualties occurred, including deaths from privation, disease, and —in the last stages—brutality comparable with that of Valeriano Weyler y Nicolau, the Spanish "butcher" whom Spain recalled as governor and military commander of Cuba in 1897 in response to American protest about his ruthlessness.[17] After the nearly bloodless conflict with Spain, the death of 4,000 American "liberators" seemed inexplicable, and unforgivable. Finally, in 1902, to put an end to this horrific impasse, the Philippine survivors accepted the Taft Commission, sent by the U.S. to substitute civil government for martial law, and entered the unspecified period of preparation for Commonwealth status and independence.

The initial military betrayal of Philippine aspirations was somewhat ameliorated by Taft's civil rule. Although still not independent, Filipinos enjoyed immediate exercise of many rights withheld by colonial Spain.[18] Codified Spanish civil law was supplemented by Anglo-American case law. The temporal power of churches was limited; still, religious freedom itself grew even when local custom technically violated general laws, such as monogamy. Above all, freedom found meaningful instrumentation through extensive health programs and public education. In thirty-five years, the number of public school children increased 1,000 per cent; life expectancy nearly tripled; infant mor-

[16] McKinley's Proclamation of Dec. 21, 1898, is reproduced in extended excerpt in Teodoro Agoncillo and Oscar Alfonso, A Short History of the Filipino People (Quezon City: University of the Philippines, 1960), p. 277.

[17] Wolff, Little Brown Brother, p. 360. See also General Emilio Aguinaldo and Vicente Albano Pacis, A Second Look at America (N.Y.: Robert Speller and Sons, 1957).

[18] See Joseph Ralston Hayden, The Philippines: A Study in National Development (N.Y.: Macmillan, 1942), in many ways the definitive work on the American occupation and the Commonwealth years; O. D. Corpuz, The Bureaucracy in the Philippines (Quezon City: University of the Philippines, 1957); Theodore Friend, Between Two Empires: The Ordeal of the Philippines, 1929–1946 (New Haven: Yale University Press, 1965). Although Friend's emphasis is on the effect of American and Japanese imperialism on Asia's first republic, some attention is also given to the earlier Spanish-American and to the more recent American-Com-Chinese confrontations of influence.

tality was reduced from 80 to 5.4 per cent; control of dysentery, beriberi, smallpox, cholera, and leprosy (but, only to a lesser degree, tuberculosis) set a standard for all of Asia. Just as exemplary was the civil service developed in the islands when only three American states had any civil service at all: but other forms of political health were only sporadically and partially achieved because of American, not Philippine, reluctance. Although the Democrats agreed to annexation only on the understanding that independence was to be granted ultimately, the Republican platform before 1924 made no mention of independence. Significantly, the Philippines was administered under War Department supervision until 1935.

So bitter had been the Philippine-American War (one guerrilla leader, Macario Sakay, refused the amnesty until 1906, and then saw some of his men hanged as bandits), two years of uninterrupted peace were prescribed before self-government beyond the municipal level was permitted. Only in 1907 was a Philippine Assembly elected and a resident commissioner permitted to join debate (without vote) in the U.S. House of Representatives. Political parties were allowed to form, provided that they did not advocate independence.

Although the Philippine Assembly and the court system provided a rich reservoir of leadership (men of the caliber of Manuel Quezon, Sergio Osmeña, Claro Recto and others), Filipinization was slow until, under Woodrow Wilson, Francis Burton Harrison was appointed governor general in 1913 and the Jones Law of 1916 was passed which, by replacing the hybrid Philippine Commission with an all-Filipino legislature, helped create conditions for a stable autonomy which officially had to precede independence. At last what the Democrats characterized as an "experiment in imperialism" was converted into a proper trusteeship.

Harrison's successor, Leonard Wood, however, who served as governor general from his appointment by Warren Harding in 1921 until 1927, created more crises than he solved, by virtually ignoring Philippine legislators. The Hare-Hawes-Cutting

Act, which established a ten-year provisional Commonwealth period, had to be passed in 1933 over Herbert Hoover's veto; and to be refined by the 1934 Tydings-McDuffie Act, which had been recommended to Congress by Franklin D. Roosevelt even while he was aware of its "imperfections or inequalities." [19] Immediately, Philippine jurists in convention drew up a Constitution (based on those of the Americas, Spain, Germany, Italy and Japan) which proved a satisfactory instrument not only for the Commonwealth but for the Republic as well.

The constitutional provision which makes it possible for a president and his vice president to represent different parties was exercised in the very first election. However, Manuel Quezon and Sergio Osmeña restrained their differences, as an example to their country, which they worked to unite more fully through provision of a national language, a larger and more literate electorate, greater economic independence from alien entrepeneurs, and social justice from absentee Philippine landlords.

The third nation to underestimate the Philippine people, Japan clearly doubted the success of these democratic experiments when it bombed Manila (which had been declared an open city) and invaded Luzon, in December, 1941. Quezon's second term of office started on Corregidor, shortly before he and General Douglas MacArthur left to continue the defense of liberty from Washington (Quezon died of tuberculosis, at Saranac Lake, in 1944) and Australia. Shortly after their departure, Bataan fell and Philippine-American troops endured the "Death March" to Tarlac together. Within weeks, Corregidor was also surrendered, after being saturated with almost two million pounds of shells daily during its last stand.

It was argued from the beginning of American rule that independence could be granted only to a people with a stable economy. Yet it has also been estimated that "an independent Philippines could hardly have suffered more from foreign aggres-

[19] Quoted in Agoncillo and Alfonso, *A Short History*, p. 404.

sion than did the Philippines in World War II at a time when it was still under American military protection." [20] Inasmuch as the Commonwealth was not responsible for its foreign relations or for its own defense, the agonies of an occupied people could easily have been reduced by neutralism or total capitulation. Instead, Filipino guerrillas—sometimes under the tactical direction of U.S. soldiers or civilians who refused to surrender when General Jonathan M. Wainwright ordered them to—fought incomparably, and incredibly. Unlike Indonesian nationalists who welcomed the Japanese, Filipinos were generally unwilling "even under pressure, to express disloyalty to the Commonwealth government [in exile] or to show disdain for American constructiveness in the previous forty years." [21]

Tomas Confesor, governor of Iloilo, spoke for them when puppet-President Jose Laurel enjoined compliance with Japanese rule: "We shall never win or deserve the esteem and respect of other nations if we lack principles and if we do not possess the courage and valor to defend those principles at any cost." Rather, it was the collaborator generally who was dishonored—the armed *makapili*, the mercenary, the power-hungry; even Supreme Court Justice Laurel himself, who had been following Quezon's specific instructions to do anything short of changing his oath of allegiance in order to protect the Philippine populace; as well as Judge Claro M. Recto, who argued that since the United States had failed, as sovereign power in the Philippines, to defend the archipelago adequately, no Filipino should be blamed for defecting from a lost cause.[22]

After the Leyte landings of October, 1944, Admiral Ernest J. King advised the Joint Chiefs of Staff to bypass Luzon and attack Formosa and Amoy.[23] General MacArthur, however, in-

[20] George E. Taylor, *The Philippines and the United States: Problems of Partnership* (N.Y.: Praeger, 1964), p. 68.

[21] Friend, *Between Two Empires*, p. 226.

[22] See Claro M. Recto, *Three Years of Enemy Occupation: The Issue of Political Collaboration in the Philippines* (Manila: People's Publishers, 1946).

[23] Samuel Eliot Morison, *The Liberation of the Philippines: Luzon, Mindanao, the Visayas: 1944–1945* (Boston: Atlantic-Little, Brown, 1959), p. 3.

sisted on honoring his promise to liberate the whole of the archipelago. He was seconded by Admiral Raymond A. Spruance, who considered China a less satisfactory approach than Iwo Jima or Okinawa to Tokyo targets. Despite *kamikaze* effectiveness greater than that later off Okinawa, successful landings were made at Lingayen on January 9. The land campaign that followed was the only one in the Pacific which had space for the mass maneuver of troops. Only the drive across northern France exceeded it in the number of armies involved.[24] Consequently, troops trained for amphibious assault lost some of their flexibility in the mountains of northern Luzon and the suicidal street-fighting of Manila.

Errors in command strategy were as costly as tropical diseases and exhausting terrain. Often badly counseled by his chief of intelligence, MacArthur ordered airdrops on towns already open or alternatively underestimated the enemy by as much as 50 per cent; set up unrealistic timetables and shifted troops just when a concentrated drive became critical; and permitted few replacements. The 93,400 nonbattle casualties were the highest in any campaign in the Second World War. After the dramatic dash to rescue 4,000 internees at the University of Santo Tomas,[25] Manila itself had to be reduced by artillery and grenade when air strikes were forbidden (nevertheless, an estimated 120,000 Philippine civilians died as a result of Admiral Sanji Iwabuchi's decision to make the Walled City a fortress and of the atrocities committed by his troops). American paratroopers had to make six-second airdrops onto Corregidor where 5,000 troops, not the expected 850, awaited. What rescued the American effort from its high command was the compensating heroism of American privates leading platoons, the fatalism of starving Japanese committed to delaying actions of attrition, and the decisive force of trained guerrillas who not only turned over most of the beach-

[24] Robert Ross Smith, *Triumph in the Philippines* (Washington: U.S. Government Printing Office, 1963), p. ix.

[25] See A. V. H. Hartendorp, *The Santo Tomas Story* (N.Y.: McGraw-Hill, 1964) for the official, painstaking history of that internment camp.

heads intact but also controlled vast portions of northern Luzon and virtually all of Mindanao.[26] Over 100,000 guerrillas were still "mopping up," at war's end in August, 1945.

When the Philippine Republic finally became official, on July 4, 1946, its economy was a shambles. Four years of war and occupation had reduced crop production to 51.4 per cent; livestock resources, to 38.7 per cent; fish production, to 29 per cent. Because the entire interisland fleet and over 75 per cent of the railroad's rolling stock were lost, the initial loss of hundreds of peso millions in the rice, mining, and sugar industries was heightened by lack of transportation for what remained. Irrigation facilities, farm implements, warehouses, and the like were destroyed almost completely.[27] Manila itself was more devastated than any world capital with the exception of Warsaw. Above all, public morality which had suffered during the dilemmas of war, was further confused by MacArthur's approval of Manuel Roxas, co-collaborator with Laurel, as first president of the Republic (only later was Roxas' service to the Manila Intelligence Group revealed); and by his support of the most conservative, self-interested social elements.[28] Nor did the United States depart, as Great Britain did later in Burma and India, without reserving for herself the right of special participation in Philippine affairs.[29] To add to the confusion, American policy on the payment of war damages and the status of forces agree-

[26] See "Colonel Yay" [Panlilio], *The Crucible* (N.Y.: Macmillan, 1950); R. W. Volckmann, *We Remained* (N.Y.: Norton, 1954); Hignio de Uriarte, *A Basque Among the Guerrillas of Negros* trans. from Spanish by Soledad L. Locsin (Bacolod City: ?, 1962); John Keats, *They Fought Alone* (Philadelphia: Lippincott, 1963).

[27] *The Philippines: A Handbook of Information* (Manila: Philippine Information Agency, 1955), passim; also A. V. H. Hartendorp, *History of Industry and Trade of the Philippines*, I (Manila: American Chamber of Commerce of the Philippines, 1958).

[28] According to Friend, *Between Two Empires*, p. 253, "the initial American years in conquered Japan conferred more benefits than did the final stages of the American presence in the Philippines—an irony not lost on the more progressive Filipinos."

[29] Taylor, *The Philippines and the United States*, p. 132.

ments changed constantly. Furthermore, Congress—against the advice of the State and Commerce departments—engaged in such blackmail tactics as making the Philippine Rehabilitation Act contingent on the acceptance of a parity clause in the 1946 Bell Trade Act.

With the accession to power of Elpidio Quirino upon the sudden death of Roxas in 1948, political corruption fed national cynicism, abetting the revolt of the Huks. Although the Communist party had been outlawed in 1932, its members had successfully infiltrated the Hukbalahap guerrillas who, during wartime, liquidated their countrymen at will and seized evacuated farms. Whatever the legitimacy of their grievances against economic inequities, clearly their motive was to overthrow the government by force of arms. Only Ramon Magsaysay's moral severity restored justice and self respect to the Philippine people. As secretary of national defense, he offered amnesty and resettlement to all Huks who would surrender, and thus broke the power of the Communist Politburo. In an exceptionally honest election in 1953, Magsaysay was made president.

Although the Philippine presidency constitutionally is more powerful than its American counterpart. Magsaysay made himself always accessible to the most common *tao*. His charisma lay in his informed faith in the Filipino. However difficult it sometimes was to implement the policy, his constabulary and special forces were expected to treat "the enemy" as friends in need of respect and deliverance.[30] A Moslem uprising in the South, typically, was settled after fierce combat by extension of political representation. Before his death in a 1957 airplane accident, his programs for agrarian reform had convincingly

[30] See Robert Aura Smith, *Philippine Freedom: 1946–1958* (N.Y.: Columbia University Press, 1958); Napoleon D. Valeriano and Charles T. R. Bohannan, *Counterguerrilla Operations: The Philippine Experience* (N.Y.: Praeger, 1962); Alvin H. Scaff, *The Philippine Answer to Communism* (Stanford: Stanford University Press, 1955); Luis Taruc, *Born of the People* (N.Y.: International Publishers, 1953); William Pomeroy, *The Forest* (N.Y.: International Publishers, 1963).

demonstrated the necessary partnership between economic and political democracy.[31]

All of Magsaysay's energy was directed toward protection of the common *tao's* stake in society. In 1954 alone, three prototype projects to this end were effected: guides against landed oligarchs—the Agricultural Tenancy Act; against Chinese entrepeneurial control—the Retail Trade Nationalization Act; [32] against American sugar and tobacco lobbyists—the Laurel-Langley trade revisions. Filipinos had never been fully reconciled to the provisions of the Bell Trade Act, which they considered made Philippine economy a captive of America by prolonging the nation's agricultural bias while encouraging a lack of diversification in crop production.[33] Taking advantage of the United States' realization of interdependence during the Korean War, Magsaysay managed in the Laurel-Langley revisions to loosen tariff controls and to remove the objectionable parity clause. Furthermore, the rate of increase in customs duties imposed on Philippine goods between 1956 and 1975 became less than the rate placed on imports from America.

During the decade after the Laurel-Langley Agreement, belated recognition by America has been given Philippine aspirations to pursue industrialization. Foreign aid to industry has increased from $1.4 to $37.6 million, while aid to agriculture has dropped from $25.5 to $10.4 million. Because exploration is still in process, the magnitude of Philippine fuel resources, metallic minerals, and hydroelectric potential can only be estimated; [34] but it would seem to be impressive, especially in iron, chromite, and copper.

[31] See Jose V. Abueva, *Focus on the Barrio* (Manila: University of the Philippines, 1959).

[32] See Remigio E. Agpalo, *The Political Process and the Nationalization of the Retail Trade in the Philippines* (Quezon City: University of the Philippines, 1962); also A. V. H. Hartendorp, *History of Industry and Trade of the Philippines*, II (Manila: Philippine Education Company, 1961).

[33] See Shirley Jenkins, *American Economic Policy Toward the Philippines* (Stanford: Stanford University Press, 1954).

[34] Alden Cutshall, *The Philippines: Nation of Islands* (Princeton: Van Nostrand, 1964), pp. 61–7.

Meanwhile, the Philippines remains basically an agricultural nation, as President Carlos P. Garcia's search for more flexible international trade and President Diosdado Macapagal's Five Year Integrated Socio-Economic Program (1962) and his Taiwan-inspired Land Reform Act (1963) have recognized. This continuing fact has been a source of consolation as well as of concern for the committed Philippine intellectual. Candidly reviewing his own history, he has been struck by its complexities and anomalies. Inclined to hero-worship in the Republic's early days when self-confidence was necessary to the establishment of a functioning nationalism, lately he has begun to realize that, like the foreigners in his midst, he too has underestimated the nature of his countrymen, their individuality, the multiplicity of their motives. The same pride that has made him research so diligently the origins of his independence as an entity in the Revolution of 1896 and the Philippine-American War has confronted him with ideological and procedural differences between Rizal and Bonifacio; and has forced revelation of the internecine rivalries among Bonifacio, Aguinaldo, Luna, and other generals, as well as the divisive motives of the *ilustrados* and the peasantry.

Typical of the Philippine historian's integrity is Cesar Adib Majul's *Mabini and the Philippine Revolution* (Quezon City: University of the Philippines, 1960) which traces the dilemmas of Apolinario Mabini, the political philosopher who, though dedicated to individual liberty and republican forms, for the sake of serving the uninstructed masses felt required to urge a military dictatorship on Aguinaldo and wanted himself to reign as chief justice empowered to appoint all other justices and even to propose legislation. The *ilustrados*, foreseeing themselves as future senators, insisted on a Congress that would not be purely advisory. Hence, the Malolos Constitution of 1899 had the republican government which Mabini the idealist had advocated but which Mabini the practical politician thought premature.

Temporarily disoriented by such discoveries (although admitting the need for their eventual accommodation), Filipinos may be tempted to divorce history from culture and to take some reassurance of fixed identity from the relative constancy of the agrarian structuring of their society. Nearly three-fourths of the people are small-scale farmers or fishermen; and although six cities in the Philippines (not counting Manila's suburban communities separately) have populations in excess of 100,000, even these are seaports dependent on plantations in the interior for commerce.

Modern elite groups, like their predecessors, are sometimes charged with being arch-conservatives committed to as much of the *status quo*, at any moment, as they can retain. Often congressmen and local officials simultaneously control commercial enterprises and vast farm tracts and therefore resent being asked to undermine their positions of supremacy by legislating change.[35] These same oligarchic elements compromised the Philippine Revolution, the Philippine-American War, and the land reform bills of Quezon which were remarkably similar to those of Magsaysay twenty years later, except that they were rarely implemented. Only the exceptional oligarch can conceive of change as corrective or progressive. Such a charge is, generally, irrefutable because the nature of Philippine society, and not just of the 1 per cent representing the upper class, has long been conservative. The *damay* or *bayanihan* society has been characterized as a tradition-bound, localistic, group-oriented, authoritarian, personalistic system in which prescribed status supersedes function in importance.[36] Its origins are manifold and self-evident: the smallness of the pioneer *barangays* and their need to be self-reliant in order to survive; infusions of Chinese patriarchism and ancestor worship; Spanish feudalism in church and family, and the usefulness of *caciquism* as a control group in a stratified society; the

[35] Taylor, *The Philippines and the United States*, p. 205.

[36] Chester L. Hunt, *et al., Sociology in the Philippine Setting*, rev. ed. (Quezon City: Phoenix, 1963); Socorro C. Espiritu and Chester L. Hunt, eds., *Social Foundations of Community Development* (Manila: Garcia, 1964); Mary R. Hollnsteiner, *The Dynamics of Power in a Philippine Municipality* (Quezon City: University of the Philippines, 1963).

resistance of American vested interests to the creation of a competitor out of a captive market.

Not least, the cause lies in the primitive and impoverishing method of wet-rice cultivation and of fishing, which the power structure recklessly reinforces more often than reforms. As a result of the 1950 Bell Mission's survey of socioeconomic conditions in the Philippines, Robert S. Hardie undertook an advisory report, *Philippine Land Tenure Reform: Analysis and Recommendations* (Manila: STEM, Mutual Security Agency, 1952), on the causes of agrarian unrest. At that time, 75 per cent of the population and 60 per cent of the GNP were rural. Over 50 per cent of the farms were owner operated, but they averaged less than two hectares (five acres). Tenancy accounted for 35 per cent of the farming group (except in Central Luzon, Huklandia, where tenancy was as high as 50–60 per cent); and 95 per cent of these were sharecroppers, the majority of whom paid over half their gross in kind, as rental. Indebtedness was unavoidable and cumulative, despite occasional gestures of paternalistic benevolence from landlords, which were more than compensated for by usury. Yet all that many tenants asked was not to be removed and replaced! Hardie urged emigration to virgin lands in Mindanao; establishment of land commissions, courts of agrarian relations, cooperatives, and rural banks; government purchase of land and redistribution to owner-cultivators, on a realistic and efficient land-area basis. One of the most startling portions of the Hardie Report, based on such earlier studies as Karl Pelzer's,[37] asserted that rural Philippine poverty was a chronic condition: the only postwar aspect of the phenomenon was its exploitation by Communists.

Despite increasingly enlightened efforts by Magsaysay and the administrations which followed, the Philippines is still burdened by the primitivism of its rural economy. Although its

[37] Karl J. Pelzer, *Pioneer Settlement in the Asiatic Tropics* (N.Y.: American Geographical Society, 1948). For contemporary confirmation of certain aspects of the Hardie Report, see Generoso Rivera and Robert McMillan, *The Rural Philippines* (Manila: Mutual Security Agency, 1952).

"nutritional density" exceeds that of Pakistan, Indonesia, China, Viet Nam or Taiwan, it is a food-deficit country. Its rice yields per hectare are one-half of Malaya's, and three-sevenths of Taiwan's. Furthermore, because its birth rate is one of the world's highest, the amount of available land per capita is rapidly diminishing. Tenant farming continues to increase (it is now between 47 and 58 per cent). Shortsighted use of capital has also prevented development of hybrid corn, high-quality copra (the Philippines is the world's leading exporter but its careless smoke cure lessens the copra's value), or the kind of by-products that can rescue the sugar industry when (after 1974) it no longer receives premium U.S. prices. Domestic fish ponds have multiplied, but there is little commercialized deep-sea fishing. The nation has a near-monopoly on first-class *abacá*, but machine-decortication destroys some of its tensility. Its tobacco is primarily cigar-filler; and it imports an imbalance of American cigarettes. Almost half the land is forested and in public domain, but Japan can buy Philippine timber and undersell Philippine plywood. Interisland shipping is inadequate; and the Manila Railroad's effort to extend the Luzon track south and northeast, beyond the central plains, is intermittent. Short of catastrophe, birth control, greater urban growth and industrialization, or far more efficient intensive farming, no escape from the present economic self-encirclement is evident. Legislation alone offers no sovereign remedy.[38]

Meanwhile, the cultural result is a reinforcement—sometimes beneficial, sometimes harmful—of traditional agrarian folkways. Slight and gradual modifications of course occur in any society, closed or open.[39] Nevertheless, Philippine culture remains essentially defensive, self-conserving. Even without taking into account numerous Asian precedents, the need to husband one's resources,

[38] Robert E. Huke, *et al.*, *Shadows on the Land: An Economic Geography of the Philippines* (Manila: Bookmark, 1963).

[39] For Philippine application, see Agaton P. Pal, "Planned Social Change in a Philippine Barrio," *University of Manila Journal of East Asiatic Studies*, V (October, 1956); Pal, *The Resources, Levels of Living, and Aspirations of Rural Households in Negros Oriental* (Quezon City: University of the Philippines, 1963).

regardless of whether one can be counted among the elite or among the insolvent millions, would be sufficient to explain the authoritarian system of allegiances that still abides within the typical family; the nepotism and bilateral extension that acknowledge primary obligations toward one's bloodlines (as well as to numerous *compadres*); consideration of marriage as an alliance of families and therefore a matter for deliberate prearrangement by elders and intermediaries; communal living; a sensitivity to status, in the name of family esteem, that registers now as shame, now as sentimentality, now as quick anger and compulsive revenge, now as wasteful generosity; the claim of the dead on the living; fatalism that, to reformers, seems indifference or sheer ignorance; an interpersonalism that in its extreme can reduce men to social means. At the same time, the patience and gentility and personal attention of a handicraft culture, to some extent, compensate for the common *tao*'s unprosperous life; and a kind of folk wisdom is accumulated and refined out of centuries of experience. History is memory and invention—an endless meditation on what Faulkner used to call "the verities," in the hope of separating authenticated constant from the mere stammer of trivia and submission to inertia.

Part of this wisdom recognizes that a traditional culture can no more be separated from history than a universal from its particulars. Too many Filipinos have stood erect—at Mactan, at Biak na Bató, at Bataan and Bandung, and at a thousand wayside *puróks*, in homely stances—to pretend contentment ever with a posture of prostration. It would be unnatural. Nor can logic long indict the colonial power, whatever its nationality, whatever the means devised, or the alien in one's midst, or the man of special class and privilege for retarding national growth, without some day summoning one's self to the hearing; and weighing then not only one's own inclination to be stationary but also the evidences and prospects of change, as well as the implication of consequences. If naive pride must diminish, an informed and maturing self-respect must gradually replace it. Every investment, every invention, every exceptional man, every substantial event is an occasion for decision and therefore for redefinition and discovery.

It would be difficult, for example, to imagine the Philippines' disengaging itself from the full international role it has assumed in connection with the United Nations, the Korean War, SEATO, the Pacific Charter, and the Bandung Conference. Recognition has come as neither a gift from condescending big nations nor an accident of history. However, modification of policies appropriate to that role is conceivable, with changing circumstances. "Apprehensive of Japan, fearful of China, watchful of Indonesia, aggravated by India, the Philippines," according to Milton Walter Meyer, "oriented its policies [over the past decade] toward lesser Asian countries and stronger non-Asian states"; and, still unfulfilled, has found its chief stimulation and strength "not in limited Asian pacts, but in extended Western union." [40]

Similarly instructive has been the recent history of Philippine claims to North Borneo (now Sabah). For services rendered the Sultanate of Brunei in 1850, the Sultan of Sulu was awarded thirty-two thousand square miles of Borneo. Great Britain, to which North Borneo was ceded as a crown colony in 1946 by the resident British trading company, has long denied the Sultan of Sulu's rights to the land but has refused to present publicly any definitive documents to support the denial. Resentful of British hauteur, the Philippines has not recognized Malaysia. However, it has pursued its claim with caution, aware of the danger of a common frontier with imperialistic, Communist-complacent Indonesia, which avoided membership in SEATO, refused to participate in the Korean War, sponsored Red China (but not Nationalist China) at Bandung, and later, while refusing to condemn Soviet action in the Hungarian uprising, was first to condemn the British/French/Israeli attack on Suez. [41]

[40] Milton Walter Meyer, A Diplomatic History of the Philippine Republic (Honolulu: University of Hawaii Press, 1965), p. 277.

[41] Ibid., pp. 121–23, 195–96, 219–40; Russell H. Fifield, The Diplomacy of Southeast Asia: 1945–1958 (N.Y.: Harper, 1958), pp. 89–94.

Consequently, even while countering the formation of Malaysia with Maphilindo proposals (to set up a treaty-bound regional entity composed of Malaya, the Philippines, and Indonesia), the Philippines acted to prevent further illegal infiltration of its southernmost islands by thousands of Indons.[42]

Such proposals and negotiations reveal a flexibility and ever-growing interfusion certain to effect the Philippine ethos in the future, as much as the quickening pace of commerce and industrialization,[43] the enlarging ratio of dynamic youth in society, the spread of unionism, emergence of self-made men from every class as modules for imitation, and the recovery of its minorities by the Philippines.

The very complexity of Philippine history and culture, their turbulence and challenge, provoke the writer into intense reassessment and redefinition—just as New England, a century ago, found a cause of some magnitude in the conflict of heritages derived from Calvin and Rousseau; just as America's southern literature today is in creative ferment, stirred by a desperate need to reconcile Christian-agrarian humanism and the doctrine of self-determination with habits of discrimination, or to separate a living and responsible tradition from rigid convention.

Nevertheless, for disorder to propagate order, even the most complex conflict must be more than convulsive, must be given recognizable shapes of awareness through the writer's craft. Otherwise, if subject matter alone were decisive in literature, the simple mirroring of Philippine society would serve as convenient measure for the significance of any published work.[44]

[42] Quentin Reynolds and Geoffrey Bocca, *Macapagal the Incorruptible* (N.Y.: McKay, 1965), pp. 187–89.

[43] See Frank H. Golay, *The Philippines: Public Policy and National Economic Development* (Ithaca: Cornell University Press, 1961); John J. Carroll, S.J., *The Filipino Manufacturing Entrepeneur: Agent and Product of Change* (Ithaca: Cornell University Press, 1965); Cutshall, *The Philippines*, pp. 68–92.

[44] Tempered consideration is given these basic socioesthetic problems by Petronilo Bn. Daroy in his pamphlet, *The Politics of Imagination* (Quezon City:

For, if the dilettante avoids all theories of literature and of society which make it possible for each to take the other seriously, the propagandist—and, often, his counterpart: the official patron—naively presumes that literature is the instinctive voice of indoctrination, the facile spokesman for a cocksure society. So natural is this error, especially among a people self-consciously nationalistic, that the response of many Philippine writers to the National Commission on Culture, created in 1964, has been refreshing. When that commission was established, the government accepted fully—for the first time since the 1940/41 Commonwealth Awards—its role as art patron and interested party. Since 1960, there have been annual Cultural Heritage Awards; but under the new act support of the various fine arts is intended to be more flexible and subsidies far more substantial.

In a corresponding move, writers used a USIS-sponsored symposium, in March, 1964, as a testing ground for their own theories on what obligations the artist owes the people at large. The spectrum of views expressed in the symposium was predictable; but there was a consensus that, to be most responsible to society, literature had to be formally responsible to itself first, that is, work hard to be powerful without being propagandistic; to incorporate, and not simply communicate, values; to become subject, and not just object, of the wholeness of history. Implicitly, the common decision was to resist all pressures to write according to government prescription.

With increasing frequency, it has been lamented by critics of both literature and society that so much of modern eventfulness—whole decades of transitional change, of experiment with self-government, of growing homogeneity; of graft, agrarian revolt, complex party loyalties; of the rise and fall of social leaders—has generated no fiction of note, no symbolic imagination to come to terms with it with an intelligence beyond journalistic recording. To some extent, such a phenomenon is caused by the

---

Philippine Collegian, 1960). For a view seemingly more attracted to polemics, see Andres C. Cruz, "The Withdrawn and the Committed in Contemporary Literature in English," *The Lyceum*, Oct. 30, 1964, pp. 5–6.

fact that creative writers closest to national events have been forced into a kind of diplomatic discretion by their very employment: many have served as ghost writers or editorial consultants to the prominent figures of their time. However, fear of libel or of retaliation so easily managed in a manipulated society such as the metropolitan writer normally inhabits is probably no more the cause than the natural confusion of any man who too long has been treated by his guest like a prisoner in his own house or who, despite his reluctance, is thrust into a world of high-velocity change.

The writer is special only in the sense that fiction is his very life, his means of inmost quest. Fiction is never adequately engaged, much less satisfied, by statistics or categorical analyses. If literature is not mere entertainment, neither is it mere illustration. Fiction is fixed in detail, in order to provide authentication, through circumstance; but to speak of a "literature made to specification" is to forget the living, developing process which separates narration from exposition.

Precisely because he is responsive to the dilemmas of his time and locality, the Philippine writer has discovered what his contemporaries elsewhere, for their own good reasons, have also discovered: that modern men write *for* self-knowledge more commonly than *from* self-knowledge. In the wary twentieth century, a story is often the experiencing of one's *in*experience. Plot is no more than the movement toward what, at any given moment, is unknown (it is in the nature of horizons to be wayward, to move with the viewer). Conflict is the friction of darkness, the resistance that incomplete knowledge offers to smooth progress. Suspense is the sense of care one necessarily feels at each step, in a place where every step has consequences; and every word, therefore, becomes an alerted, open eye. All imperfections, together, constitute a perfect means for communicating not some sublime, preselected wisdom but the intensely human process of struggling toward (or away from, or beyond) some insight, some redefinition, some working approximation of truth within the small context of one's flesh and daily neighbors.

Consequently, the *creative* writer is the one who proceeds with a diamond-cutter's caution, but also with his courage, realizing that after long concentration a diamond is cut totally along its flaws. His society's dilemmas, its language difficulties, his own personal mysteries—these are among the flaws that shape the Filipino's telling and that test his commitments. Although it is a labor, he writes because in the eternal process of change and becoming, the insights of literature which modify or intensify man's view of his world and which therefore help sanctify human endeavor, are among the few kinds of finality that he can have. For, like a diamond once cut, what is said can never be unsaid.

Western literature, in the twentieth century, has grown up with a sense of flux and subjective entrapment; with relativity, and the reduction of matter to insensible fields of force, and the physical principle of indeterminacy. These have had their visible influence on the Jamesian point of view, the Imagists' desperate arrest, the Joycean stream of consciousness, the non-heroes (clowns, outsiders, scapegoats) of a thousand novels, and reliance on symbolic revelations (O'Neill's masks, Eliot's archetypes) in several generations of art whose "trial truths" have to speak for the inarticulate modern.

Nor have the craft and art of the Filipino remained untouched by these subtle developments. Rather, to such subtleties he finds added his own special problems of discrimination: is a novel a costume farce, or a rich allegory in disguise, in the nineteenth-century tradition of Balagtas' poetry which had to avoid Colonial Office suppression; is the underwriting in a story sign of clumsy imprecision or of a delicacy in language, a courtly Malayan indirection more appropriate than blunt Anglo-Saxon to the sensibility being characterized?

Furthermore, the Philippine writer in his hour of doubt—while he wonders where the hard-carboned diamond can be wounded, to release its light—has only a token audience and few trained critics to assist him. Who will help him know whether he is an imaginative writer, a nonimaginative writer, an unimaginative writer, or an imaginary writer? The overburdened teacher resists the "philosophical implications of form" and settles for primitive, unconditioned subject matter. Whatever is Filipino is enduring epic or divinely inspired lyric. Or the political columnist who doubles as reviewer and is impressed by dust jackets, all that he has time to examine carefully, may decide that no author in Manila is worth reading while the New Deluge is submerging France.

Among such notoriously indifferent Uncritics, Father Miguel Bernad's collections of essays, *Bamboo and the Greenwood Tree* (1961), cannot fail to be a welcome exception. Only momentarily does personal affection ever waylay critical propriety. Even the collection's faults are those of the pioneer: withholding comment altogether on poets, the volume assesses barely a handful of contemporary authors. Of compensatory value, however, is the appendix, which provides letters of self-explication from both N. V. M. Gonzalez and Gregorio Brillantes. The professional analysis of formal functions in their works, by these two authors, is convincing proof of the maturity of Philippine writing in English (and of the courage of the critic with whose interpretations of their stories the authors sometimes disagree). Nick Joaquin has said that the coming of the Americans ended Philippine culture just as it was blossoming in Spanish, and that the reseeding in English has been painfully slow. Others have asserted that only in one of the vernaculars (less surely in Pilipino, the nationalized language) can Filipinos express their innermost selves: but there is only a trickle of durable literature to summon as evidence. *Bamboo and the Greenwood Tree* is significant as one of the first books to take seriously the incomparable achievement in English, in this century.

Nowhere, perhaps, is the silence of the systematic critic-in-depth so noticeable as in the explication of Jose Rizal's novels.

These have been studied, even under compulsion of law, a sufficient number of years now for a body of illuminative (rather than enumerative) literary criticism to have appeared. However, after one has surveyed fugitive attempts at literary history in scholarly magazines and Sunday supplements and stray collections of essays, he is likely to be still uninformed, if not dismayed. Almost the only detailed contemplative discussion of Rizal's art is that by a Yugoslav—Ante Radaic's *Jose Rizal, Romantico Realista* (Manila: University of Santo Tomas, 1961), which is always provocative even when it reads like a Dominican apologia or strains comparisons with Spanish masterpieces. Rizal's Spanish censors were not subtle enough to distinguish author from character, and executed Rizal for inciting rebellion; but injustice is still done Rizal, though dead, through the scarcity of close readers. Why do the *caballeros de Rizal* too frequently insist that Rizal be read exclusively as propagandist, not as artist? Indeed, some of them have made Rizal their *kabayo* and have ridden off in strange directions.

The question is a crucial one because the same historians and social observers assume that Rizal's epoch-making novels can never be excelled. It is true that the firing squad which ended his life in 1896 ensured the ultimate acquisition by Filipinos of a free press and democratic procedures capable of correcting society more directly than Rizal ever could: and, so, limited the need for the novel-as-propaganda. Nevertheless, it can be argued that, despite historical implications, the *Noli Me Tangere* (1887) [45] is not a manifesto, but a full-blooded act of literature —a realistic novel as readable today as ever, wherever second-class citizens struggle to know the right way to rise. Less attention is given political ideologies than descriptions of Manila and the provinces, and whole cross-sections of townspeople, individually characterized: Maria Clara's father and his doll-like household gods; the wife of the civil guard lieutenant, capable of

[45] In the 1961 translation (Bloomington: Indiana University Press), by Leon Ma. Guerrero, then ambassador to Great Britain, the novel is entitled *The Lost Eden,* a phrase taken from Rizal's poem, "My Last Farewell," written while awaiting execution.

drowning a man by degrees; comically illiterate Doña Victorina, who wins arguments with her husband by seizing his dentures.

Structurally, the *Noli* is interesting because of a reversal of roles as neat and as credible as that of Prince Hal and Hotspur in Shakespeare's *Henry IV*, Pt. 1. Ibarra refuses to join in armed rebellion even when authorities dishonor his "heretical" father's corpse and excommunicate the son. When Elias the outlaw reminds him of rampant social evils, he still counsels gradualism through education. Only after Ibarra is exiled on false charges of masterminding revolt and, consequently, loses long-betrothed Maria Clara, does he swear venegance. By then, ironically, he has converted Elias to peaceful ways.

Suppose Rizal found attractive not this ingenious reversal as a gratuitous irony, but the opportunity, through a composite Elias-Ibarra, to project and test indecisions within himself. Rizal traditionally is acknowledged to have been a reformist, not a separatist; and consequently he is placed at the extreme, opposite Bonifacio the firebrand. Yet both positions are weighed carefully, in the persons of Ibarra and Elias, and it is the armed subversive who emerges. What prevents Ibarra-Elias from representing the wavering mind of Philippine culture, as well as two conflicting, never wholly resolved inclinations in Rizal himself, traditionalist and revolutionary that he was; in addition to the end-of-century dialectic between liberals of peninsular Spain and its repressive Colonial Office, between church and state, between the virtues of freedom and of independence? Is Maria Clara herself, then, intended less as a model for all Filipinos than as a symbol of human dilemma and unhappy compromise?

Such readings would confirm, rather than contradict, realistic qualities already evident in the *Noli*, a novel which could not be published in the Philippines because its tale of civil and clerical abuses was far from imaginary. Too much has been made of Rizal's youthful admiration for Dumas' *Count of Monte Cristo*. Whatever may resemble gothic melodrama in this quick-paced novel of satiric-pathetic adventures owes far less to imported literary formula than to recorded Philippine history. Is some degree of melodrama not inevitable in a conservative Victorian society, some amount of coincidence not natural to a closed colonial society?

In fact, life sometimes imitated Rizal's fiction. When hostility at home drove him abroad once again, his fiancee Leonor Rivera, at the command of her parents, was married to an Englishman, almost in parody of the Maria Clara episode. In Belgium, in 1891, he published *El Filibusterismo*,[46] whose central character Simoun is generally conceded to be vengeful Ibarra, disguised. Simoun is not heroic but troublesome, at all levels of society using money to "hurry up" evil. Dying, after an abortive attack on Manila, he is told that evil cannot redeem evil, but only "goodness, sacrifice, and love" can. Despite such continued caution, when Rizal returned to the Philippines he was deported, like Ibarra himself. On the Mindanao frontier he lived a model life for four years. Always compassionate, still he felt revolt premature and refused to join those kindled by his accounts. Nevertheless, when the revolt of 1896 seemed to follow the pattern of Simoun's in the *Fili*—and similarly failed, Rizal was returned to Manila, summarily tried, and executed for treason. Ironically, his martyrdom inspired a full-scale revolution which later broke Spanish resistance, even while Commodore Dewey awaited troops in Manila Bay.

The *Fili* has usually been considered an inferior, less realistic novel—a contrivance of mirrors, somewhat like the decapitated head at the Quiapo fair, in Rizal's second novel, which tells a tale of ancient wrongs paralleling nineteenth-century colonial rule. The novel may well seem, at first, propaganda too neatly reflected without those enigmatic shadowings which indicate human involvement. Partially it is the fault of history and of the similarity of men everywhere that so much of this record of modern revolution which in its day was prophetic now has become overfamiliar. Land is falsely claimed by the powerful, who proceed to charge exorbitant rentals; the tenant's sons are con-

---

[46] *The Subversive*, in Guerrero's translation (Bloomington: Indiana University Press, 1962).

scripted or jailed; his daughter is defiled; and the classroom, place of final hope for change, is the epitome of petty dogmatism; and society at large is scandalous. The pattern of inhumanity is unfortunately commonplace—although Rizal, of course, must share some of the critical blame for relying on caricature to reveal the turmoil of his society.

Only with two characters does one begin to sense a Conradian dimension beneath the flowered Dickensian vest. Simoun the jeweler is the once-naive Ibarra returned after thirteen years to avenge the loss of his father, his fiancee, and his rights. His method is disguised in simplicity. Hoping to speed the day of collapse and of public wrath, he urges the Spanish administrators into every excess. Unfortunately, Simoun works in such secret ways that he is invisible most of the time and what he is doing is largely left to the imagination—except for his less subtle activities, such as the gathering of explosives through blackmailed Chinese traders. When the uprising that he has long planned fails, Simoun kills himself, ostensibly to let his identity die with him (but it has been revealed several times already). His despair seems premature if his impulse to revolution is elevated, as he declares after the death of Maria Clara, from the personal to the national. More likely his death is required by Rizal's diminishing sympathy for him. Ibarra-Simoun is an embittered cynic, too confirmed to be the solitary spokesman for Rizal. His opinions are always startling ("There are no tyrants where there are no slaves"). But the extremity of his actions makes his wisdom appear the property of some other person, perhaps an earlier self. Father Florentino reminds the dying man that evil cannot cleanse evil.

Greater attention is paid Isagani, the young medical student. Isagani not only defends the worth of the Filipino against his Dominican professor but also proves in person the Filipino's integrity. His fiancee is faithless; yet when explosives are planted at her wedding party in order to assassinate or maim the Spanish officials present, he risks his life to save them all. Simoun has attempted, vainly, to create by destroying. Can the more traditional Filipino, given the courage and inbred decency of an Isagani, destroy by creating? Such seems to be the question raised by Rizal; and neither he nor the enigmatic Isagani as the latter is last seen is sure. But the very existence of the question, of the open mind, of the nonviolent heart and its dilemmas seems to be attractive to Rizal here, just as in the *Noli*.

If the counterplay of idealist Isagani and realist Simoun, of love and hate as forces of freedom-with-dignity, is too attenuated, too transparent in the context of panoramic descriptions left tangential only, nevertheless this fault in characterization is not so great as it seems if the *Fili* is read as a separate novel. Actually it is more than a sequel to the *Noli*; together, the *Noli-Fili* constitute one novel, with a single geometry of unresolved oppositions whose purpose is to do more than merely prophesy or confirm history. The dilemmas of Rizal and the people of his time—how to rescue freedom with or without independence; how to change without coercion those permissive of tyranny; how to be equal without being interchangeable— such dilemmas were brought to a decision by the Katipunan uprising and the hasty execution of Rizal. Decision, of course, is not always resolution: and the same problems are still explored by today's writers of fiction: still in search of a hero, still seeking direction through indirection.

By any number of criteria, therefore, the *Noli-Fili* is a modern novel far more valuable than those who prize it may realize. Beyond that, it provides one kind of model for properly humanized historical fiction, by which such Rizaliana plays as Severino Montano's *Parting at Calamba* (1953) and *The Love of Leonor Rivera* (1954) seem sentimentally contrived; and Adrian Cristobal's *The Trial* (of Bonifacio: 1963) too literally transcribed, immobilized, and antidramatic.

Certainly the *Noli-Fili* is more modern than, for example, is Emigdio Enriquez' novel, *The Devil Flower: A Love Story of the Philippines* (1959), which is an "entertainment" constructed around the suppressed passions of a Zamboanga girl who is reputedly a Maria Clara type. Enriquez' story is less a tale of disillusionment than a carefully composed illusion in itself. Resplendent details of dress and food, of landscape and local custom are provided generously, not as modes of characterization but as substitutes for characterization. The language is bold, with its references to Spanish fly, exposed anatomies, and multiple seductions; but the sentiments, though screened, are as conventional as those in *Camille*. (The relative delicacy of *The Devil Flower* can be measured against such erotic fantasies as Antonio E. Sta. Elena's novel, *A Voyage of Love* (1961), which, pretending to be a transcribed *rite de passage* experienced in trans-Pacific Skid Rows, is a simple, indulgent directive from a non-marriage manual.) Ercelia Fernandez, supposedly, spends most of her thirty-five years inwardly rebellious against her reputation as a "paragon of virtue." In her twenties, she succeeds in having herself attacked by Don Miguel Sta. Romana, the town lover and one-time seducer of a nun, and now Ercelia's uncle. She is upset by none of these facts so much as by his hairiness (a "popular science" explanation later relates this revulsion to a traumatic childhood memory of her father's hairy arm, butchering). In self-punishment for arousing Don Miguel but also for—very indirectly—causing her father's death after he confronted them, and for causing Don Miguel's death as well (a secret lover has denounced him falsely to a Moro *amok*), she renounces the young man, Larry Leyden, who genuinely and honorably has shared her affection. Only after eleven years of such guilt does Ercelia, now tubercular, decide to accept Larry; but, following a brief Wagnerian dream of ecstatic ravishment, she is discovered dead on her threshold.

There is no sense of quest in such a novel; there is only ancient formula—the woman of singular virginity which miraculously survives all temptations—in modern costume: the ultimate sophistication being that she survives even the terrible temptations she wishes on herself. Under its sensual facades, *The Devil Flower* seems dependent on an almost childlike faith in the inviolability of innocence. Motives, the propriety of symbols, even chronological sequence cannot bear severe scrutiny. Rather, a suspension of both disbelief and belief are required, as if one were watching the pale make-up and bright costumes of a centuries-old, stylized *moro-moro* play; or the exaggerations of children playing grown-up. That particles of the formula have been reversed or placed out of scale (Maria Clara is far more credible than this woman who, we are to assume, had little else in her life except sexual passion to suppress) only indicates that the child is bored or is trying hard to act bad.

Rizal's language is more discreet, his incidents less spectacular: but his novels seem realistic, compared with the romance of an Enriquez; and if serious writers sometimes resent having their work compared with Rizal's as the constant model, their objection may well be that the reasons offered for the comparison are mistaken and, above all, that Rizal himself would have been the first to claim that any man or any of his works is only tentative, only exploratory.

William Dean Howells once called the *Noli* the greatest novel in any language in one hundred years. Although Filipino claims are more modest, Rizal's novels have been required reading in all educational institutions since 1956. If contemporary authors are discouraged from imitating Rizal's type of panoramic novel, the monumentality of his success is to blame as much as the difficulty always inherent in adding historic and social dimensions to the private imagination. No one denies that the Philippines has its grievances—its commercially aggressive Chinese communities, its misunderstandings with American pharisees, its anxious resettlement of the Huks, its Moro uprisings. But it becomes simpler to pass the job of protest on to journalists from the abundant free press. Besides, newspapers have what writers lack—a relatively captive audience and a definite commitment to one of the several major languages competing in the archipelago. Writers envy Rizal, who, fluent in twenty-two languages, chose Spanish because he knew exactly what readers he wanted to reach. (However, like many Filipinos, Rizal had to subsidize his own publication; and, in fact, condensed the *Fili* in revision to save on the cost of printing as well as to improve the text.) Faced with such circumstances, often the writer settles for a more intimate subject matter and a limited readership.

He remembers also that of all the socially conscious stories of the 1930's, perhaps only Manuel Arguilla's compassionate, not propagandistic, tales of the Sakdal socialists ever entered permanent literature. Similarly, the novels of Japanese occupation —Juan C. Laya's *This Barangay*, Stevan Javellana's *Without Seeing the Dawn* (its title taken from the *Noli*), and Edilberto Tiempo's *Watch in the Night*—all are flawed, with unassimilated speechmaking and sometimes implausible characterizations.

As if to reassure themselves of some inner resource before reentering the larger world (or as if responding to the startling responsibilities of a people at last liberated), the outstanding writers in English today practice a new virile *delicadeza*. Theirs is an attentive, subtle restraint, comparable in precision with the Anglo-Saxon manner but free of its bluntness. This is nowhere more discernible than in Bienvenido Santos' *You Lovely People*, unsentimental stories of expatriated Filipinos—the American "Pinoys"; or N. V. M. Gonzalez' *A Season of Grace* which is concerned less with class struggle than with the ritual of long-suffering pioneers restoring a reluctant jungle to its garden state. Nick Joaquin, a translator of Rizal, is constantly tempted to feel indiscriminate nostalgia for Spanish custom and stability. Yet indirection and inner ironies, and not simple chroniclings, are the mark of his best work, *The Woman Who Had Two Navels*, and his play, *A Portrait of the Artist as Filipino*.

At the same time, such writers seem aware that introspection's minute observations can become—as in the case of Jose Garcia Villa's poetry—overwithdrawn, private, or repetitive. Consequently, Santos has allowed a national image—the Filipino Dream—to emerge from his personal experiences; and in *Villa*

Magdalena has turned to intercontinental fiction. Gonzalez' latest novel, *The Bamboo Dancers*, also resorts to international scenes, to measure the distances between men epitomized in the post-Hiroshiman radiation within mankind's genes. Such writers present a view of nationalism no longer naive, a world-wide commitment parallel with the Philippines' role in the UN and SEATO. In poetry their counterpart is Alejandrino Hufana, who, since the dramatic monologues of *Sickle Season*, has expanded his effort to make epic equivalents of tribal verse still chanted in the mountains. The Philippine experience has broadened, deepened, in search of a center and circumference.

If this movement succeeds in adding the delicacy of understatement, of exact self-knowledge, to the reconsideration of man in his broadest obligations and inheritance, the scope even of Rizal's fiction may some day be excelled. For a poise will finally have been secured, between the infinitesimal and the infinite.

Folk Culture and City Commerce: Confrontations

OFTEN, in contemporary Philippine literature, there is a slowness of motion which owes something to timeless folkways' sacred, seasonal mysteries, but as much again to the questing spirit for quietly profound consequence which is appropriate to an open, developing society. The most exemplary fiction shares a kind of restraint and virile delicacy, a precision by indirection suitable to the people's heritage of courtesy and courtliness, but suitable also to the inner-turning, patient, modern probe for reassurance. The function of imaginative literature, such writers know, is not to take for granted, but to recalculate; to validate one mode of experience by another: and thus to assist the conservative toward an appreciation of what is worth conserving; and the liberal toward a knowledge of what is worth liberating. Above all, the burden of the writer has been that of Rizal—to startle into image the Philippine presence, beyond all question of human worth.

MANUEL ARGUILLA

One of the greatest temptations for the folk writer is to falsify the human image through oversimplification. The startling depths of even primitive art—Navajo sand painting, Cro-Magnon cave drawings, the stone heads on Easter Island—like the intricate totems and taboos of the oldest societies, deny the common assumption that man at any place or any stage is ever simple long. The reckless writer stops short: where fulfilled art, by its thorough ordering, its intimate placement, eventually achieves a complex illusion of simplicity (just as in the tribe

or in medieval society every gesture is ritualistic and, in the hier-
archy of events, there are no accidents, no mysteries allowed).
This is Arguilla's dilemma in *How My Brother Leon Brought
Home a Wife and Other Stories* (1940).

Occasionally Arguilla entertains the temptation to write of
the prehuman or the misleadingly overexclusive experience. His
bar-bell idylls, "Elias" and "The Strongest Man," are entertain-
ing but easily forgotten. On the other hand, the display of muscular love in "Midsummer" and "Heat" is rescued by the fragility
of more subtle emotions, shyly visible, restraining passion and
giving it the grace of form.

Restraint is Arguilla's virtue. Usually his stories are praised
for their realism, therefore their capacity for release, the naturalness of their details. The realism is pervasive, and invigorating.
Yet one of the major functions of that realism is to allow the
romantic inclination—devotion to the natural man, bone and
sinew, hip and thigh—to exist without the extravagance of sentimentality. The paradox of mature fiction is that simultaneously
it allows the experience of release and restraint. Uncontrolled
release is a bare spark leaping a gap in a Leyden jar: immediately
lost, however spectacular. Fiction directs and contains that release: and there is electricity, a constancy of illumination. Unless
Arguilla had withheld himself at times, what he gave would have
been less valuable.

It is such restraint which makes "Morning in Nagrebcan"
tense after, not during, the father's brutality. When the brothers,
ex-rivals, bury their puppy, the quiet cornfield with its spent pol-
len is agitated only. An ironically golden sun wastes itself on the
disturbed ground of the grave. Tears form, instead, in the chambers of the heart, more powerful for not being visible. The story
aches—and that is a greater achievement than catharsis. The
function of art is to reconstruct living and felt experience,
wholly; not to divert or avoid or ease it, and lose it.

"A Son Is Born," that nearly ritualistic record of flesh, fer-
tilized, making flesh, is kept unsentimental and tangible by its
last sentence: "And that was how my brother Jesus was born,

in the year the locusts came." Besides, the birth belongs not to the parents, but to the young, initiate, onlooking brother.

The most enduring experiences in Arguilla stories often are those of his young-boy narrators. And his lovers, too, are most erect and presentable not when lusty but when innocent—boy-like, with the manly dignity of a sometimes solemn boy, respectful of life. If "How My Brother Leon" is a magnificent story, it is managed through the combination and intensification of these very elements. The eyes of a child, half-knowing yet all-caring, provide the ideal device for leaving the most important narrative matters unmentioned but not therefore untold. Arguilla's subtlety has been too long overlooked. It is the source of that intimate-yet-objective quality which gives these stories their peculiar strength.

Moreover, the idyllic and pastoral flute tones of certain of these first stories are composed further and rendered harmonic by the substantial, more somber bloc of "oppressed labor" stories at the end: "Caps and Lower Case," "Apes and Men," and the Sakdal tales. Except for brief outbreaks of violence, even these are noteworthy for their welling but not yet overflowing emotion, their silent threat. "The Socialists" has one outburst of lyricism:

> Comrade Lirios had a sudden vision of 16,000,000 people of the same cast and mold, capable of the same direct, unself-conscious, child-like simplicity and earnestness. They till the soil and plant rice and know the quality of rain and sun. The feel of pure honest earth is in their work-hardened hands; they stand on it with bare feet, toes spread apart.

Yet this excess is not Arguilla's, but Lirios', a man just learning the shabbiness, by contrast, of the Socialist Club of Manila; and the necessity of contrast justifies the exaggeration. The full story itself is not blind to the heroic posing of the farmers, reciting "The Man With the Hoe."

Actually, Arguilla's best stories of protest, "Rice," "Epilogue to Revolt," and "Caps and Lower Case," avoid becoming propaganda by holding fast to the individual, the variation within the scheme, and not to the overgeneralized and therefore over-idealized masses, abstracted by doctrine. Thus Arguilla avoids the self-deception of other protest writers of the thirties abroad, who took ten years to realize that Communism-real is not Communism-ideal, and to withdraw their allegiance from "the God that failed." Time and again Arguilla demonstrates that he is writing not only Ilocano stories: that, paradoxically, when one seizes a particular firmly, he holds a universal in his hand.

Only in the middle stories, the marriage group, does Arguilla's craft falter. The bathos of projected suicide in "The Long Vacation" recalls that of the actual death in "Ato." "Elias" is a strong-man exhibition, material for a Tagalog movie. "Imperfect Farewell" tries to evoke pity without providing substance, and must be contrasted with the sensitive handling of "Felisa," where again the unspoken, unspeakable words are the most moving: they are the major sign of tension which the story has to resolve.

The triangular situation in "The Maid, the Man, and the Wife" stays undeveloped because only one of the three characters (the maid) seems unfictitious. Yet a similar triangle in "Mr. Alisangco" succeeds in its telling, even though one character is seen through the eyes of others only. But character and situation develop each other: man and wife, here, become involved in the bitterness of their own humor; and Mr. Alisangco's last vision of the girl, Araceli, is in the best Arguilla tradition of restrained breathing, the choked heart at an instant still indecisive, still indescribable as the end or the beginning of something, the straining creative anticipation. It is the same sort of last-minute ironic but subtle twist that gives authority to "Though Young, He Is Married."

Even the strategy of placing this marriage group between two stronger blocs fails to cancel the full effect of the unevenness. However, the weakness of even the worst stories is at least mitigated by Arguilla's consistent (if intermittent) and un-ashamed directness with language and therefore with the persons, places, things which language represents. A language that touches truth—the surface under the surface, and the surfaces beyond—in as many ways as Arguilla's, can never be romantic, or exaggerated, long.

N. V. M. GONZALEZ

The folk quality in the works of N. V. M. Gonzalez has been placed under even more severe formal restraint. The simple style and structure of his first novel, *The Winds of April* (1941), might be expected of a modest young man engaged in semi-autobiography; but there is a sense of propriety-beyond-decorum in the book, inasmuch as it is a child's enlarging world that is shown, as his family moves from Romblon to the frontiers of Mindoro. Furthermore, every volume since Gonzalez' first is so noticeably underwritten that he runs the risk of being misread, of having subtleties overlooked, of leaving unmoved those readers used to bathos. It is a professional hazard, accepted by the responsible artist convinced that he must write about his people, as they are, even if not always (or not immediately) for them.

Often, in *Seven Hills Away* (1947) there is a near-static quality that suggests the slowness of change beyond the *barrio*, in the *kaingin* clearings of islands south of Manila. What otherwise might be considered sketchiness is evidence of the quiet, sometimes desperate, peasant way of life. The sense of incompleteness is deliberate; but when the collection of stories is considered as a whole, even the truncated ones begin to absorb and imply one another; and their movement becomes less subliminal. The first and last stories establish the wave pattern within the total structuring: in "Pioneer" a young man, having made too many friends on the frontier for his comfort, pushes on once again; in "The Happiest Boy in the World" a father relinquishes his son to his landlord in the *barrio*, so that the boy will be educated. Except for this boy, whose future is unknown, the recurrent theme of the stories is that every departure is a return, every change mere repetition, and that every man finds his true self by fulfilling ancestral patterns—of burning off a field in lonely self-reliance, of taking for himself a hard-working, child-bearing companion, and of someday sending his son off to the next horizon. "The Planting" and "The Baby," separate stories, are overlapping segments of this cycle. Whatever injustice or hardship become their lot (nature, their animistic minds tell them, waits eagerly for their slightest misstep), they are unsurprised. Part of the static quality of these stories lies in the stoic nature of the characters. Dignity has rarely found a symbolization superior to that of the starving family, in "Hunger in Barok," which chooses to plant the seed rice lent them for eating!

Moreover, even where melodrama is available, it is undercut. "Far Horizons," the story of a drowned son and his stricken mother, is controlled by a style as stark and impersonal, unlyrical, as a Malayan sea captain's log book might have been in the days of the great wanderings. Or the fire in "Seven Hills Away" that destroys a house and all its implements of hope is protectively seen, dreamlike, through the unwilling eyes of a boy who simply cannot face the reality of seven years' rebuilding.

Something of this same primitive, experiential quality is achieved in Gonzalez' next collection of stories, *Children of the Ash-Covered Loam* (1954), through the choice of children and plain women as either his narrators or his central characters. Gonzalez writes of those who make of volcanic ash a sacred tabernacle to house their human love. The threat of the volcano, the crippling part of man, is always present, mitigated by the love which must make violence come to proper terms. Gonzalez' characters are believable, a race of common men, without being reduced to the usual (for-export-only) stereotyped lovers of *tubâ* and cockfights, and haters of spinster chaperones. Although they believe in the *anting-anting* and the *anitos*, his characters are interesting not because they consider themselves instruments of some dark misfortune, but because in the midst of suffering they assert their worth, and care bravely for one another. Consequently, they have a full and handsome, an unashamed dignity.

Even the experience of children is respected. The title story itself, as well as "Lupo and the River," are told from the point of view of very young boys. With a gradual increase of wisdom not unlike the quiet oncoming of another season or the slow freshening of a woman's body, Tarang encounters the source of life, the sacred mystery of reproduction. He finds it with equal amazement in his mother, the new rice in a *kaingin*, a littering sow. In the second story, Pisco has revealed to him, with this same ease of unrolling experience, the damage that can be done man's innermost heart by a girl's careless and uncaring feelings. Finding the man whom he half-feared, but still admired, dead in the heart of a fish trap, Pisco is suddenly forced to be grown up.

These two initiations into birth and death are lovingly and honestly handled. They are filled with youth's sense of wonder: those strangely beautiful moments that fill one with awe and then as suddenly with the feeling of awful consequences. Man grows away from the garden of his first innocence; he grows through guilt, but guilt redeemed by the saving grace of occasional beauty.

The same sensitiveness, the same breadth of feeling are displayed in all the other stories. Miss Inocencio, the lonely schoolteacher of "The Blue Skull and the Dark Palms," is tempted to accept the school inspector's offered protectiveness. Instead, she chooses to stay loyal to the young dead guerrilla, Pepito. Love does not prevent suffering; it only seals off complaint. Marta, in "The Morning Star," is another example of uncomplaining love. She blames no one for the fact that she is about to bear an illegitimate child in a strange wilderness, with its father irretrievably beyond their reach. Instead, she accepts the company and comfort of an old sailor and a mute, so that her pain and even the loss of the child are bearable. Here the birth and death themes of the first two stories meet: these are necessary conditions of life, and Marta, however physically unlovely, is morally attractive for having endured so well the full human burden.

This is the burden that Elay, the servant in "A Warm Hand," reaches for in the dark night. It is her sophisticated selfish mistress who struggles to make herself the center of attention on their sea voyage. But it is simple Elay who finds an answer to her own desire; who finds that she is wanted. The sophisticate recurs with Mrs. Bilbao, the woman in "Where's My Baby Now?" who cannot grasp her failure as woman and wife. Her time is filled with clubs and lectures and the Women's Social Action Committee. She has only public responses, but not any private feelings except irritation.

The final story compares life, with its weight of death, to the condition of war. While her husband is dying aboard ship among strangers and the haste of a busy merchant world, a young wife is tortured by her feelings and by their lack of feeling. Just as she and her suffering are impaled by the ruthless headlights of a dockside jeep, so the whole story is framed unmercifully by the conscientiously curious but, ultimately, forcibly distinterested tone of the narrator, a commercial traveler. The result is painful irony.

It is the fully beating heart, human awareness and compassion, that Gonzalez has exposed in these stories, not the cancer of a diseased social system. It is the same slow pulse of life that he presents in his second novel, A Season of Grace (1956). His characters are adult children, Mindoro pioneers, not unlike those in his earliest stories. They live in a land of neither clocks nor calendars but only almanacs marked with the seasons of seed-time, caretaking and harvest, for indivisible earth and man. Gonzalez' language rhythms are those of untranslated speech, indebted in tempo, pause, and prolonging to the natural work rhythms of farmers and fishermen, so that the cadences themselves become rituals of survival, of primitive sense.

Although A Season of Grace is a novel of pioneers, the motives of Sabel and Doro, who leave the overworked, overclaimed plots of Tara-Poro and the fishing barrio at Alag, to go clear kaingins of their own in the interior, are far from those of historic American gold-seekers and land-grabbers west of the Mississippi. These pioneers have no expectation of getting rich, no desire to escape the claims of deserved private pasts: they are simple, strong, and enduring, the heroic average whose dreams are modest. The triumph of Gonzalez as an artist is that he has avoided the other shore as well, has refused to make his innocents the happy savages of Rousseau's sanitary jungles. *Kaingineros*, by burning over forested areas, make easier the destruction of land by typhoon and flood: there is this ironic undertone, this knowledge of the potential for self-destruction mingled with the title's more affirmative tone. Payment of Doro's debts is extended: is disaster simply delayed? or is some goodness more durable than disaster born of submission to the natural order?

Gonzalez' landscape has been lived in; these characters suffer, sweat, and bear, as both structure and texture testify. The novel traces through a jungle the track of a man and woman whose intent is to restore that wilderness to its garden state. The action encompasses one year, one turning of the seasonal cycle. Yet within this eternal return runs the individual rhythm of Sabel and Doro's life. From harvest to harvest Sabel bears one child after another, but of course they are not the same child; nor are the young parents so poor after twelve months as they were before, though they will always be burdened. Epe Ruda and his wife, offered as a second couple of quite different temper and status, suffer a series of miscarriages; yet each is more than a repetition of the first. Each brings them closer to some kind of personal disaster, even while the common laborer's indebtedness to them doubles. Three mats are taken from Sabel at the book's start, and at the end three from Clara, the girl with the withered leg. Although the petty officials requisitioning them remain the same, a transfer of skill and therefore of identity (with the suggestion of transferred vitality, too) has been achieved between the grown and the growing woman.

When Sabel says, "There are others on the land. . . . People not our kind," she refers to the long-snouted rats which devour her *palay*; but the chambers of the book resound with this phrase, in the figures of Epe Ruda and the municipal visitors. Yet there is little bitterness spent on such twilight antagonists;

and the pioneers succumb to neither system nor surroundings. A *Season of Grace* is not a proletarian novel. Without lifting its voice, it commemorates human worth in a few persons making a ceremony of living within the limits of their souls and a troublous soil. It is precisely this ceremonial quality that protects Sabel and Doro, and reduces the importance of impediments to their progress. Institutionalized religion is so remote in this novel that the figures of saints function chiefly as a display of social status; and the church building is swept out, at the last moment, only in time for a funeral.

Yet grace as an inner quality of equilibrium is everywhere present, even transfiguring superstition through the innocence of the believers' faith; grace is a spiritual underlay, the wine in human blood. These are gentle people, gently portrayed. Eloy looks like a seed, as he sleeps: and what sleeps—a seed—inside Eloy? What lives in spite of life?

If the *kaingins* for Gonzalez are no romantic paradise, neither are they a spiritual wasteland. For Sabel and Doro the cycle of seasons becomes a spiraling toward gradual fulfillment. They not only endure: they prevail. Although they are twentieth-century figures, they seem related to those pre-Spanish inhabitants of the Philippines whose social codes of justice and decency made possible their relatively easy conversion to Christianity.

The *kainginero* is less visible in Gonzalez' 1963 collection, *Look, Stranger, On This Island Now*, particularly in the second section, whose stories are placed in Manila and its adjacent provinces. Nevertheless, the *kainginero's* loneliness as well as his powers of endurance are felt constants, like an inherited secret or second identity, underlying whatever social changes have moved the peasant to the town of Buenavista, in Romblon; and thence to the commercial centers of Luzon. Although Rizal himself wrote principally about and for the *ilustrados*, here he becomes associated with the *kainginero* through the epigraph (stopping at Romblon shortly before his death, Rizal remarked, "The port . . . is lovely, but sad and solitary") and the title as well, inasmuch as we are told that the "stranger" is Rizal being invited to reassess "the changed and changing Philippine society." Together these figures serve as a conscience, marking progress and corruption.

All of the characters in the Buenavista section suffer some manner of loneliness, but for each there is consolation. The bachelor-teacher in "The Whispering Woman" knows, even as he mourns all trapped and dreamless wanderers, that in the dark of his corridor the landlady's daughter Charity waits wordlessly, to bring water or to hear the outcry of his need. The frightened boy in "The Wireless Tower," climbing to see if lightning ever split the tower top, can write later, simply, "It is true"; he has been made fearless by some discovery in himself. Another boy, in "The Eternal Fort," translates the fever of his flu into an electric recreation of Spanish times. A third boy, in "The Bread of Salt," is disillusioned when his wealthy girl friend overcharitably forces fancy cakes on him at a party where he has played violin; and he returns to the street and to *pan de sal*, anyman's crisp, warm daily bread. Especially this last story presents a perfect metaphor for Gonzalez' choice of style; just as "Sharks, Pampanos, and the Young Girls of the Country" signifies the role of the artist as fisher of men. Bert is the inside-outsider, the man who has fished for years but not for money, as have those with whom he finds himself. When, at the end, he turns off his flashlight after catching his young guide urinating in the dark, he is accepting the privacy that remains no matter how close their companionship (he is accepting his wound, as it were, though far less dramatically than a Hemingway hero).

By contrast with these quiet triumphs, there is a great sense of loss or waste, of uneasy apprehension, in the second, or Luzon, section. Tony Cruz, in "The Flight of Gentlefolk," is being sent back by his aunts for a three-day visit with his mother in a destroyed and occupied Manila, and to a stepfather who does not want him. In the story he never reaches them, but spends the night with his grandfather in the home where he once grew up: like the old man's orchids, entrusted to a neighbor, they are all derelicts now. In "Dry Heaven" the visiting fishermen cannot conceive of Father Eugenio, once head of his class in Rome, as anything less than an exile in the poverty-striken fishing *barrio*. Although it is clear that the problems brought to the confessional are perplexing, the priest himself feels his inadequacies. Even greater is the sense of failure of Lopez in "On the Ferry." After excessive deforestation on Mount Halcon, floods have broken Badjao Dam, which he helped construct. He invents a dozen distractions so that he will not have to face the cause, in himself, of his failure while in the company of his son whom he removed temporarily from college. But a foundering boat betrays him to his conscience. Above all, "The Popcorn Man" exposes the inner corruption of Filipino faculty members, "educational concessionaires" at a university extension that resembles Clark Field. The compromises—with teaching standards, illicit PX trading, patriotic self-respect—multiply until the protagonist has nothing left except contempt for his own weaknesses. Yet perhaps such knowledge is at least as valuable as the near-naivete of boy or native in the Romblon stories; and is probably superior to the perfection of disintegration disclosed in Gonzalez' novel, *The Bamboo Dancers*, in which for the first time simple style and almost random structure indicate not innocence but evasiveness on the part of the character.

It is neither an accident of the author's curiosity nor Cook's Tour extravagance that spends so much of *The Bamboo Dancers* (1959) on international panorama. New York, Vermont, Montreal (the least exploited scenically), Tokyo, Hiroshima, Taipeh, Sipolog—these, despite their variousness, have to suggest a constant human condition and interior state. The novel is more than an indictment of indiscriminate atomic destruction. It follows a fugitive antihero through a series of underwritten, dedramatized events. Such a design can only be intended to demonstrate man's failure to understand his fellow man, through natural inarticulateness—the innate imperfection which limits self-knowledge as well as communication—and through perverse, semiwillful evasiveness. Here is the seed of inhumanity. It is this that makes the war that makes the Bomb that makes the silent fallout of rushing consequences and ever-ongoing secret radiation in the stream of genes.

Is the shadow of silence that falls between men caused by the unspeakable horror that is nuclear war or by what is inadmissible by men, because it is too personal though common? The scenes in Hiroshima are underwritten not simply because the narrator is still desperately detaching himself in the midst of involvement, but also because Genbaku the nuclear cloudburst is only the Gorgon-head epitome (Sphinx-head, in Dali's representation), and not even the culmination, of man's self-reduction to inert, nonradiant leadenness. If in a sense *The Bamboo Dancers* is a narrative fable treating the second law of thermodynamics—the gradual unavailability of energy, as matter is not lost but converted downward to some physical hell at the bottom of the table of active elements, then the quickening pace of the novel, although appropriate to the increasing tempo of the *tinikling* and its hazards, is a grand irony among ironies. Man, still falling, accelerates; as if increased corruption, the measure of the distance fallen, multiplies his weight and therefore the agony of velocity.

However, more truly, what adds weight and pace, as the novel progresses from its quiet, almost random start, is the natural accumulation of significance to the drift of event, in spite of the narrator's resistance. And it is this impending meaning which, being the negation of human denial, paradoxically may also negate the completeness of the fall by giving illuminative configuration even to descending night. Milton would have called this "darkness visible," describing not only hell but the saving act of description itself, the act of art, a kind of Bergsonian *élan vital* which is counterforce to the second law of thermodynamics. But if darkness is properly visible in *The Bamboo Dancers*, it is in spite of the sightlessness of Ernie Rama, who is often more stone than sculptor.

Clues to the novel's procedures are presented by Gonzalez in various ways. There is the epigraph from Henry James, warning that one is in the presence of design even if it is emergent rather than apparent. There is the quotation from the art critic speaking of Gauguin: "The artist seeks something underneath appearances, some plastic symbol which shall be more significant of reality than any exact reproduction can be." There is Ernie's commentary on the perennial star-gazer at the Greenleaf Writers' Conference: "We all have our own galaxies to describe in a book, only we are doomed right from the start by the finitude of our watch." There are the seemingly casual, buoyant negotiations of the carp, in the pool at the Hotel Kika-so, which draft a geometry among the reflections of stone lanterns, a testimony to intelligibility. All these and others are warnings that the reader who seeks that enrichment of awareness of which Ernie speaks but too rarely manifests must bear patient, responsible witness, for that is the author's plan.

Henry James, after the subjective psychology developed by his brother William, established narrators as rigorously limited angles of vision. But Ernie Rama's is a restricted point of view in a double sense: his sometimes deliberate coldness to any human embrace reinforces the native imperfection of human understanding. Is it not appropriate that he is professionally a sculptor who persistently and naively thinks of truth as a granite core underlying obstructive chips and flints which the chisel has only to remove? This is characteristic of Ernie, this rejection of his own experience of knowledge as something processive, cumulative, incomplete, peripherally arrived at, tenuous, and tentative. He is never seen as a practicing artist but rather as a wanderer across continents and oceans, the international scene being employed to suggest not the oneness of man (alike only in alienation) but the distances between them.

The motif of incompletion is recurrent, and at first may bother the reader who, expecting narrator and author to be alter egos, wants to be guided by Ernie, not to be lost with him. But Ernie and Mimi take separate subways home, after long silence; the lonely USIS girl whom he planned to meet disappears in Kyoto, unknown; enroute to Hiroshima, time is wasted with an interpreter who does not interpret; Miss Page, the photographer, vanishes after they have barely met; the star-gazer waves a message never delivered; the Japanese switchboard operator and he are mutually unintclligible. Everywhere Ernie sees, he says, strangers and mountains, a zoo of exiles. He is an outsider among outsiders. What does he make of the Hobbses, those resthouse owners in Hiroshima; or of the Hayden heiress whose secluded house he stumbles on in the woods of Vermont; or of Cardinal Mann; or of the bamboo dancers themselves, whom he meets in Taipeh? Each seems to want to be lifted, like a vessel, to have his urgent symbol poured out. But to Ernie's hurried passage these and others are little more than "the imprint of what might have been shadows of people running from the atomic cloudburst" (which *is* their running, their flight from each other). Is it so inappropriate, after all, that his brother Pepe should suggest that he take up driftwood art?

Of his fellow countrymen, Ernie is wary—skeptical and sometimes even scornful of their collections of miniature weapons from Moroland, their doilies, their provinciality, their dollar-buying, their "luxury slums," their little vices and darkened intellects. Only occasionally does he accept them as companions. For fear that they will lead him to self-knowledge? Old people of all nationalities he avoids like a bad conscience, afraid of their need, their outcry and its truth. The beggar with the timeless outstretched hand, he finally realizes, is his father and more than his own father. It is whatever claims him; and he rejects it, and therefore his fullness of self. Why should he not fail Helen then, who turned to Herb Lane originally to shelter her in a Kansas tornado and who turns to him again when Ernie, careless of the consequences, plants radiant seeds of death in her? It is his unlove, the germ plasm of his living death, that is fulfilled in her miscarriage. "I had too long fallen out," he says of his lonely apostasy, although a pagan choir manages hymns to the Christian God overhead. He is victim of the fall of man, and of his own intransigence: he *is* the fallout. He has no vices except major ones.

Ernie Rama is a Fisher King inseparable from the Waste

Land for which he is responsible and whose reflection, in turn, he is. The subtle orientation of the novel around the "Lament for Tammuz" and its ancient identification of kingdom with king's doom is significant. "They grow not"—man does not progress in wisdom. However, Ernie resembles less the allegorical Fisher King of T. S. Eliot's modern epic than he does the Fisher King's counterpart, Jake Barnes, marshal of the walking wounded in Hemingway's *The Sun Also Rises*. The parallel is strengthened when one compares the function of the fishing scenes—"men without women"—in both books, or recalls how Ernie even refers to Helen as Lady Brett Ashley, or thinks how similar to Hemingway's taxicab scene is that in which Helen murmurs that she feels safe with Ernie. In the Fisher King tradition, Ernie even has his own groin wound, presented as a kind of latent homosexuality to be interpreted, under the circumstances of the book, as a result or symptom rather than as a cause of his behavior: his constant ambivalence and hesitation. He finds a far greater attractiveness in men than in women. At Greenleaf, wondering if Helen is "offering" him Herb, he reflects: "A fine time to remind me about myself!" And later, in Herb's presence, he thinks, "I had to take my hand off his shoulder, for fear that one moment more and I couldn't help myself." His ability to perform the sexual act with Helen comes to her as "a complete surprise"; although it must be remembered that he thinks her handsome (not beautiful) and prefers her because she is "mannish."

What should have been a climax in Ernie's experience occurs while he is, characteristically, sick and therefore incapable of being even a shocked spectator. An accidental death, a miscarriage, and a murder occur in rapid succession, while he feverishly sleeps. The Philippine consul in Formosa revises the facts so hastily, for diplomatic purposes, that the truth hardly leaves any lasting imprint. Ernie does his best to help Helen escape unscathed—that is, to avoid publicity which might endanger her reputation! Eventually she is still a fugitive from herself, in Macao; the thought of cosmetics revives her effectively, after her fiance's death. As for Herb, Ernie sentimentalizes his "good will and innocence" in an epilogue; Herb Lane is the young artist cut down in his youth, alas, after his soulful eyes have already been compared with those of Roger Joseph, who died on the beaches of Leyte.

This apostrophe in honor of a man whom Ernie hardly knew would seem strange, were one to forget that Ernie knew Roger Joseph even less, and that this semiabstraction Herb Lane is in fact being used as a kind of mirror in which Ernie, in concealed self-pity and admiration, can see himself—as he is not. The exchange of roles and of personalities in the epilogue has to be read as a continuation of Ernie's sickly evasion, not as a reassuring sign of health restored. Ernie never wonders about the twelve-year-old Chinese girl run over by Herb. He can only reach out to others who, at least as he knows them, are not "other." He is the perfect epitome, therefore, for those victims at Hiroshima who asked to be remembered by the Filipinos: "Tell them how we suffer"; without a word of guilt for suffering caused by them or a sigh of commiseration for others who suffered or a sacrificial silence for the grace and good of others. Hiroshima has erected itself as a symbol of self-pity; and it is this self-love without understanding which is the cause of Genbaku and the undying radiation in the plasm. The Hiroshimans in this novel speak of their new sense of "social responsibility"; but their young march in the street not in redemptive brotherhood, but with the same fierce solidarity, totalitarian will and unconcern for the exactitudes of truth that fired the Kempeitai and the Knights of Bushido. Ernie is true to his character when he does not join in the cry of his begging father or of Helen falling, until he himself nearly drowns; for he can know little of genuine compassion, which requires care and knowledge. He is outraged only that no one realizes his danger; but the others look at him "as if confronted by a stranger speaking a different language"—and, whether he cried out or not, he is that stranger.

He has finally, in the roil of "death by water," been involved despite himself. But it does not necessarily follow that he has reached an adequate understanding of himself and of man. Nevertheless, even his failures or half-truths can be guides to the reader's discoveries.

The last word from Ernie Rama comes by mail: he is happily tending his own garden, in Project 17, like Voltaire's Candide. Has the Fisher King "at least set my lands in order? . . . These fragments I have shored against my ruins" as Eliot's protagonist suggests? Or is this gardening part of the same indulgence that makes possible the death of fish *en masse*, by dynamite?

ARTURO B. ROTOR

The quietness, the underwritten quality representative of the stories in Arturo Rotor's prewar collection, *The Wound and the Scar*, owe an immeasurable debt to the author's modesty, which nearly prevented first publication in 1937 and which has resisted appeals for their reprinting ever since that date. Nevertheless, their reserved tone is equally appropriate to his most characteristic protagonists: the interne, and the prisoner.

The fledgling doctor in Rotor's first three selections encounters courage in, and learns compassion from, long-term convicts assigned to penal colonies on Palawan island or in Davao. Their calm, their gentle patience mask no vengeance or cunningly restrained violence. The prisoners have the endurance of peasants because, for the most part, they come from peasant stock, but also because it is their good fortune to serve out their sentences on penal farms, separated from their wives but not from the communal spirit of rural life. That human bond, reinforced by an unstated, unsentimental alliance with all living things, is nowhere more naturally represented than in Rotor's "How They Transferred the Convicts to Davao." Surrounded by a terrible jungle, "one immense death-house," the prisoners become so dependent on one another's decency and on the cleared plantation which they work and on the wild game at its edge, that when one of them dies, it is questionable that his closest comrade any longer wills his own release. The image of their inseparability comes earlier: clearing a *kaingin*, the convicts cut all the huge trees only part way through; later when one is felled, a whole forest is brought down.

It is this empathy beyond pity, this direct acknowledgment of essential man through the unspoken outcry of outlaw to outsider that gives importance to Rotor's stories. His internes are aware of the agonies of others (whether prisoners or patients) and of their own inadequacies as healers of man. For the young doctor in "Because I Did Not Ask," his own failure and that of his chief even to find their patient's appendix during a routine operation reinforces his rejection by the coterie of his beloved. Referring to both events, he writes her, "You see the scar; I saw and remember the wound. You know only the song; I know, and I'll never forget the silence after the song."

Rotor can mock high society, for its duplicity, its ruthless infighting, as he does in "Dance Music" or "Flower Shop," which have virtually no characters but which focus instead on impressionistic and cosmetic-colored poses that appear like some residue left by the mannered rich. However, his fiction prefers to probe not the weaknesses of the strong, but the strengths of the weak. His prisoners, relaxing in the dusk, look like children playing "*patintero* in some remote *barrio*." They sustain each other in their hardships, and when that is not enough, simply endure. The same reverence which Rotor, once prison doctor, gives to their courage he gives, in "At Last This Fragrance," to the taxi-dancer who, dying soundlessly, drenches herself in an emptying vial of perfume. Another story, "*Dahóng-Paláy*," finds valor in Sebio the Weakling who risks snake bite for his true love; still another, "Kingdom by the Sea," honors the constancy of Totong the Crazy, who is accidentally killed while taking a bride in a mock ceremony underground. Similarly, "Zita" is the story of a romantic girl's initiation, despite her disenchantment, into uncomplaining womanhood. The power of transformation that she represents allies her with Zitas in two other provincial stories, episodes together in an unfinished allegory of the dream, that fragrance in imprisoned, exiled, stricken men's imaginations which is their prayer and refreshment.

ESTRELLA D. ALFON

Since 1960, Estrella Alfon in restless self-dissatisfaction has turned, temporarily, from short fiction to the drama. Excessively conscious of her lack of formal training (although, as one of the younger prewar Veronicans, she must have learned much from such writers as Arguilla and Arcellana or such distinguished editors as A. E. Litiatco, A. V. H. Hartendorp, and Francisco Icasiano), she has sought to discipline her writing under the direction of Severino Montano and his Arena Theater group. In that short time she has won an astounding number of awards, because she has never lost her intuitive understanding that all matters and techniques are, ultimately, modes of characterization.

The quality of the stories in her collection, *Magnificence and Other Stories* (1960), is uneven; but the successful ones, interestingly, seem to find a form in formlessness. Often they are placed either in rural Cebu or on "Espeleta street," an urban neighborhood whose mores, perhaps because of the peoples' poverty or the recentness of their arrival, do not seem remote from the *barrio's*. So close is the author to her characters that, time and again, the shared identity of author and I-narrator is taken for granted; and because the author is curious and observant, because she is telling the story to herself, as it were, in order to comprehend the implications of its startling facts, the narrator is not only rarely identified but keeps vanishing as a presence until she is most evident in the compulsive empathy that remains.

"The Gentle Rain," for example, has a somewhat rambling epistolary form because, in fact, it grew out of a letter the author once wrote. It concerns a family on Espeleta street whose members do not even realize how alike they are. The father brings home a stepmother for the children, and she is already pregnant. The son emigrates to America because the girl he wronged is demanding marriage. His utterly lonely sister bears a child by a man who turns out to be married. Not these vulgar events but the terribleness of the privacies that separate father, daughter, and brother in their need is what the letter form's personal-impersonality provides. The letter-writer remembers how at a party she once, having mistaken this girl for a servant, asked her to serve the trays. On a later occasion, however, she recalls that "for the first time it occurred to me that whereas to her aunt, to me, and to any other person but Maring, her life was merely something to talk about perhaps, something to tell for a lesson maybe, to her it was something she had lived, and had yet to live." It is this realization that compels Estrella Alfon to keep writing. A similar house of mirrors in which, ironically, only the blinded live is constructed in "Mill of the Gods." A young woman is pleased at the death of her father because he has long been unfaithful to his wife; however, in the meantime, the daughter herself has fallen in love with a married man.

Although the situations in such stories are occasionally harsh or even savage—desertion, voyeurism, near-rape—it is this protective note of naivete, this implicit will to define and to understand rather than to judge which dominates. In "Low Wall," the outraged object of a Peeping Tom's adventures ends by feeling guilty "of some fault, some vague shortcoming I had, that was responsible for that lad's being what he was." Or there are the two stories, "Man With a Camera" and "The Photographed Beggar," which are antagonists in a silent debate. The camera-man has taken a revealing, off-guard picture of a professional beggar; and the beggar calls "Thief!" and weeps—for the truth of what is exposed. But the photographer's lack of compassion, his own loneliness which has left him inhumane, are betrayed, too: and there is a pity apparent, that these two fail to see themselves in one another.

Two other stories, although not paired, seem inseparable— "Compostela," which relates the strange peace discovered by the narrator as a refugee in a seabound fastness in the midst of war; and "Perfect Day" which, at the height of happy adolescence, projects the estrangements, disappointments, and sorrows unseen ahead. Estrella Alfon writes of life's tissue of ironies not from despair but from a kind of folk wisdom and perspective that immunizes. "Today was perfect," she writes, "not just because it held laughter; but because like every other today, there were yesterdays to remember, to cry about and to be glad about; and tomorrows to look forward to in fear and hope."

FRANCISCO ARCELLANA

The unique contribution of Francisco Arcellana to the underwritten story—his obsession with simple repetitions—may seem to have been influenced by ancient tribal or epic traditions of the hypnotic, rhythmic utterance. Whatever its origin, the technique is not instinctual but consciously functional, as anyone is assured who has watched the slowness of the creative act as it occurs in Arcellana. Revision becomes genuine re-vision. Furthermore, even after a story is published, it still may not satisfy his flowing estimate of life, so that through other stories with nearly identical themes and situations he writes more and more variations on the original.

That such writing is an art and therefore not the automatic stammer of the mass unconscious can be illustrated by the changes visible in "Divide by Two" when it is compared with the earlier "Divided by Two." The original version was separated into three sections, the first of which was a lengthy description of place—the muddy University of the Philippines housing compound—and of two neighboring households. The third section (four sentences long) introduced a last-minute character only to make possible the comment that the real spite fence in the protagonist's life was not between cottages. The final version discards or absorbs all the exposition of the original prologue and epilogue into the ongoing narration of the central section. All else is left to inference, made sharply clear, however indirectly, by reliance on overrepetition to establish the theme of inner conflict.

Eighty per cent of "Divide by Two" is dialogue, but not conversation. Every line of dialogue is accompanied by an "I said," "Belle said," "Belle asked," to suggest that the narrator and his wife are merely speaking in one another's presence; their togetherness is an accident of ceremony. This fundamental relationship is reinforced by Belle's anger at the fence being built by their neighbor. A whole history of hatred is suggested by the story's being launched by an outburst, which is undercut by her husband's quietness and his dissociation from more than the argument. "I . . . walked to my room," he says; never to *our* room. In the process of criticizing their neighbors, they begin to accuse each other of associating too closely with them. Slowly the narrator is maneuvered to the point where he has no choice but to confront his neighbor; but meanwhile he has been forced to face himself—his inadequacies as a husband and as a creative artist. The ultimate admission—that not his neighbor and not even Belle but he himself is his own adversary—occurs when he chases Belle back into the house. The epigraph is fulfilled: "Is it really violence I cannot stand? Isn't it rather truth?"

Arcellana's use of repetition in "Divide by Two," in order to let the story tell itself, is typical. Its purpose, going beyond that of the musical refrain (just as his rhythms are more than biblical), lies in cumulative effect. One is reminded of the Imagistic poetess, "H. D.," and how she exploits the psychological fact that apparent repetition can involve new contexts and therefore slightly modulated meanings, ironies, even equivocations; and the tempo itself of reiteration can be constructive. The resemblance to Imagism would be more pronounced, could one conceive of the defining, reductive, empirical process being reproduced in its entirety, because this is what occurs in Arcellana.

With some stories one can go further: what at first strikes one as simple repetition gradually builds momentum and the creative or destructive energy of a single particle whirled in a cyclotron. The mechanical whine slowly becomes a function of things in motion, the tightening, narrowing circles of consciousness, like a metal noose inside the mind. Such an effect is apparent in "The Yellow Shawl." [1] Arcellana describes a lovers' rendezvous, first from the man's point of view, then from the girl's. The details recorded by the man, before their meeting, seem distractive—and are intended to be so. So stunned is he by the mysterious failure of their love, that he reads every artifact in the world for a sign of explanation—every bush, every step on the stairs, every dimension of the room. The very superrational formality of such a survey keeps his mind from shattering. The girl's experience of their meeting does not so much duplicate as overlap, envelop, refract his; because their failure is a mystery to her too: until stricken she cries. The third section, objectively narrated, relates the terrible brutality of the Japanese to her mother, nine years earlier, while she and her father could only wait helplessly, unable even to weep.

A spiral development in tempo also marks both "The Mats" and "The Flowers of May," confirming the complementary nature of their content and theme (a 1963 television adaptation melded them successfully). In "The Mats," Mr. Angeles brings home from his southern inspection trip sleeping mats which he unfolds and describes for all his children, including three dead daughters: "Do you think I could forget them?" The question, like the slow ritual, is agonizing, not festively sentimental. The same three deaths are mentioned in "The Flowers of May," but that of Victoria is especially commemorated in each flowering

[1] An earlier draft of this story, impressionistically and artificially arranged into numbered quasi-stanzas, appears to have been influenced by Villa's "Untitled Story." The experiment ended after several months, with one of the few tangibles, the yellow shawl, as the only surviving remnant.

season, by her father, because she had reached sixteen. Two months after Victoria's burial the children's routine of gathering flowers suddenly makes that death undeniable. For Arcellana the fiftieth round in a routine revolution can be critical; in his deceptively linear, circling geometry, nothing is final that may not also be first.

D. PAULO DIZON

Early in *Bamboo and the Greenwood Tree* Father Miguel Bernad observes that Arguilla's influence was decisive in returning Philippine literature to the *barrio* for its subject matter, late in the thirties, despite the fact that few significant writers settled permanently in the provinces. It might also be observed that when city life has been described in Philippine literature, the action typically has been scaled down to the poorer neighborhoods—as Estrella Alfon does with Espeleta street—and to the remnants of *barrio* attitudes there.

D. Paulo Dizon's collection, *Twilight of a Poet and Other Stories*, investigates these remnants without romanticizing them nostalgically. Both the dual prefaces by Alejandro Roces and Celso Carunungan, with the same unfortunate opacity with which these writers have viewed their own work, emphasize the element of humor in Dizon; but there is virtually no comedy in these stories, and what little humor does emerge is wry, bitterly satiric, defensive, Chaplinesque—humor of the Absurd, rather than of the simply incongruous. Rather, Dizon's concern is with presenting his characters' desperately static lives. Sometimes their problems originate in the rural conditions of the culture and its related conservatism—there are two stories of forced elopement, for example, because under the civil code parental consent is legally required, but it is not easily obtained even for adults long physically mature; there is the story of anticipated "miscegenation," with no more respect for private wishes than any small village would permit. But these laborers migrant from tenant farms face, in the city, *barrio* problems without the small village's comforts and consolations. They have sacrificed their communal identity in search of some personal self: and have found, too often, only anonymity.

Dizon's stories are about the bored and the lonely, in rented dorms, boarding houses, and broken homes. "Not Enough Fuel in the World" epitomizes them: the family is slowly chopping up and burning its own house, in order to survive. Husband and wife are alienated in "Twilight of a Poet," alienated and miraculously restored in "Once Upon a Christmas Eve," alienated beyond each other's realization in "The Boarding House." Nearly all of the stories use a personal narrator, but the "I," far from being a device for immediacy or insight, adds poignancy by being an uncomprehending spectator. Life attracts him compellingly (the student in "A Story Told in Anger" says, "What happens to individuals, whether I know them or not, also happens to me in fancy") but eludes him. Moreover, the narrator customarily is either a featureless artist—violinist, harmonica player, but above all a "poet"—or an admirer of one. He is long on suffering but short on sensitivity of the kind that leads to explanations.

Not in spite of but because of this sense of dissolving personality; because of the disembodied sympathy without understanding which seems to parallel the disoriented detached lives of the lonely urban dweller; and because of his obsession with the romantic image of the poet-*manqué* and the imprecision of Dizon's often hackneyed language—whether accidentally or not a forceful experience of a pathetic human condition sometimes issues.

None of the stories engage "social consciousness" in the semi-abstract fashion of the thirties, when Dizon reached manhood. Even his widely known "The Man With Trembling Hands" is, essentially, not about class struggle and betrayal, but about the fumbling confusion of an isolated human being in a time of decision. That he is a company guard felled by strikers he could not shoot is the vehicle for Dizon's irony, not its destination. The very absence of any possibility of identifying with class, or organization, or dramatic cause seems to emphasize the pathos of Dizon's characters, and to make more significant that pathos' temporary amelioration by man's inexplicable need to aspire, as well as to be forgiven for failure.

ANDRES CRISTOBAL CRUZ and PACIFICO N. APRIETO

The salvage of dignity, achieved almost by accident in Dizon, is managed with the utmost craft in *Tondo by Two*, Andres Cruz and Pacifico Aprieto's joint collection. With harsh honesty they have detailed a Manila slum that would make anyman protest, with the protagonist of "Heir": "I want to die living," not live dying. The tuberculosis that racks him finds correspondence in the gnawing vermin that will bring down his father's house yet and destroy those hardwood figures lifted in oblation to an absent sky. "When I was a little kid," another character says in Aprieto's "Night," "I thought the Canal de la Reina was a big beautiful river." But especially since the war, these historic *esteros*, once huge typhoon drains and waterways for commerce brought from the sea on barges, have become open sewers. Into the hot, rented warrens of the *accesoria* the civilized crawl with their Wordsworth ("The world is too much . . ."), hiding from the landlord's threats. Even cottages in the new government compounds are no more than modern slums, where windows of adjacent houses literally open into each other and flower beds are better thought of as rock gardens. In his introduction to *Tondo by Two*, N. V. M. Gonzalez refers to these unblinking disclosures as the "corpse of youth"; but quickly adds, "Perhaps, to the student of anatomy no human body really dies."

The dignity of man is salvaged particularly in the stories of Andres Cristobal Cruz; the irreducible in man is discovered. His lovers are elevated above their pitful circumstances simply by feeling no self-pity. If they had really submitted, the stench would go unnoticed, they would compete to make their little compartment of space as filthy as the rest; but because they are sickened, they prove their health; because they do not despair, they cut the darkness like diamonds. In "The Quarrel," Nina, who has lost her baby, can be driven to hysteria by the landlady; or say an "oddly beautiful" grace over breakfast; in "White Wall" Cris can surrender Magdalena to Victor, the Tondo tough guy, who convincingly says, "I'll do my best." The girl in "So" can wait out the months quietly until her child is born and her angry relatives will no longer imprison her, because along the seafront with Cris she has felt "life, out of their sowing into each other, perfect into and out of each other like the waves." Cris sings to her in his place across the *estero*; and the mating sound of lizards drowns out the creak of orange crate shacks.

The rhythms that Cruz invokes wash over and through the slums, not concealing the stark, bleak details, but nevertheless cleansing; not transfiguring, nevertheless transforming. As Carlos Romulo said of him during the 1962 "Ten Outstanding Young Men" award ceremony: "The objectivity of his representation amounts to almost rejection. But it is a criticism that is equaled by his power of love. His poems and stories testify to the muck of *esteros* and alleyways 'so narrow only lovers could pass.' " The endurance of his lovers is identifiable not with inertia or with insensibility or with undernourishment, but with the kind of unconscious strength and will to prevail that Faulkner would have recognized. It is a strength given not *by* such a leanto society but *to* it in order to sustain it.

These forces for endurance find special forms of corroboration in Cruz's *White Wall: Selected Tondo Stories* (1964). A third of the stories deal with the dilemmas of Ismael del Mundo, son of a provincial judge with political plans for him which Ismael rejects, even though the alternative left him and his wife Nina is impoverishment in the "Interior" (the innermost ring of shantytown), obstetrical difficulties, regrets. After disinheriting himself, Ismael is assailed with loneliness: "It was as if some love within him had just died, but that his beating blood refused to acknowledge death." Temporarily he compromises, by ghostwriting for a senator. Still, he cannot help but be honest with himself; and quits at election time. He has voted for selfhood—and suffers the pains of freedom.

ALBERTO S. FLORENTINO

What often conjugates so many rural and urban stories in the Philippines is the dire poverty of the characters. Under such conditions the writer is tempted merely to describe—hoping that the enormity of the social crime will elicit sympathy—or to incriminate those from a wealthier class who may not have a conscience. Alberto Florentino is distinguished not so much because he is one of the most awarded younger playwrights but because, as Severino Montano says, he has sometimes achieved a "poetic vision of social protest."

Perhaps only the title play in his volume of one-acts, *The World Is an Apple and Other Prize Plays* (1959), is satisfied with relatively direct, naturalistic presentation. Despite his wife's protests, Mario rejoins his old partner-in-crime because he was fired when he stole an apple from a warehouse for his sick child. The play depends on type characters and a predictable formula of event. It is static—except for whatever emotions are engaged by the implied analogy itself: an apple is so little to want; it isn't the world; it *is* the world, the right to want, to become. But this is a kind of poetry precipitated by a play that is otherwise almost a charade, a dumb show. The action does not speak as eloquently as the analogy; Mario does not speak the metaphor so much as it speaks him, without it he is no one.

The other plays may also be disguised poems; but if so, their whole presence, their undiffracted presentation, is involved, and therefore whatever they are, they are more powerful, more memorable. The cemetery in Manila, which in "Cadaver" has been converted into a slum for the living, is itself an expressive character as well as symbol of the quasi-death of the young squatters. It is perfectly appropriate, not contrived, that Torio should have been injured and infected by a corpse whose grave he was robbing. The squatters have been considered no better than the dead so long, that his actual death seems to be the same effect viewed differently. In "The Dancers" an idling father forces his youngest daughter to become a taxi-dancer and prostitute on the excuse that she will simply chaperon her sister. The revelations are all subtly managed through a choreography of character relationships, befitting the ironic subject.

In each of these first three plays, appeals to God—not hysterical or involuntary but sincere and personal—have been made by various characters whose faith is tested by events. "Cavort with Angels"—a quiet play of self-delusion, disillusionment, and finally self-destruction—resembles the enactment of a case before some divine judge who is himself placed on trial because of the innocence of the character. The younger sister who dreams only of "a man just like rainwater" and mothers a drunk in the hope of marriage says that God "must have a purpose. . . . He's only trying us." The drunk not only flees but also kills her pet mouse in doing so. Staging the suicide is managed with lights: she has been gradually poisoned to death by life. "Oli Impan," which sees through the eyes of two children the routing of postwar squatters in Manila just five days before Christmas, is also an indictment of a crime deeper than any social crime defined by the class-conscious. The implied protest is against inhumanity in the largest sense, the betrayal of Christ and the divine in man, through lovelessness, lack of basic hospitality. Whoever treats another man like a beast becomes that beast. The children do not know this, of course. Distraught, they cling to what is familiar to them, a Christmas carol—which they mispronounce, epitomizing the babel of human divisions itself, the failure of communion.

Such plays are prayers, more than social pleas in the bureaucratic sense; their appeal is not to organized charity nor to the social welfare agency, but to any man with self-respect and self-knowledge who would be lessened by the symbolic death of any other man. Everyman is a squatter; the world is someone else's apple. Florentino is concerned with what the haves have not, and what the have-nots sometimes have.

CARLOS BULOSAN

Most of the stories of Arguilla, Gonzalez, Rotor, Alfon, Arcellana, Dizon, Aprieto, and Cruz are serious stories, even those that are not quite solemn or sober. Essentially, Carlos Bulosan, too, was a serious man, whom Leopoldo Yabes once considered the successor to Rizal. One of the great ironies of Bulosan's unfortunate career is that he is more likely to be remembered exclusively as a teller of comic tales (if not as an alleged plagiarist or leftist sympathizer),[2] unless *Sound of Falling Light: Letters in Exile* (1960), edited by Dolores Feria, can reverse a trend. There, in a letter dated 1955, a year before his death, Bulosan says urgently, "Let me remind you that *The Laughter of My Father* is *not* humor; it is satire; it is indictment against an economic system that stifled the growth of the primitive, making him decadent overnight without passing through the various stages of growth and decay. The hidden rottenness in this book is so pronounced in another series of short stories, that the publishers refrained from publishing it for the time being."

To some extent this must be read as the afterjudgment of a man who had become progressively disillusioned with his own fortunes as well as with social progress. He had little more than a year left to live; and his failing health must have assured him that the dead-serious novels and other projects that he planned would never be finished. Undoubtedly, he regretted the kind of popularity that his collection had brought him ten years earlier. Yet it is also true that, beneath the stories' hilarity, one some-

[2] See Dolores Stephens Feria, "Carlos Bulosan: Gentle Genius," *Comment* 2 (First Quarter, 1957), pp. 57–65.

times senses a subtle complaint against the near-penal conditions of the economic structure; and under the sentimentality, a genuine affection for those whose good humor and capacity for love survive this captivity. In his two dozen tales, the antics of Bulosan's Ilocanos typically are a response, desperately overcompensatory, to flood ("My Father Goes to Court"), wartime decimation ("The Soldiers Came Marching"), land-grabbing from the illiterate ("The Tree of My Father"), child labor ("My Uncle Manuel's Homecoming"), avalanches and house-burning ("My Father Goes to Church"), and similar catastrophes.

Bulosan, who often spoke of himself as an exile, must have thought of his homeland with mixed nostalgia. He wrote his title story in 1939, while he was broke and unemployed in San Pedro; he found it in his hat late in 1942, when the world writhed in pain. Inevitably he remembered his people's travail and betrayal, and the patterns of their immunity. Even though his identification with the Pinoy workers in the fields and canneries on the American West Coast prevented his deserting their cause, his craft suggested a way of sustaining his faith in Philippine peasant endurance. He tried—unconsciously, he insisted—to link his people with the timeless races of the sturdy.[3] As he wrote to Jose de los Reyes early in 1948: *"The Laughter of My Father* is actually a book of modernized folktales from all over the world, but adapted to the Philippine scene and embellished with my kind of humor"; and, at their best, with Bulosan's kind of humanity, the same sort that makes his painful personal history, *America Is in the Heart* (1946), so moving.

The ultimate irony is that successful misreading of Bulosan, along with the influence in the Philippines of Saroyan's stories of West Coast Armenians, Steinbeck's mock-heroic *paisanos*, and the lesser tales of Erskine Caldwell, has encouraged imitation of the most pretentious sort. Reviewers incapable of distinguishing between enduring literature and transparent local

[3] Compare *Filipino Popular Tales*, ed. Dean S. Fansler (Hatboro, Pa.: Folklore Associated, 1965), a facsimile of the original 1921 edition; or Manuel and Lyd Arguilla, *Philippine Tales and Fables* (Manila: Capitol, 1957).

color share in the responsibility which continues to promote, in foreign eyes, the oversimplified image of the Filipino as Peter Pan or as the lovable village idiot, everyman's eccentric uncle.

ALEJANDRO R. ROCES

When *Of Cocks and Kites and Other Short Stories* failed as a television play in 1962, blame was laid variously on over-acting, underdirection, and the difficulties inherent in producing a composite (the 1959 collection included seven stories) or of transferring a work of the imagination from one medium to an-other. However, a reexamination of the original volume reveals that, by selecting a few episodes only and foreshortening these, the adaptation was an improvement on the original, overrepeti-tive formulas.

What provides unity to the collection, even more than the recurrence of Kiko-the-cocker in all but one of the stories, is Roces' dependence on burlesque and "situational comedy," at the expense of characterization and emergent theme. Although the humor is leveled at the lowest common denominator, it fails to provide the sly insight that one expects from genuine folk humor such as Faulkner reproduces. So indistinct are the human characters in Roces' stories, that simply by contrast the fighting cocks have more interesting, if hardly intricate, personalities. There are the hermaphrodite who slays an entranced opponent, the supercock who stabs himself by mistake, the cock who wins by *rigor mortis*, the king cock brought down by his crown, and so on. Nevertheless, despite the noticeable superiority of cocks to the *sabungeros*, no satiric correspondence is intended or achieved (as in the animal allegory, for example, of George Orwell).

Because Roces has imitated directly "The Celebrated Jump-ing Frog of Calaveras County," he has often been called the Mark Twain of the Philippines. Unfortunately, he offers none of the moral and social complexities of Twain in *Huckleberry*

Finn or any of the other deceptively simple, postjournalistic works. The manneristic writing of Roces is more reminiscent, perhaps, of Bret Harte at his worst. However, where Harte sometimes let medieval phrases intrude in order to suggest the knightly quality of his gentlemen cowboys, improprieties in Roces' language represent inexplicable lapses. The most striking examples come from the title story: "All the domesticated fowls scampered for cover, except the mother hen which flushed after the gallinivorous bird and engaged it in aerial combat. The three flapped downward—in pennate confusion—till they hit ground. And the next thing you knew the raptorial bird was fleeing the field with the rasorial fowl still in truculent pursuit."

The high reputation of these stories must be blamed on the critics, for it is doubtful that Roces could have had any illusions, originally, about the literary value of these slight, episodic, artificially heightened, embarrassingly depopulated anecdotes. Even if there is some small truth to Arturo Roseburg's remark that, were cockfighting to disappear completely from the Philippines, its lore could be reconstructed from Roces' stories, perhaps the cultural essayist, not the writer of fiction, should have been charged with that minor obligation. And what could be more comic than the serious tone of Roseburg's assertion, in the introduction to *Of Cocks and Kites*, that "Roces has done for gamecocks what Melville did for whales"?

CELSO AL. CARUNUNGAN

The synopsis on the dust jacket of *Like a Big Brave Man*, in its 1960 American edition, wrongly explains that the novel's young hero, Crispin, returns to the Philippines upon learning of his father's death (actually it is his uncle who dies). For such an error, an editorial assistant undoubtedly must answer. However, the same jacket quotes Celso Carunungan in an even grosser misreading of his own work. With complete seriousness, the author argues that his intention is to demonstrate that whatever distinctions may arise in their social status or wherever they happen to live—at home or abroad, in *barrio* or city—"through the deeply ingrained seed of religious faith and traditional passion, they have remained the same real Filipinos at heart." Whether "traditional passion" means "passion for tradition" or "customary emotionalism," there is little of either in the novel. Crispin's obedient return to his father seems less a mature acceptance of family obligation than a contrivance to end a structurally defective narrative. The novel is artificially divided into two parts (joined by an interlude: the air flight), established by place: rural Philippines and metropolitan America. The boy, Crispin, is provided with mobility (a G.I. who takes a fancy to him wills him free passage to—of course—Brooklyn) but with little opportunity for maturing. Although Crispin occasionally discovers things, there is no sense in the novel of growth and development. Nor is the mechanical nature of the movement disguised. Crispin's arrival in America is as contrived as his departure: it is not until Thanksgiving, long after his arrival in New York, that Crispin is invited to the home of the dead soldier who made his trip possible.

If the phrase on the dust jacket refers to "emotionalism," then it must be observed that a number of episodes in the novel concern "puppy love," or sentimental attachment to a carabao or (as Crispin leaves the islands) to all the birds he ever shot or to Filipino recipes (in an incredibly cartoon-like chapter, Cris's Aunt Sally catches a thief because he cannot resist her chicken *adobo*). Some of the more genuinely moving scenes involve not Filipinos but Americans—the divorced woman on the plane who stoically surrenders her son to his father; the predicament of the dead soldier's fiancee who has married his cousin—or the Americanized boy, Eddie, distraught over the imminent break between his parents. (Not that Carunungan has tried to do justice to Americans: the incidence of divorce is stunningly high in this novel.)

The fact is that, with some notable exceptions, all the characters in this novel are presented so superficially that they are incapable of genuine emotion, motivation, energy, and involvement. It is this blurring reduction to nonentity, rather than any incisive perception, that makes possible the author's claim that he sees a oneness among all Filipinos, whatever their external distinction. Carunungan speaks of their having in common "the deeply ingrained seed of religious faith"; but only the most routine—or questionable—examples are given. When Crispin "gives up" Rosa, the barmaid, to her fiance because both are religious (she will play the part of the Virgin, he means, in the Easter festival; her fiance attends church), he feels he has learned more of life than he ever could in Father Sebastian's class in holy doctrine. The chief function of the priest himself is to defend, to the M.P.'s, the American soldier who gave Crispin's family pieces of parachute nylon for clothes and Father Sebastian pieces for altar cloths.

Selection of a boy's point of view, which permitted a structure based on the growth of an intelligence from innocence to experience, as in Gonzalez (or to a very special kind of corruption, as in Henry James), seems in Carunungan to serve merely the purposes of evasion noticeable elsewhere. Certain of the chapter divisions evidently were afterthoughts: Eddie's moving story is stuffed so tightly into its chapter that Crispin, the observer, might as well have left the room, for all the response he fails to make. Despite the serious intent offered on the dust jacket, the author clearly does not want to get deeply involved with life. *Like a Big Brave Man* is less a novel than a series of caricatures pasted together to give the illusion of motion. Even Carunungan's humor tends to be fragmented and momentary, rather than connected (although there are numerous repetitions of the same device: Restituto Fruto becomes Tutti Frutti, and Rolando Policarpio, Roly Poly, for example). So often does the narrative seem to exist for the sake of the gag-lines, and the Pinoys or common *tao* for broad burlesque, that the reader wants to flee, for justice's sake, to the finer proportionings provided by Carlos Bulosan. Or he turns hastily to Gonzalez, whose more subtle folk humor provides a better clue to what keeps sub-

merged, impoverished man from despair. It may be true, as Cris
is told, that "the simple people don't ask much"; but, being
much, they deserve the respect of an honest portraiture.

JUAN C. LAYA

In "Renaissance in Many Tongues," [4] the report Wallace
Stegner made in 1951 on the condition of literature in the
Philippines, he noted the rural orientation of most urban writers.
Then he added: "They write with anger and bitterness of what
the war did to the Philippines, but they write of what it did to
the villages, not of what it did to Manila." Not only is it still
true that all Philippine novels about the Second World War
have been novels of guerrilla action rather than of metropolitan
military occupation, but at least one—Juan Laya's *This Barangay* (1950)—is less concerned with violent action of any kind
than with how ancient tribal social structures kept war refugees
alive and responsibly organized in their jungle fastnesses.

Laya's first novel, *His Native Soil* (1941), watched while a
young Filipino too long absent in a foreign land rediscovered
home and the roots of self, sometimes by being made to realize
the inappropriateness of rapid change and alien conveniences
to his rural birthplace. The theme of *This Barangay* also involves
a return, redemption through a heritage sometimes forgotten,
the tribal now becoming a communal spirit. Because of Laya's
persistent attempts to revitalize the past, it is not easy to understand his comment on his first novel: "The author gets uneasy
and bored whenever people mention the novel, for it is of the
past, and there is too much present and a little future left to
attend to." Perhaps this is an instance of premonition; perhaps
it shows how present even the past had to be, in order to interest
Laya. There is something of that sensing of the vital passing

[4] *Saturday Review of Literature*, XXIV (Aug. 4, 1951), 27–8, 52–3; excerpted
in Miguel Bernad, S.J., *Bamboo and the Greenwood Tree* (Manila: Bookmark,
1961), p. 21.

moment in *This Barangay*, a quality that both excites and occasionally confuses.

"Barangay" is the name that schoolmaster Emilio Veloria and his bride Nena want to give to the cluster of guerrilla huts in the Pangasinan hills. Because Emilio has intelligence as well as strength, he is made *barrio* lieutenant of the young settlement. His most immediate problem is to restrain Tony and Itong, two hotheads, whom he prevents from assassinating Attorney Benig, neighboring puppet-mayor. Although Emilio's father was killed by Benig's brother during a tenant-*hacendero* scuffle not long before, Benig himself has just saved Nena from the Japanese invaders.

Then Emilio is free to solve the daily dilemmas of the *barangay*. He assigns one hour of guard duty and two hours of community labor to everyone except rich Mr. Sabias, who hires a substitute. He spends his own savings on tetanus serum. Nena has to run a store. Finally, he trains the men to use bows and arrows, for defense and for hunting. Emilio gives himself so wholly to the present work, that he seems easily to forget the past, especially the murder of his sister Lily by the Japanese.

Gradually trouble infiltrates: Lieutenant Aldecoa, suspected deserter from USAFFE, who is finally told by Emilio to leave for talking against the American army; and Filipino bandits. Through a warning from Attorney Benig, the *barangay* captures the weapons from the bandit gang during a raid, and then gives Benig sanctuary. One of the community, Pidiong, courts Josefina, another refugee recovering before she passes on to Manila.

Later, Japanese soldiers are ambushed after degrading an old woman in the market. Benig dies, killing his own brother Innong, the traitor. There are terrible reprisals; yet the guerrillas continue to fight not just for their safety but, as one Filipino says, for their dignity as a people. However, when Lieutenant Aldecoa returns, claiming authority as an army officer, they surrender their guns to him. He turns out to be a bandit and is killed with an ax in a neighboring town while attempting rape.

For a while, things go well in the *barangay*. A school is organized, with a practical curriculum in which books play only a secondary role. Their weapons are restored; they celebrate the rice harvest. When Sabias is robbed and Emilio's house burned by bandits, the whole *barangay* helps the latter rebuild. Sabias, who cannot live a poor man, kills himself; but Josefina lets Pidiong accompany her to Manila, Emilio learns he will have a child, and at the end defeated but strong Filipinos and Americans from Bataan come to reinforce their numbers. The *barangay* now has resources for survival.

For all its realistic detail, Laya's novel, like Emilio himself, often misdirects its devotion. As *barrio* lieutenant, Emilio pays less and less attention to his wife so that he seems more than surprised that she is going to have a child. The promise of birth at the novel's end is a sentimental device to support the other suddenly fashioned symbols of hope, permitting a triumphant ending although the action has barely begun.

As a matter of fact, there is no sign that Emilio has learned to understand himself or his relation with his wife. As he is presented, Emilio is not a man of ideas but of certain aptitudes —he has a teacher's knack for organization. While he builds the *barangay*, he puts aside his sister, his father, his wife, one by one. Yet the author holds Emilio up for emulation. The novel suffers from a major indecisiveness on Laya's part. He seems unable to decide where the center of his story should lie: with Emilio the person or with the community concept represented by the *barangay*. That a group, without leader or spokesman, can be the "hero" of fiction has been demonstrated by Ignacio Silone's *Fontamara* or Jean Giono's "The Corn Dies." Laya's choice here, however, is to treat Emilio with special importance, so that the theme of civic spirit can emerge only when Emilio sacrifices his family to it. No real adjustment of self to family and of family to society is indicated. By novel's end, the *barangay* has improved the safety of its members without their having grown in dignity.

Whenever Emilio's feelings are exposed, the author expresses them with the false lyricism of Hemingway's romanticized primitivism in *For Whom the Bell Tolls*. Other characters are equally cosmetic types, from beach resort billboards: Virginia Fe (who first appeared in *His Native Soil*) and Statesman. Perhaps this occasional retreat to personality betrays a shyness on Laya's part to accept wholly his own revived and sentimental notion of the *barangay*. Perhaps for nationalistic reasons—encouraged by his subject: survival in wartime—Laya relied on an old heritage which was inadequate to express his own ideal society. (His history of the community school idea, *Little Democracies of Bataan* (Manila: Inang Wika, 1951), was published only a year later.) At best, a *barangay* can be called a primitive democracy. It is too feudal, too tribalistic, too centralized in authority and power to compare with enlightened democracy.

The resultant confusion in novel structure is shown also in *This Barangay's* overreliance on melodramatic skirmishes with the Japanese and with bandits, despite Emilio's early realization that disease is by far the worst enemy of the *barangay*. Consequently, although the separate incidents are often exciting (Aldecoa's peculiar offstage death is exceptional), the novel gives the impression of being episodic (the numerous arbitrary divisions are disturbing), a series of undirected climaxes, and therefore more a retouched diary than a well-formed novel. Still it is less cluttered than the first novel. Had Laya lived, a third novel might have shown mastery at last in characterization and full-length structuring.

EDILBERTO TIEMPO

By far, the most provocative Filipino war novel in terms of actual events made available to the author is the semihistorical *Watch in the Night* (1953). But importance is a gift to his subject which a writer's craft makes; not the reverse. Too often, in this novel, Edilberto Tiempo offers information uninformed further by imagination; and, so, nearly defeats the purposes of fiction.

Ramon Cortes, a Protestant minister whose thinking is considered unorthodox by church elders because he believes in evolution, wears polka-dot handkerchiefs, and has fallen in love with a Catholic girl, becomes a chaplain in Cebu during the Japanese invasion. He experiences selfish hoarding by town officials, the collaboration of his expected father-in-law, the terrors of scorched-earth policies, occupation, underground resistance, and retreat to Negros. After Wainwright orders the USAFFE to surrender, four Filipino envoys from Cebu advise Negros to capitulate. Impulsively, Cortes who, no longer calling himself a minister, has been assigned to guard the envoys, shoots them to death. To protect his fellow soldiers from reprisal, he decides to surrender himself to the Japanese, but his mind is changed when the boat taking him to Cebu is strafed and its passengers are forced to swim for their lives. However, doubts of conscience still abuse him; so that, although occasions for murderous violence present themselves during his encounters with Filipino informers and men mutilated by the Japanese, Cortes refuses to kill more of his country's enemies. Instead, he devotes himself to working the soil and to pitying himself when, for example, in a preying python being destroyed by two victimized boars, he sees his own predicament: legend wants to force him to continue the role of killer. Only when he officiates at the funeral of another minister who once reminded him that man's duty is to bring good out of evil, does Cortes feel that he has begun to return to his proper service.

His own sermon suggests to the resistance movement that individual identity is earned through communal sharing. Feeling that he himself is the result of all the men whose suffering he partly shared, Cortes is prepared to suffer too, whatever his new-found sense of mission dictates to him: "There were things that had to be done no matter how revolting."

In synopsis, Watch in the Night has all the mature sense of a solemn promise, but the actual telling is a betrayal. Scene after scene is left undeveloped because the author's strategy depends on public addresses, lengthy sermonizing, and one-way conversations. The assertive quality of this speechmaking is especially objectionable because it finds no compensation in a felt human presence: the book's thought passages are generally confused, and its actions seldom graphic.

The early part of the novel, which should have established the reality of place and person, the climate of credibility, is singularly fugitive. Because the author has chosen to make Cely Castillo a Catholic, he is faced with the problem of having the heroine of a novel whose religious implications are enormous and crucial discard her faith for the man she loves. Cely is offered as a simple woman, long-suffering, well educated, warmhearted —but apparently as superficial in her religious commitment as in her paintings. Consequently the minister who would choose her for a wife is equally suspect. Cortes himself, as first presented, needs strength to borrow, not to lend: the details of the polka-dot handkerchief and the quarrels about evolution are badly chosen if they are intended to establish Cortes as a man advanced in thought and capable of the unexpected. Little insight into the character of the minister of the Gospel is provided before Cortes becomes a killer. If Tiempo means by this careful lack of characterization that Cortes should be considered capable of anything, it is at least equally valid to argue that without an identity Cortes is capable of nothing. Whatever he does is gratuitous, and his subsequent self-examination is superfluous.

Cortes and Cely are shadows further darkened by the author's avoidance of a sense of place throughout the novel's first quarter. The book's forepart lacks exacting images, fleshly details—as if nothing mattered. The surprising fact is that, shortly thereafter, during the Japanese invasion, Cortes thinks of Cebu City with diminishing emotion as if at the instant that places die, men tend to impersonalize them. The experience of the book, however, is exactly the reverse of Cortes' conclusion. As threats of destruction spread, the sense of place gradually awakens and intensifies. Typically, author and character are at odds.

Although occasionally and momentarily realism informs the broader outlines of *Watch in the Night,* as the novel proceeds

Cortes himself becomes increasingly incomprehensible and therefore an inadequate center. He deserts his ministry to become a soldier; then impulsively kills four men entrusted to his care. Immediately he is filled with doubts, which he tries to satisfy by offering himself to the Japanese for execution; but when he is accidentally prevented from sacrificing himself, he makes no second effort. Instead he attempts to employ himself in the more peaceful ways of resistance. He will plant and harvest and carry; he will not fight as a soldier, even under conventional rules of warfare. However, a Japanese strafing attack sends a second revelation: burying a fellow minister, Cortes regains his vocation —he wants to be again the "militant minister" whom admirers once pictured; but now he will be capable of killing, in the name of the Lord of the Old Testament, with a righteous anger that will justify the use of any means.

Thus he glorifies his former action by dressing it in ministerial robes. But the author, as if aware that some readers might be more scrupulous than Cortes, has at least made him suffer a brief purgatory of doubt. If the solution seems too easy and its arrival too contrived, nevertheless it is the only one to be expected of Cortes. His mind is consistently fumbling, shallow, displaced, evasive, and pitifully rationalizing. When he wants to admit evolution into his sermons, he speaks of the Old Testament as allegory. When he wants to justify his mysterious impulses, he turns to the Mosaic God of wrath for comfort. He is willing to murder others coldly, whose actions he condemns, although he is never sure of their ultimate motives. Yet he forgives his own actions, because he assumes that his ends (almost undiscoverable) are beyond question. Cortes' real game is to hide his individual soul within mass responsibility. The philosophy of solidarity which he finally advocates is not earned but seized in desperation.

Because Cortes is the point-of-view character, the impression is given that *Watch in the Night* is a serious book about redemption in a difficult world of corrupt means. Once Cortes is observed objectively, however, so that the reader is not included in the man's self-deception, the book can be read as the progressive deterioration of an intellect unprepared for either the world or religion. Even then, the subject wears an air of abstraction, not of reality. Tiempo has failed to discover the fictional eye (it need not be the narrator's) capable of seeing itself.

The final disappointment derives from the failure to develop other significant elements, in addition to Cely's Catholicism: the collaboration of her Spanish father; the selfish acts of town officials during the seizure of native Japanese goods; or characterizations such as Rufino's, the dwarf who insists on enlisting. These remain tearings from a notebook. Even if there is a kind of excitement in the thought of Tiempo's stealing the original data for this book (a history of the Seventh Military District, "They Called Us Outlaws") out through a blockade by submarine, the circumstances of composition hardly compensate for the lack of vividness and concentration in the finished novel. *Watch in the Night* is a short novel without accessory compactness of precision or dramatic compression.

One of the unfortunate results of the novel's failure to define its purpose is that American publishers of the very slightly revised edition, *Cry Slaughter* (1957), themselves apparently misled, further muddied the book's intention by such announcement as: "This is the [guerrillas'] story, raw, honest, unprettified —and the story of the hungry, love-starved women who waited for them in the hills."

Tiempo's most recent novel, *More Than Conquerors* (1964), is less digressive but also less compelling, because it scales down the area of agonized decision and action in order to dwell on tests of physical, rather than moral, courage. Only the dust jacket simulates a mission for the novel that is other than modest: "Andres and his brothers call up echoes of the Christ figure in the midst of temptation and at Calvary." Actually, a Philippine "Magdalene" sacrifices herself so that the alleged Savior can escape to meet the Allied invasion forces.

The story of the capture, torture and escape of Andres Bantayan, who helps run an underground press, is thoroughly credible but equally predictable. While any comparison with such subtle and labyrinthine classics as E. E .Cummings' *The Enormous Room* or Arthur Koestler's *Darkness at Noon* might be invidious, it is not unjust to lament the novel's failure to match the power of such recorded anguish and sustained heroism as Lord Russell's *The Knights of Bushido* or A. V. H. Hartendorp's *The Santo Tomas Story*. Fiction justifies its being taken seriously only when it is "superior history," an image of life larger than that in any archives.

STEVAN JAVELLANA

For many postwar years Manila wore the air of an occupied city. The black market in Quiapo, the fortress houses with broken-bottle walls and barred windows, the wallets buttoned against the skin—like the rubber gas masks in downtown surplus stores—all these were leftovers of war. Perhaps they were symptoms too of its causes. Is there ever conquest without some consent? Like many Filipino cities, Manila was still occupied by fear—of itself.

One of the signs of maturity in Javellana's *Without Seeing the Dawn* (1947) is that occasionally it recognizes that inhumanity can be the trait of a man regardless of nationality. The "hero" is accurately called at times a "male carabao," at other times a "demon." From the start, he is as much his own enemy as are the Japanese. The author's preliminary note, therefore, is wrong when it implies that, before the war, all Filipinos were industrious and their wives pious: "One night disaster like death came to this village . . . with the coming of the Japanese." Actually, disaster like death comes inch by inch for many months before its last arrival. The novel itself knows this, even if the author at times does not. Like his own subtitles, Javellana inclines to divide life too easily into Day and Night. When Ricardo Suerte, at the end, asks for and receives forgiveness from his wife for crimes against the living and the unborn, he achieves a stature hardly foreseeable in the book's earlier half but recognizable as human and deserving of (in the author's words) "respectful understanding."

Without Seeing the Dawn does not start promisingly. Carding and Lucing consummate a marriage of mutual lust. He works hard, like any other healthy animal on Panay; but when their first child is stillborn, he fails to see why his wife must weep. Her sensibility too is short-ranged. Soon she welcomes the body of their landlord's "princely" son and earns back her husband only by concealing the truth of her passion. Carding's turn to be unfaithful comes when, after the landlord repossesses their land, they are forced to live in the city. Carding makes money as a stevedore and as the bodyguard of Rosing, a cabaret entertainer; finding her attractive, he lives with her until, just as abruptly, he decides to return to his wife who has gone back to the *barrio*. Their wayward passions spent, they settle down, helping each other survive fever, childbirth, and flood. The last, however, destroys their crops, so that Carding thinks of migrating to Mindanao—just as orders come for all men over eighteen to report to the constabulary in Tarlac.

Book II finds Carding returned to Panay, having survived Bataan, the Death March, and imprisonment. Believing resistance useless, he refuses to join the guerrillas, although he does help kill the Filipino bandit Morada. Later the Japanese, in search of "Indians" (guerrillas), start a burn-rape-mutilate-kill campaign. When Lucing tells that her unborn child might be a Japanese and that her father-in-law died trying to defend her from assault, Carding ambushes and mutilates one of the enemy and joins the guerrillas. He deserts his wife. Later he murders her uncle Jaime, an anti-American serving the Co-Prosperity Sphere. His shocked *barrio* mates call him a demon, especially when he also slays his cousin, an armed collaborator. Finally he assists his wife in childbirth, intending to murder the child. However, when it is stillborn, he feels reprieved and even cleansed, as if all his urges had originated somewhere beyond his personal will. But Lucing, knowing his intention, says that he should have wanted the child to live because it was at least part hers. She sends him away.

In town, Rosing, the cabaret prostitute, destroys an ammunition dump for him; and though he is tortured by the Kempeitai, her execution releases him. After killing their informer, he organizes a bolo battalion which makes a suicidal attack on the armed town when all surrounding inhabitants have been ordered into a "collective *barrio*." Along the line of march, Carding stops to ask Lucing's forgiveness. Moved, she decides not to flee but to wait for his dead body to be brought back to her.

As animal-Carding finally stands erect, the author too, despite two-thirds of his narrative, achieves a characterization that can stand. What compelling reason can Javellana have had for making Carding a bull carabao? The seduction-counterseduction seems planned largely to satisfy the supposed tastes of "The Fighting Men of America" to whom the book is dedicated. From unbridled flesh, the temper's demon can emerge—but hardly the vertical human that Carding becomes, whose death is cause for lamentation because he knows sin.

When his violent instincts are left unsatisfied by the stillbirth of Lucing's third child, Carding tries to draw merit from that accident and forgives himself for his murderous intention. Neither his wife nor the author allows such unearned absolution, however: and here the novel justifies its existence. Carding has to grow through suffering and self-realization, he has to see that the severest struggle is within himself, before a clean death can be granted. Actually no visible revelation, after he is outcast, prepares Carding for his birth as a human. Even the Kempeitai torture can hardly be the turning point. Probably, therefore, the reader's sympathy is won by proxy—the suffering of legless Gondoy, the abducted Alicia, the innocent old man with his son in the death cells. This is, strangely, not predominantly a novel of hatred for the invaders. The Japanese become opportunities which allow Carding's victory over his instincts. The scene of greatest combat is inside the man. The fact remains, however, that the conclusion is won largely by proxy—another sure indication that the first half of the novel should have treated Carding in a way that would not make his final rise miraculous.

Furthermore, although the early characterizations and offhand seductions (as well as the romanticized behavior of Rosing, early and late) are formulas borrowed with little conscience, they find little support from language that is surprisingly uneven. Javellana fails to exploit properly the clash with Morada and the ambushing of Polo, both of which are dismissed before they have fully developed as scenes; and the mutilations of Flora and Lucio, which are intended to be vivid in horror, are less realized than the later restrained descriptions of Gondoy's wound and Alicia's dilemma.

Nevertheless, because it becomes more and more honest, and less melodramatic, and more visibly not a story of glandular impulses, *Without Seeing the Dawn* is not a novel easily ignored. It is only regrettable that it did not understand sooner and better its own nature, so that the personal struggle could have been substantiated less by dreams and superstitions and more by that full, if instinctual, apprehension of the human predicament of which the simplest Juan de la Cruz, the commonest *tao*, is often capable.

AIDA RIVERA

Japanese occupation was a more than special time for the Philippines: it was a late stage in the long ritual of its tempering. The bending and testing of those days left misshapen many who, in their effort to survive, rationalized each weakness into a necessity. Consequently, when Aida Rivera chose wartime as the dark-fired crucible for three of the five stories in *Now and At the Hour and Other Short Stories*, she was not only exploiting a natural symbol for human strain but also preparing a matrix (ideally a deeper receptacle than she managed) for the remaining stories, whose relationship in this collection otherwise would seem tenuous or accidental. The close geometry of a poet's kinship with wife and *querida,* or of kitchen maid to her ex-lover and the child of her unloved husband is congruent with the fractioning of people dividing themselves among conquerors and liberators and their own elaborate disguises; and this congruence is clearly not the artist's work but a design in nature seen and respected with something dangerously close, at times, to speechlessness, to awe.

Aida Rivera gives the impression of assigning herself, against her will, a special role in the craft of fiction. What she writes is too knowledgeable to be called sketches; but if these are short stories, they are short with a vengeance: their knowledge lacks one dimension. The context often is so compressed that the crisis is overpowering; its sharpness is felt like a sudden twinge. But the reader who stops to wonder, to understand, finds that the pain is a symptom of something unexplained and, worse, unexplored. The story steps back at the threshold of sensation.

Is this not what Nolan Miller meant when, after judging this collection worthy of the 1954 Hopwood Awards at Michigan, he still complained that "Young Liberator" should have been told from Ling's point of view, not from one noticeably alien to Miss Rivera? Em is alien not because he is American; nor are only his speech and actions contrived. Typically, the author has been satisfied with staging the gesture of crisis, a kind of charade; no byplay is allowed, no dramatic proliferation, no cross-examination of motive. "Young Liberator" barely escapes being a stereotype; Ling is nearly as alien as Em; and what Miller was asking is, "Where is the insight? At what turn is the unspeakable somehow spoken?" Here, even the speakable is unspoken; the author's words, like her characters', have the ring of convention, not of conviction. Here was material for a short story: Philippine hospitality, left hand openhanded, right hand shriveled by Spanish colonial custom; innumerable other fictions dependent on the interest that would individualize boy or girl. All Aida Rivera has done is to illustrate the drained and fleshless line drawings made for her text by Teresita Sarmiento. When structures are so compressed that one senses poetry as model—

lyric, rather than narrative—the suspicion grows that the author, laboring too long to avoid overwriting, has failed to see or say enough.

Although none of the other stories, fortunately, are quite as pale as "Young Liberator," two others re-present the same esthetic problem. The situation in "Now and at the Hour"—murder of the collaborator falsely accused—is substance for minute inquest; but it is relegated to the status of "thriller" only, an entertainment in grotesque irony, because the killer-*malgré* no sooner emerges from the community of characters than he vomits once and fades back into anonymity, leaving the story to superstition and St. Elmo's fire and other theatrical inconsequences. The texture of "The Madonna Face" is equally promising—the casual camaraderie of events in a girl's life during occupation; one waits, refreshed, for these to be given significance—but judgment passed on the girl friend who gives comfort to the enemy is so stock and standard that the earlier details of day-to-day are not so much enlivened by the climax as absorbed and deadened by their routine. The impulse to feel shocked is checked by recognition of the mere incongruity of what is allowed to become only an incident.

What redeems "The Madonna Face"—the girlish excitement and naivete associated with its young narrator—becomes, in "The Chiefest Mourner," a resource for authority. The commonplace quarrel between wife and *querida* is nourished by the absence of the man in question (his death makes human judgment trivial), but particularly by the ever-presence of its complicated adolescent observer and commentator. Her innocence is both amusing and instructive; too young to be commandeered for acts of prejudice, she is capable of unself-conscious pity and unreasoned understanding at the apparent retreat of the *querida*.

The same paradoxical knowing-naivete, this time in a young mother, gives "Love in the Cornhusks" its quality as firsthand feeling. That her Bagobo husband is not described or discussed is as characteristic of Tinang as painfully copied language is of Amado, whose first love letter, arriving too late, suggests the failure of communication between person and person, for whom these troubled lovers are epitome. But more important, her sudden shake-up when the child is threatened by a snake takes us to the other side of Tinang's dreams, one of those reserved places that literature is authorized to penetrate.

Here Aida Rivera is at her best: the lyric-like tale of inexperience fumbling toward a definition of what threatens the undefended shores of its consciousness; the young passion trying to take on weight and stature, trying to survive initiation without violation. But such tales can achieve proper form only if attached to characters appropriately sensitive and available: for then the central character is not so much a way into the narrative as the narrative is a way into the character.

EDITH L. TIEMPO

Most of the characters in Edith Tiempo's *Abide, Joshua and Other Stories* are white-collar professionals whose low incomes find partial compensation by their positions of authority in rural communities. Conceivably, therefore, they should be expected to inhabit the best of two possible worlds. Instead, they express an uneasy poise between conflicting pressures. Most typical of them all is the Prufrockian principal/teacher caught in the agony of a kind of living death and far from the stereotype of the Visayan islander as reckless hedonist.[5]

Mr. Rosales, principal in "The Dam," regrets not having been stern enough with his mischievous young teacher, Conde; yet, knowing how the other faculty members—childlike, in his view—resent his "officialism," he yearns to cry out "brother" to Conde or to his own young cousin somewhere on the Korean

[5] For further corrections of the stereotype, see Donn V. Hart, *The Philippine Plaza Complex: A Focal Point in Culture Change* (New Haven: Yale University Press, 1955), *Securing Aquatic Products in Siaton Municipality, Negros Oriental Province, Philippines* (Manila: Bureau of Printing, 1956), and *The Cebuan Filipino Dwelling in Caticugan: Its Construction and Cultural Aspects* (New Haven: Yale University Press, 1959).

front. Mr. Perfecto, principal in "The Corral," wins Pilar, but only because, despite her unspoken love for a woodchopper, custom and her own humility require that she submit to Perfecto, her former employer and the friend of her father. In "The Dimensions of Fear," middle-aged teacher Agujo, made vindictive by loneliness, is reduced to cheating and stealing, which he cannot bear to admit even when a student becomes his scape-goat. Moved by the Auden line, "In the depths of myself blind monsters . . ." he—unsuccessfully—attempts suicide. Equally lonely and displaced is Tío Teban, in "The Chambers of the Sea," who, having relinquished his father's rice fields to a man not carrying the family name, has become a perpetual college student and a dependent on his female cousin Amalia. He identifies his predicament with half-human sea monsters stranded on the beach, although he likes to believe that "they must be beautiful and graceful in the deep!" A similar prodigy, fearfully ambiguous, is the old female "healer" in "The Hound," who nourishes superstition and the avoidance of responsible action among her impoverished townsmen. After Padre Renardt says that she has been "shaped . . . out of our tiredness," Mayor Simeon is moved to break his connections with smugglers whose accomplice he has been ever since the war permitted him a motive.

The difficulties of leadership, the dangers of change—these seem related in Edith Tiempo's stories, many of which can be read as a warning against self-elevation, the separation of individual (by education, by rank, by whatever circumstances) from the group that provided him with the warmth of human identity. In "Abide, Joshua," for example, seamstress Natalia finally suppresses her dream of expanding her business with capital from the sale of the parental house. Her brother Silverio selfishly has always used the rental to forestall the necessity of his earning a living. Yet, in memory of her childhood with him and of family piety, she capitulates—although with ambivalent emotions. In "The Beach," Camilla too returns to the quiet town of her past with mixed reactions. She cannot reject totally the interim life given her and her child by her engineer husband; yet against an intruding, thieving outlander, she stands proudly with her kin and their common mores. Later she tries to accept life with all its apparent contradictions: "It was really neither the present nor the past that one looked at, anyway. There was only relentless change and how to catch its quality, this good and friendly destroyer."

More than Wilfrido Guerrero or Gilda Cordero-Fernando, Edith Tiempo's criticism of the lower echelons of the Philippine power structure is moderated by compassion, and therefore is managed by indirection and a high regard for rhetorical order. Perhaps she has simply chosen to make narrative comment on those persons less excessive in their pride and, for that reason, less beyond the reach of informed forgiveness. Or perhaps any will to indict is stopped by the wisdom that comes when weakness is too generally witnessed to be a matter for private guilt exclusively. Not only her stories but also poems such as "Green Hearts" and "The Fisherman" know intimately the expense of life: how nature is ransacked to sustain mankind; how age is ravaged by covetous youth and by the recollection of vigor beyond retrieving. But dismay seems to be turned back short of despair, by philosophical acceptance of human imperfection. Although her rhythm of phrasing is forceful and accusing, her imagery urgent, yet the very formality of Edith Tiempo's poetry has more the shape of a shield than of a weapon.

WILFRIDO MA. GUERRERO

In an underdeveloped country whose resources have been wasted by unenlightened farming methods or cornered by colonial powers and foreign entrepreneurs or destroyed beyond belief by devastating war, the middle class is likely to be small, and to be turbulently engaged in its struggle with circumstances and conscience. Although the *nouveau riche* may arise in any *población* and continue to dwell there, in a baronic "robber's roost" of surrealistic architecture, more commonly they begin and end in the commercial centers of the country where the desire to be corrupted can be satisfied more easily. In Manila or Cebu City or Davao they may be tempted to pay only token taxes, yet spend a fair portion of their income on the government, buying personal services wherever possible, to avoid the bureaucratic impasse. Thus they make a travesty of their culture's age-old emphasis on the discreet offer of assistance and on paternalistic obligation.

Wilfrido Ma. Guerrero, the Philippines' most prolific dramatist, employs twisted idioms and the gauche gesture to help expose the inner compromises and failures of this insatiable part of society. He has sometimes been placed in the tradition of Ibsen; but one searches his three volumes—13 *Plays* (1947); 8 *Other Plays* (1952); 7 *More Plays* (1962)—without finding more than a shadow of Ibsen the technician of the theater, although some passing resemblance can be seen between Guerrero and Ibsen the iconoclast. He has denounced the strait-jacket authority of the traditional Philippine family, which too seldom consults the feelings of the young, in such early plays as "Half an Hour in a Convent," "Wanted: A Chaperon," "The Woman Surrenders," and *The Forsaken House*. Similarly, he has tried to liberate the Filipina from a male-imposed double standard, in "Forever" and *Frustrations*. Yet Guerrero's reputation more clearly depends on his work as a satirist; as a social critic who, at his best, comes closer to Molière or Aristophanes than to Ibsen. Even "Wanted: A Chaperon" is near-farce; and a comic subplot in "The Woman Surrenders" almost destroys the credibility of the poignant climax. Similarly, Guerrero has proved capable of mocking gently those whom elsewhere he has protected: youth, in "The Young and the Brave"; women, in "Modern Girls" and "Women Are Extraordinary."

So gentle, in fact, is Guerrero's mockery of social excesses that sometimes evil of the most consequential sort seems no more urgently in need of removal than do the petty foibles in his farces. "Opisina Ng Gobierno" and "Blessed Are the Grafters" can be said to parade corruption as a postwar entertainment little more dangerous than the division of sports-fan loyalties in "Basketball Fight" or the insatiable flirtation of the monologuist in "What a Guy!"

To some extent the limitations of Guerrero's effectiveness as a critic of his times can be argued to be a sensible compromise with the conditions of the Philippine theater. Genuinely professional troupes are rare, even in the larger cities; and audiences, too, generally have lacked experience. In the remotest rural areas, folk epics and other semidramatic forms of vernacular literature have survived, by oral tradition mainly, for centuries. Poetry, song, and play have become inseparable in that process. One of the most popular forms of self-entertainment during fiestas is *balagtasan,* a kind of spontaneous debating in verse, to test wit rather than reason. To the same heritage belong the *duplo* and *karagatan,* dramatic debates employed to fulfill social requirements at a wake, to relieve the living during the interval between religious ceremonies. For more elaborate occasions, there are *moro-moro* plays representing colorful conflicts between Moslems and ever-triumphant Christians, or *awits* (chivalric-heroic romances) and *corridos* (legendary or religious tales, adapted from Spanish sources long ago).[6] Despite topical references, Guerrero's plays seem part of this tradition of melodrama and extravaganza; and indeed, since 1962, he has led a mobile theater through the provinces, bringing simple productions of his and other playwrights' work (often in translation) to the *barrios,* after the precedent established by Severino Montano's touring Arena Theater.[7]

The attention span of audiences in a tropical country may also explain, in part, the disproportionate number of one-act plays written by Guerrero (who has proved in his rare three-

[6] E. Arsenio Manuel, *Dictionary of Philippine Biography* (Quezon City: Filipiniana Publications, 1955), p. 420; Alejandrino G. Hufana, *Mena Pecson Crisologo and Iloko Drama* (Quezon City: University of the Philippines, 1962), pp. x–xxii; Nick Joaquin, "Popcorn and Gas-Light Era," *La Naval de Manila* (Manila: Florentino, 1964), pp. 39–56.

[7] For a contrast between rural and metropolitan forces in the Philippine theater's struggle for emergence, see the remarks of Montano, Guerrero, Rodrigo Perez III, and Lamberto V. Avellana in *Literature at the Crossroads,* pp. 111–49.

acters that he can develop characters profoundly through the unfolding of event), as well as his inclination to use comic sub-plots in serious plays or irrelevant incidents in satiric plays. The confusion of clerk and janitor is irrelevant to "Opisina," just as the slapstick underpass scenes in "Blessed Are the Grafters" add only confusion, not insight even of a comic sort. "In Unity," a didactic play intended to prove that democracy gives the indi-vidual—and the local community—the right to be self-reliant, gratuitously has a series of burlesque incidents deriding a new bride from the city.

In short, there is the sort of contrivance and irrelevance and spectacle and disregard for architectonics which made medieval folk drama in Europe so lively just before Shakespeare gave it form. Sometimes it seems less that Guerrero's plays exist to make a point about a social ill than that the social ill is seized to make timely spectacle for author and audience. Undoubtedly Guer-rero, who can see through the illusions of others, has few illu-sions about the limitations of his own art so far demonstrated. His inclusion, in 8 *Other Plays*, of Arsenio Arabia's mixed criti-cism of his efforts indicates the degree of his self-knowledge. It is also true that, on certain occasions and with special audi-ences, Guerrero has prepared the way for acceptance of such younger writers as Virginia Moreno, Wilfrido Nolledo, Jesus Peralta, and Amelia Lapeña-Bonifacio, whose idiom and struc-turing have diverged noticeably from the path of his own.

GILDA CORDERO-FERNANDO

Too many of Gilda Cordero-Fernando's earliest stories, pub-lished in weekly magazines and Sunday supplements, took so much delight in ridiculing the more obvious superficialities of bourgeois taste that penetration into cause and person was hardly attempted. The glittering artificiality of suburban society was overmatched by a sophisticated style as brilliant and indiscrimi-nate as any tour de force ever written by F. Scott Fitzgerald before he realized that he himself was succumbing to the sickness around him. Fortunately, most of those suicidally clever, anecdote-ridden stories have been excluded from *The Butcher, the Baker, the Candlestick Maker* (1962). "High Fashion" is pure caricature and fable—as much a cold cameo as the society model for whom Gabinito the designer rashly spends his strength and talent; "The Race Up to Heaven" is essentially a sociological essay, in pseudo-dialogue and logically mechanical form, contrasting the machinelike American with the unprogressive but humanly warm Filipino; "The Level of Each Day's Need" is an undisguised fairy tale about the importance of humility to the family with a growing income: one of the housewife's three wishes should have been for flesh and blood.

Nevertheless, other stories such as "Magnanimity" expose not only the conspicuous consumption of the Philippine status-seeker, but also his corruptibility, his commission of worse than white-collar crimes, his ready sacrifice of love. Two stories about the same *barrio* in Bataan, "A Harvest of Humble Folk" and "The Visitation of the Gods," present through the person of a schoolteacher profoundly perceived all the virtues traditionally associated with an agrarian society, and all their struggles to survive, inviolate, visiting supervisors and other antichrists. These stories are long but remarkably underwritten. So is Mrs. Cordero-Fernando's modern classic, "People in the War," which tests family devotion during the incredible terrors of wartime occupation and liberation. Understandably, human flaws are discovered; and just as understandably, forgiven. Often Filipinos boast of sentimentality as if their national identity depended on it. But there is nothing sentimental or melodramatic, nothing excessive or contrived, about the young mother's suffocation of her two-month-old baby, in order to prevent detection by Japanese troops; and her trancelike return to bury the infant, out of love and guilt, when the rest run off to safety.

Such stories—or "Sunburn," which concerns discrimination against Filipinos in New York by persons themselves members of minority groups, indicate that the author is still a woman with a cause. But she has learned to discipline her impulse to interrupt a story once it has begun to tell itself. Details no longer are hoarded as if they were ends-in-themselves, but are correlatives suggestive of subsurface truths of character. Gilda Cordero-Fernando has experimented with stories about children and —especially from the awkwardness, the sense of displacement and of quiet, adolescent needs in "A Love Story"—has learned the reality of the tremulously emergent emotion and the inexpressible motive. Experience with human intangibles of this sort may account for her now less facile stories about suburbanites who are possessed by their possessions.

F. SIONIL JOSE

Philippine history in its proper sense—documented and candid—is only now being written. Teodoro Agoncillo has shown, in *The Revolt of the Masses* (Quezon City: University of the Philippines, 1956), how the *ilustrados* used Aguinaldo against Bonifacio, whose sympathies were closer to the peasants; and, in *Malolos: The Crisis of the Republic* (Quezon City: University of the Philippines, 1960), how the *revolucionarios*, having proclaimed a legitimate republic, suddenly found themselves *insurrectos* and involved in the Philippine-American War. Similarly, in *Mabini and the Philippine Revolution* (Quezon City: University of the Philippines, 1960), Cesar Adib Majul has explained how the republican form of the first Constitution grew from the *ilustrados'* fear of the uninstructed peasantry measured against their even greater fear of Aguinaldo's military dictatorship. The relation of province to province, class to class, individual to society is the subject for careful study by historians, especially as the period of Philippine independence enlarges and the honest intellect is moved to admit that not all Filipino difficulties have been imported and not all importations have been harmful.

In this act of self-discovery and assessment, fiction has its own responsible and difficult role. Edilberto Tiempo's unique dynastic novel, *Daughters of Time* (*Weekly Women's Magazine*, November 23, 1962—March 8, 1963), tries the improbable —to trace in one moderate volume the lifetime of Lamberto Alcantara from 1892, the year of the Katipunan's founding, to the aftermath of the Second World War. The pace is too great to permit the sense of panorama that a Tolstoi or a Dos Passos can manage; and in the process, individual characterizations themselves are blurred. There is no time for intensity.

F. Sionil Jose, on the other hand, has set lighter limits on himself and has projected a whole tetralogy on the subject of Ilocano migration. In a family-oriented agrarian society such as the Philippines, the serial chronicle would seem to be appropriate as an expressive art form, just as it was found to be, in the American South, by William Faulkner, Caroline Gordon, Evelyn Scott, and others; or by Rizal himself in his *Noli-Fili* composite. F. Sionil Jose's tetralogy, however, whose first part was published in 1962 as *The Pretenders* [*and Eight Short Stories*] is a rare example of this device. (In his November 2, 1949, letter to Jose de los Reyes, Carlos Bulosan speaks of his plans for "four novels covering 100 years of Philippine history." He had no opportunity to complete these plans. More recently, Linda Ty-Casper has published *The Peninsulars*, the first part of a trilogy covering three centuries; and N. V. M. Gonzalez, having outlined a novel cycle that may reach nine volumes, worked on the first three simultaneously in Rome, throughout 1964/65; the period covered, apparently, will be from the Jones Law to the present.)

As Leonidas Benesa pointed out, during a Congress for Cultural Freedom forum at Ateneo de Manila in 1962, "The use of the Ilocano as the Filipino wanderer par excellence, the Filipino in search of his soul, his identity, takes on the significance of myth." Furthermore, the actual subject matter selected by Jose would seem rich enough to lead to revelations of the most powerful sort. The mountaineer father of Antonio Samson dies in jail because he fought for ancestral lands to which he lacked title. Although Tony weds not Emy, his first cousin and first love, but Carmen Villa, a wealthy Manila mestiza, he promises himself that he will return to the mountains some day to find his roots. By the time he actually does return, he feels corrupted by the modern *ilustrados*, the Philippine elite—industrialists bent on selling the right of exploitation to former enemies and to alien capitalists; members of the free press whose opinions are easily bought; deans who plagiarize; and wives who think childbirth a kind of disfigurement. But in the mountains he finds not only his grandfather's remains but also his son, who has been secretly born to his cousin. She now rejects him as he has rejected the ancient folkways. Since he is everywhere an outsider, having sinned even against himself, his pride leaves him only one alternative: suicide.

Unfortunately, the style of *The Pretenders* is so simplistic, so undistinguished (except for an occasional wrenched metaphor) that one wonders if the author understands just how complex and demanding his subject is. The novel can be read on the run, whereas the problem implied in its epigraph—do the modern *ilustrados* really desire freedom, or simply access to power? — is worthy of the most serious scrutiny. As he emerges, Tony Samson seems to be another Ernie Rama, the pseudo-intellectual in Gonzalez' *The Bamboo Dancers*—with one significant difference. We are asked to pity Tony. In a long epilogue, his American friend Bitfogel indicts the whole society that, he says, conspired to kill Tony. If Tony must be considered the world's unwilling victim, his suicide—which elsewhere is suggested as being a protest more appropriate than revolution, and, elsewhere again, the only way under some circumstances that an Ilocano can save his self-respect—seems suddenly much more defeatist and cowardly and irrational. It contradicts the Ilocano sense of self-possession which, the novel otherwise romantically implies, is in the bloodstream. Either way, of course, Tony as individual and free agent hardly exists. In the absence of characterization-in-depth, the novel inclines to become a struggle between two giant forces—the agrarian mystique and the metropolitan temper—with Tony a temporary and rather trivial battleground for that struggle. But one suspects that this was not Jose's intention.

Far more credible and admirable than Tony is Don Manuel Villa—admirable because he has more self-knowledge than anyone else; and is it not lack of self-knowledge, if not lack of self, that really betrays Tony? And why is no attention paid the remarkable similarity between Tony, as ambitious rising Ilocano, and Don Manuel, the Spanish mestizo whose father was a poor furniture-maker in Intramuros but who entered high finance himself through the construction business? Or the parallels between Ilocano loyalty to the tribe, and the family allegiance of the *ilustrados?* At what point does a virtue become a vice? When does freedom of movement, in an opening society, become a death-wish? These are crucial questions in the history of cultural growth whose counterpart this novel pretends to be, but they are never asked, or even noticed. Nor, in the midst of innuendoes against foreign control of capital, does anyone notice the irony that exploitation of Filipino by Filipino goes unchecked.

A number of such momentous correspondences are ignored, left inert, in order to maintain a specious division between the incorruptible mountains and the cataclysmic plains. The seeming realism of this novel, therefore (in some ways it is a *roman à clef*), is misleading; its secret lies not behind thin disguises but in depths never plumbed. Tony Samson, "intellectual," hardly begins to define what being an Ilocano means: incest in *The Pretenders* takes on none of the symbolic dimensions that Faulkner, for example, provides in *The Sound and the Fury* or *Absalom, Absalom!*; Tony's premarital relations with Carmen are calmly identified as the sort of trial marriage practiced in the mountain *ulogs.* He is never sure whether he loved Carmen (or Emy?) or was simply lonely when they met; and, when she has an abortion, he is outraged principally because in Bontoc this would be improper.

It is the author, not the city, that corrodes the human image into a mechanism of convention. Jose's premises are presented, not explored. Characterization complex enough to be subject to decay, rather than pseudo-characterization decadent in concept, is lacking. In short, Tony seems to react, rather than to act; to be a toy of the author, if not of some force in the lifestream: and his suicide strikes one ultimately as being not so much ambiguous as simply evasive.

F. Sionil Jose, as bureau chief and editor once and later PRO for the Colombo Powers, has had adequate opportunities to watch the rub of Organization against individual and to calibrate the many kinds of corruption. But in his first novel he provides not the insights of an F. Scott Fitzgerald but the oversights of a Budd Schulberg in *What Makes Sammy Run?*

Jose is far more successful in humanizing the strain between ancient and new, highland and low, landlord and tenant through such short stories as "The God Stealer" (when Latak, a white-collar Ifugao, steals for his American friend the household god of his grandfather and the old man collapses, Latak reenters the tribe in propitiation and carves another god) or "Graduation" (the landlord's son learns self-possession from his tenant's daughter, when he loses her). Another mountain story, "The Cripples," outlines the conflict between two brothers over a widowed stranger; and tension is heightened because they will never come to blows: the hands of the elder brother have grown soft during his years as an acolyte. He is as crippled as his father or the woman's husband, both of whom have had hands mutilated for theft. Again, in "The Monkey," Jose proves that he can work out briefly and unsentimentally the perplexing geometry of emotions involving a boy who takes as pet the monkey that killed his grandfather, but who surrenders it when his mother is ailing for lack of meat. It is the thoughtful discipline of such stories that will be required in the next portions of the Ilocano's search for definition.

KERIMA POLOTAN

The Hand of the Enemy (1962), Kerima Polotan's Stonehill Award-winning novel, resembles *The Pretenders* in a number of ways. It too contrasts *barrio* and metropolitan virtues; its expressed philosophy is fatalistic; it ends in suicide. Perhaps, however, the contrasts between the two novels are far more instructive. *The Hand of the Enemy* provides the sort of textured precision that comes naturally to a writer whose short stories have won premier prizes over a decade. (Large portions of this novel, in fact, had already been published as stories before the possibilities of a novel were conceived.) With that precision is an intensity of perception that suggests an underlay of ironic reality very different from what any character imagines.

Emma Gorrez, who is the principal point-of-view character, is a woman of sometimes proper instinctual feeling; but her intelligence is not adequate to the fluctuation of events in her life, signified by her constant change of place. She leaves rural Luna to study in Manila; disillusioned, she goes to teach in the quiet northern *barrio* of Tayug where she marries the editor of a small newspaper and attracts Rene Rividad, the school principal troubled by a promiscuous wife. The Gorrezes become involved in the grass-roots campaigns of 1953 and, for assisting the Cosios' candidates, are given by these Manila socialites a press in that city. Eventually Emma's self-respect makes her flee back to Tayug, while her husband Doming as PRO is escalated up through the pitiless higher echelons of business. For awhile, Rividad and Emma console each other; but she can feel no genuine love for him until, rejected, he burns himself and his wife to death in their house.

Rividad speaks for the confusion of the others when he says flatly, "Life—is the enemy," or, on another occasion, declares to himself that "life was something outside him; a great big something, a mighty merciless great big hand picking up people and lives and hopes and tossing them athwart the sharp prow of circumstance." More dramatically, Emma nearly amputates the offending hand of Nora Cosio with a paper-cutter just before her flight from Manila. Yet, if the characters are doomed, they are doomed by their lack of self-knowledge: the hand of the enemy is their own, as surely as in Arcellana's "Divide by Two."

Not their desire, but their desire misinformed, deludes them. That Rividad should be the chief spokesman for their blind fatalism, therefore, is an appropriate irony. Self-righteously he leads an ascetic life as if in penance for his father's having led a bloody but unsuccessful peasant uprising in 1931. The same cold virtue turns him against his wife Norma when she aborts her illegitimate child; and he takes her life with his own as a kind of double judgment against her adulteries and his frustrated lust.

Rividad's consistent failure in judgment confirms the pattern of all those others who, in their desperate loneliness, seek substitutes to love and scapegoats to hate. Norma herself accepts Rividad's courtship only when she seems temporarily set aside by the vice mayor, her extralegal father; later, trying to compensate for Rene's cultivated lack of warmth, she affects the promiscuity that marked her mother. Emma too, when her father disowns her for leaving Luna, sails to the south in search of a former fiance (now married), leaves Manila for rural Tayug instead of Luna, and when she loses Doming to his young sophisticated *querida* and to the Manila he said he loathes, transfers her affection—at first halfheartedly—to Rividad.

Studied in the light of such groping exchanges and reversals, the corruptions of politics and high finance become psychological, rather than merely sociological, symbols. Nora Cosio says cynically, "It's bad enough having the poor around us all the time, but not to use them, their loyalty, to fail to harness them. . . .": and she proceeds to buy the common *tao's* vote in order to put aside a graft-ridden administration. The intrigues of the Quality Products Corporation are equally private, their viciousness screened from the public eye as surely as the manager's side-office seductions. Such fraudulent concerns for The Image become projections—although of a less innocent sort—of the main character's self-delusions. Perhaps even the loop-stitch arrangement of time which this novel occasionally uses is intended to suggest the snares set by the characters to trip themselves.

Only the ending remains ambiguous. When Emma calls out "I love you" to Rividad in his flaming house, is this a true act of suddenly discovered love, or of gratitude for *his* love, of admiration, or of pity to console his loneliness; a wishful act on her part by loving dramatically to give herself one last illusion of self-possession; a combination of these? When she writes of these final events to her husband and ends by saying, "Goodbye, my dearest Doming," what does she mean? Leonidas Benesa, in his Ateneo de Manila discussion, wondered if she planned suicide. Probably not, or she would have joined Rividad in his pyre. Nevertheless, there is a tone to her words that mark, if not the end of her life, the end of her relationship with Doming or of some crucial stage in that relationship. Which is it? There is an emotional catharsis unrelated whatsoever to understanding. Benesa properly complains that the conflagration and Emma's climbing of the Rizal statue as Rividad's mother did years before, to comfort her outlaw husband's gallant death, are melodramatic. The fact would not be objectionable, however, if the author intended melodrama, as a last ironic confirmation. Does Emma love Rividad because he is dying, because he and the dilemma his presence caused are being removed, because she has never loved well or wisely, never loved what was but its appearance only and love for a dead man is safe? Does the author know how unheroic an act his is and how ridiculous a gesture hers? That would be a perfection of criticism, perhaps; but the reader is uncertain: it may simply be an imperfection in form; the novel may be unfinished.

Early in her career as a teacher in Tayug, Emma tells her students to think hard about the 1931 uprising: "You must ask questions. It is the only way to keep from dying for foolish things." Although there is less inert material here than in *The Pretenders* and although *The Hand of the Enemy* is exceptional for a first novel, still it leaves several questions unanswered. It is unfortunate that Norma, who comes closest to self-knowledge, is removed so soon from the novel. She would have been a more refined instrument of revelation than Emma is.

A People of Many Pasts and Complex Parts

THE painful changeover from *kaingin* to commercial metropolis provides occasion for innumerable reflections on the proportion of loyalty a man will give to self-reliance or to larger allegiances—reflections on what in general might be called nationalism, but what actually involves decisions about a variety of commitments and dispositions, and therefore involves the problem of human integrity itself, or self-possession. States' rights and Jeffersonian individualism are not dead issues in America or in fiction such as Faulkner's. The Philippine people and their literature are equally concerned with the shifting balance of power between self and society.

One extreme can be represented by Jose Garcia Villa's poetry, which seems more concerned with self-expression than with self-exploration. The other extreme was urged twenty years ago in the collected essays of S. P. Lopez, *Literature and Society*. Both extremes tend toward abstraction; but, fortunately, most Filipinos cast their minds somewhere between. Within their means—the indirections that imaginative literature necessarily follows—they are concerned with reevaluating the extended family and its pieties, with respecting the presentness of the past and therefore with measuring what Faulkner would call the "erosion of living traditions into hollow forms."

JOSE GARCIA VILLA

Although five of his earliest tales were reproduced in the *Selected Stories of Jose Garcia Villa* (1962), in tribute to the first prolonged revisit by the distinguished expatriate in nearly thirty years, the fiction of Villa is mainly an academic curiosity today.

103

When Scribner's published his collection, *Footnote to Youth: Tales of the Philippines and Others*, in 1933, Villa had already committed himself to writing exclusively as a poet. Consequently, the stories are primarily of interest as commentaries on the kinds of attitudes and techniques now associated with his poetry; and, ultimately, Villa's importance to fiction is as its critic, not as its writer.

A third of the twenty-one stories in *Footnote* are semiautobiographical and as casual as diary entries. Rarely are the great plains of the commonplace interrupted; and then by minute near-mirages, apocalyptic consolations for the hermit-protagonist who has driven himself out into the wilderness. His world is so walled in that the irony of recurrence becomes a constant theme and monotonous structural device. There is a repetitive pattern of illegitimate children, unwanted or inadequately cared for; of alienation between father and grown son, between protagonist and his temporary intimates; of a love-hate identification with Rizal as father-image whose parenthood is clouded; of rejection in courtship and marriage; of renewed self-importance recovered through (usually sentimentalized) association with the suffering Christ.

In his introduction to *Footnote to Youth*, Edward O'Brien speaks of Villa's combining a "native sensuousness of perception and impression" with the traditionally Spanish "expression of passionate feeling in classical reticence of form." In actuality, Villa contrives a sort of artificial cellular geometry, within numbered paragraphs that roughly resemble stanzas isolating act from act. Routine incident, therefore, is permitted no opportunity for rescue through dramatic association. Such configurations, at best, convey the mechanical aftermath of loss, rather than—as the story line itself suggests—the gradual process of becoming totally dispossessed, and the forestalling of this process, the recovery of person through passionate intimacy with God. Vision is proclaimed, not presented as experience. The static quality of many of the stories is antinarrative.

These stories have the same frail romantic quality that was

being developed in the same period by Khalil Gibran in Boston's Chinatown. However, self-consciousness too often is pushed to the brink of self-pity, and the vision of God invoked only so that His divinity can be borrowed by man, as reprieve, as proof of importance. (Eventually in Villa's poems God was reproached as man's Foe and Suppliant—a later stage in postadolescent self-definition.) The same psychology of projection and identification is evidenced by the abundance of stories concerned with "sons," "daughters," and look-alikes of Rizal; the same sentimental piety in still other stories.

The remarks of Edward O'Brien in 1933—that Villa belonged "among the half-dozen short story writers in America who count"—have to be placed in historical context. *The Best Short Stories of 1932*, which O'Brien dedicated to Villa, is a remarkably undistinguished volume more than half of whose contributing authors have remained nonentities. The modern American short story was still in its infancy. At the very moment that O'Brien was prophesying a career for Villa as a novelist, the writer was making a more accurate assessment of himself. He found his rhythmic repetitions, his sense of the cyclic, his delight in color symbol and allegory, his inability to sustain narrative momentum, his passion for the ineffable or the aphoristic, as well as the sometimes bizarre wrenching of his words,[1] more appropriate to experiments with lyric poetry. *Footnote to Youth* has become a footnote to Villa.

As for his poetry: Villa's *Selected Poems and New* (1958) proves that he has always struck a not incongruous revolutionary pose. As an expatriate from the Philippines, he scorns in various disguises his people's most sacred images—the father; the homeland: that residue of ancestor worship visible in oppressive family circles. (An early poem, not reprinted, is titled "Father, on His

---

[1] Two sentences from "The Man Who Looked Like Rizal" typify early Villa attempts to elevate the otherwise pedestrian language of his tales (and are reminiscent of Roces' failure in taste): "He was a vicinal acquaintance, a big massive fellow with a quadrate face and pileous arms and chest. Pedrong Sabong the people appellated him." The story is among the five chosen by the author for inclusion in the 1962 Peso Series reprint.

Unsonment" and does not seem Freudian.) Paradoxically, his work is therefore representative of his abandoned countrymen's long-standing demand for self-determination, and for personal contribution to tradition. (Even the occasional strain of pompousness is reminiscent of what Rizal once asserted: in order to be accepted as equals by their Spanish masters, Filipinos had to become superior to them.) Theirs is a peculiar kind of rebelliousness neither tolerant nor liberating, but more than willing to be bound by taboos—of its own making. In spite of himself, Villa speaks for the Filipino whose requirement is that he be defined by his own history, not by any other's. His poetry's near-blasphemy, the unconvincing pretense at repentance, have some portion of their origin in the sometimes careless religious observances among Asia's only Christian people, who were left a lasting taste of distrust by Spanish religious orders that served as arms of the Colonial Office.

What is too often mistaken for mysticism in Villa—challenging "Christ Oppositor" to single combat—is surely better understood as unmediated defiance, resolute aspiration, the refusal to be humiliated by anyone. In this passion for denial lies Villa's strength and, unwittingly, his weakness for self-imitation.

Poems of the order of "My most. My most. O my lost!" kindle like a condescension into heaven. Here the theme of man's daily wrestling with God for supremacy is Promethean, therefore appropriately luminous. But more typically the fire lights only itself, failing to reveal any developed sense of even that destinate "genius" so often proclaimed. The sort of criticism by word count which Richard P. Blackmur once turned against E. E. Cummings would be disastrous in Villa's case, whose rubrics also grow repetitive, rather than resonant, in a stammer of imagery. Skull rose flame eyes Christ gold tiger ruby—the romantic vocabulary is small, solipsistic. The poems therefore tend to be more cavalier than metaphysical. The theme diminishes as what at first seemed sacred or profane poems clearly become manifestations of the same self-love; and that self is never doubted, never explored, only praised and presumed. Villa is no modern

John Donne. Despite a tightness of sound pattern and stanza often as intricate as any Provençal *trobador*'s bird flight variations, an essential looseness due to the loss of substance and consequence cannot be ignored.

The same reduction to absurdity, through excess, threatens the famous "comma" poems. Before Villa, E. E. Cummings liberated syllables, letters, and conventional signs for visually dramatic, often ironic rearrangement. Villa has specialized in a small reserve of words and what looks like a comma but actually provides an overriding continuity rather than, as punctuation might, separation. Where a sort of processional measure is desirable, the "comma" in fact does distribute equality of weight among words. But for other poems it is as demonstrably malfunctional as a dragging foot. Being invariable, it allows no subtleties of suspension, syncopation, etc.; being identical, visually, with actual commas, it hinders the exploitation of punctuation in general. In "Anchored Angel," a recent and otherwise considerable poem, Villa still uses the "commas" with inadequate understanding and skill, although nearly ten years after his original commitment.

Nevertheless, there would seem to be more potential in such devices (if used, for example, as equivalents to musical "holds") than in what Villa calls "reversed consonance." The consonantal order of "Si*ng*" is offered as a mirror-image of that in "be*gins*," although clearly the *sounds* have not even a reverse identity. The ear cannot, the uninstructed eye will not, note such patterns which, in the very poem offered by Villa for illustration, are dissipated by slant rhymes, multiple alliteration, and assonance. The "purpose" of reversed consonance therefore is calisthenic only, or exhibitionistic.

Such devices, however, have long been both means and ends in Villa's poetry. Can his origins as a rebel account for the fact that he has constantly relied on reversals, negatives, and reductives; definitions by rejection? To "bring the watermelons pigeons," according to one poem, "would be artistry." Another counts the permutations on pink and blue monks eating blue

and pink raisins. Again: "The wind shines,/ The sun blows . . . ";
or "Yesterday,I,awoke,today." These are anagrams, simple exchanges no more profound than those early pseudonyms, for
instance: O. Sevilla; or Doveglion (dove-eagle-lion). Occasionally,
however, the results fall into meanings:

> *Myself,as,Absence,discoverer.*
> *Myself,as,Presence,searcher.*

Here, opposite ends of an experience, curved in accordance with
the geometry of narcissism, converge with all the ease of a snake
devouring its tail.

Throughout the *Selected Poems* it is equally natural to encounter unnumbered deprivatives. The "not-face" and "un-ears"
of the younger lyrics are preparation for

> In,my,undream,of,death,
> I,unspoke,the,word.

Such conjunctions of word-unword become as elementary as
those of stress-unstress; and even if, in an age of Manichaean
depressives, pompousness bears a certain attraction for readers in
need of reassurance, contrived complication passes for pro-
fundity only at the risk of pretentiousness. Where Villa's meanings are most immediate, as in his "Aphorisms," their triviality
is undeniable.

Villa's fifth volume of poetry (the third in America) is more
representative than selective, and therefore most valuable as a
little archive for the historical critic. Has the rebel run out of
manifestoes and will he not bring himself to trial? The essential
sameness of so many of these lyrics is not lessened by the fact
that they are at a loss for titles and, despite Villa's experience
with short stories, have no significant narrative order. Although
a number do emerge, as does "The,bright,Centipede," with distinction deserving of Dame Edith Sitwell's extravagant praise,
they bear no relation as climaxes or epitomes to the others with
which they are indiscriminately mingled.

One would like to say that each of these others is a point of voluminous light, a graded off-color in a Seurat painting, whose figure descends from a distance; or that each represents some slight alteration in angle of view, passage of time, the revolving interplay of attitude reflected in the portrait of an object deprived, as by a Picasso, of its inflexible uniqueness. But while the human eye locks Seurat's particles into indivisible quanta, composition in Villa is too often the result of kaleidoscopic accident. And while flux is fundamental to Picasso's multiple vision, Villa's is largely predictable and therefore, in a sense, arrested, immoble, unmatured.

These are strange conclusions to have to reach about an avowed progenitor and poetic experimenter. Still, they are borne out by his latest profession of originality, his "adaptations," the editing of imaginative prose (by Rilke, Gide, *Time*, etc.) into line and stanza. There is as yet no clear indication that such minor adaptations are moving in the direction of Robert Lowell's "collaborations" which he modestly calls *Imitations* (1961), or of the translation/accommodation/mutation pattern of Ezra Pound's development. Meanwhile, these classroom mechanics do indicate Villa's skill at restyling and arranging; and perhaps, as well, betray by this aggressive borrowing unconscious acknowlment that his own poems too long have lacked specific presence and circumstantial detail.

Nevertheless, even after the worst that can be said of Villa's poetry for corrective purposes has been said, his reputation as the premier poet of the Philippines is secure. It is difficult, therefore, to understand the repressive nature of the Villa cult among the young poetasters, except as identification with the *arrivé* or as adolescent self-defense. The cultist's own insecurity, personal and professional; his own unintelligibility and self-doubts; his own linguistic inadequacies—all these he manages to protect by refusing to discuss positively the Villa text or poetic.

Villa, of course, is partly responsible for the arrogance of the cultist: his anthology, A *Doveglion Book of Philippine Poetry* (1962), is unique not because of the unevenness of quality in his selections—every editor is guilty of some imperfection in judgment—but because of its absolute intolerance, its disdain for all other editorial judgments. Villa is discourteous; but, worse, he is uncritical—that is, as indiscriminate in his opinions as if he had stopped reading Philippine poetry the day of his expatriation. There is something equally old-fashioned about Villa's dogmatic separation of form and meaning; or of prose and poetry: "the two disciplines," he writes, "are as antipodal as night and day —in genesis, in language, craft and all." He has conveniently forgotten the history of his own artistic growth and of the manner of his recent adaptations, in order to defend what he calls Expressive Writing (romantic poetry). Villa's place in Philippine letters is secure; but his image, as it clarifies, may be modified. The arch-rebel may prove to be even more conservative than his society; and far more anachronistic.

SALVADOR P. LOPEZ and
R. ZULUETA da COSTA

Defending the proletarian writer in *Literature and Society* (1940) because his work is "an instrument of social influence," S. P. Lopez nevertheless had to admit that "passion for a cause alone cannot make the artist." His chapters on Villa's poetics and practice complain about the "obstinate meaninglessness" of Villa, his unrealized mysticism, the vulgarity of his eroticism, and his unashamed egotism. However, the nature of Lopez' deepest preoccupation is suddenly betrayed: the only poems of Villa about which he is enthusiastic without qualification are those which were shown him in the privacy of Villa's apartment and which no longer were "innocent of any social consciousness." When he exclaimed, "Almost it could be said that they were written on the basis of yesterday's headlines!" Villa felt compelled to apologize for having made the poems defective by supplying polemic purpose.

The earliest of these complaints originally appeared in Lopez' introduction to Villa's 1939 volume, *Many Voices;* and the new enthusiasm was assimilated into his introduction to *Poems by Doveglion* (1941). In the latter, Lopez takes particular delight in some of Villa's most pretentious poems, simply because they are entitled "Philosophica," and in others because, whether Villa would admit it or not, these, "especially the satirical ones, are a sharp commentary on the foibles of man and the society that environs and nurtures him."

Consequently, although Lopez has made brief excursions into textual criticism,[2] Ricaredo Demetillo (in *The Authentic Voice of Poetry,* 1962) quite properly belittles Lopez' overriding naivete: "Lopez was asking poetry to support a sociological program, while Villa was just concerned with writing poetry to express almost compulsive ideas and feelings." The most convincing evidence of where Lopez' sympathies have lain is his introduction to Zulueta da Costa's *Like the Molave and Other Poems* (1940). There, of the two foreign influences on Philippine poetry—Whitman and the French Symbolists—which Lopez considers significant, Villa is assigned to the ivory tower of the latter; while da Costa is called a successor of Whitman, because he affirms the common man without excusing anything. His is an "excellence of substance."

Unfortunately, *Like the Molave* shows less restraint than evasiveness. Its sentiments are abstract, its allegories trite, its repetitions monotonous, its sarcasm obvious, its rhetoric theatrical, its lack of self-knowledge appalling. Perhaps patriotism can afford to be tenuous or cliché-ridden, but not poetry. Rarely in this long colloquial declamation is there a single phrase as forceful in rhythm and imagery as the epigraph from Quezon, from which the title is taken. Whether the poet is cynical or hopeful matters little when the country of his poem is underpopulated. Da Costa's language is as vague, as vacuous as the promises

---

[2] *Literature and Society* is largely theoretical (it makes detailed analyses only of the poems of Villa), in part because so few writers of substance were apparent in 1940. The Commonwealth Awards were intended to initiate a literary movement; the 1964 Cultural Act, to sustain a movement.

which he complains the government leaders make. It is only slightly superior to Bulosan's utterly prosaic, unconvinced, and unconvincing *Voice of Bataan* (1943), whose soldier voices lack individuation. Whitman specifies; da Costa disinherits; Whitman breathes into the nostrils; da Costa bleaches. All the Philippine circumstance and human splendor which he supposedly apotheosizes is absent, interred. Yet this is the poem which Lopez has called "an eloquent statement of Filipinism."

Along with the title poem, Zulueta da Costa published a number of others, chiefly impressionistic footnotes to his first love—opera, symphonies, piano concertos. These are, understandably, immaterial. However, da Costa's clearest desertion of the declamatory style is evident in the newest poems added to his 1952 edition. Several—such as "Half a Sonnet"—are experiments without apparent reason; others—"Of a Dead Rose and the Sea"—are dadaist combinations thirty years too late. Nevertheless, the experiments prove that da Costa cannot be dismissed as a poet. Poems such as "July 4th, 1946: Not for the Books" and "Still Life" evidently have learned from the Symbolist tradition which bothered Lopez: da Costa has traded Stephen Crane for Hart Crane. The rhetoric is intense, while the reference has grown more tangibly Filipino.

Besides the latter-day da Costa, a number of Philippine poets have shown the possibilities of commemorating local circumstance without sacrificing passion or universal implication. Virginia Moreno's poems are emblems in motion, as if figures in a tropic entrancement by Henri Rousseau suddenly stirred, then reassembled at intervals in momentary stances. The sensuous effect is that of a daylong primitive marriage preparation, the alternations and exquisite pain of a prolonged ceremonial tattooing. The poems are symbolic witness to the wedding of personal and collective wills; just as Oscar de Zuñiga's stalking passage through immovable objects (in *Love Song and Other Poems*, 1960, and some of the lyrics in *The Arid Year*, 1962) can be read as allegorical journeys in search of a direction. Each of these is a perceptibly different landscape; but each is inhabited and therefore can be called a contour of some total truth.

In addition, there is the underscored political-social bitterness of the "Clarius Poems" and of "Cabcaben," in Andres Cristobal Cruz's *Estero Poems* (1960); the courage of the castaway, in Tita Lacambra-Ayala's *Sunflower Poems* (1960); the postwar city seen as mechanical labyrinth, in Dominador Ilio's *The Diplomat and Other Poems* (1955); the post-1950 poems of Amador Daguio, cryptic messages from distant expeditions; or reflections in the connoisseur eye of Emmanuel Torres, engrossed in containing the self-contained, thereby making icons of familiarity out of the ancient and the foreign.

Rarely are such poems caught daylong at their own mirrors, as Villa's sometimes are; rarely is the full experience of man sacrificed to a social premise, as it is in the detached rhetoric of da Costa's manifesto, *Like the Molave*. Carlos Angeles' *A Stun of Jewels* (1963), for example, celebrates the sun and its counterpart, the conscientious eye: but, unlike the self-consuming fires of Villa, these conspire to converge on man's barbaric nakedness, exposed along a death march of his own making. Similarly, Epifanio San Juan who, as an undergraduate, gained notoriety for the narrow view expressed in "Man Is a Political Animal" writes poetry, in *Godkissing Carrion* (1964), rarely attached to national circumstance. Nevertheless, selections taken from the gargoyle-grotesques can be interpreted as allegorical commentary on modern politics, in the tradition of Goya's *Los Caprichos* or his *Disparates*. Speaking for younger poets faithful, even in failure, to their need to find a ceremony appropriate to their search for self, San Juan acknowledges that "vision is an enterprise" —a commitment through the fullness of craft and not through accident.

RICAREDO DEMETILLO

In "Jose Garcia Villa vs. Salvador P. Lopez" (*The Authentic Voice of Poetry*), the sympathies of Ricaredo Demetillo are clearly with "gnomic brilliance" and not with the "poetry of utility." Nevertheless, his ability to discriminate between these two does not prevent Demetillo from realizing Villa's limitations. He laments the fact that the latter's poetic depends too much on naivete and inner compulsions and not enough on conscious ordering or the external human condition; that, after *Have Come, Am Here*, Villa's "mystical furor" has worn thin, leaving him with "dead forms" and an occasionally "eccentric" and "juvenile" following; and that he is hardly the Blake with whom he so often has been compared. How then can one explain Demetillo's extravagant remark that "the full stature of Villa will be realized in the future, for we shall either grow towards him or perish"? Not "beyond him"—a phrase that would do Villa justice without requiring that his limitations be imitated—but "towards him."

Undoubtedly this lapse in objectivity on Demetillo's part comes, unconsciously, from the attractiveness which Villa's attitudes and themes have always had for Demetillo as poet-rebel. When he writes that "more positively, Villa believes that the moral values which most of us hold petrify the spirit and subtract from the full life" and therefore commends Villa's "conscious blasphemy," he is defending his own early work. On the other hand, the growth of Demetillo from self-interest to the epic-historical dimensions of his *Barter in Panay* indicates that he himself is capable of pioneering provinces of literature outside Villa's domain.

Much of what is protestant in Demetillo's *No Certain Weather* (1956) seems to derive from the proposition that as long as one man is yet unborn, it is too early to define humanity; therefore, let each man be free to make himself up as he goes along. The poems rebel against all "who plan tomorrow like a meal"; or tailor the man to fit the suit; and such rebellion, the assertion of selfhood against the ancients, perhaps is natural in a first work. But if some part of the future is unmade, is pliant to a man's strong hand, the prophecies of even a poet must be as tentative as the yardstick has become ever since Einstein. The future need not conform to the weather's forecast, any more than the poet to current codes of conduct.

The reader is asked to see himself as the poet sees him, his average profile silhouetted "in a time of darkness" and "tea-cup age." Although the ground beneath his feet is about to vanish in a rainwash of universal solvent, Mr. Average Man complacently fattens on Christ's blood or, in trousers "a faultless shade of grey," decorously passes through forgotten family graveyards. "The Storm" strips off their inadequate flesh from seven frightened people, each ready for shipwreck with his weather-bent spar of self-delusion. In Balara Park, the jungle's retreat seems temporary only, since the wallowing heart still chokes with kangaroo grass. Don Angel flinches, drenched and disfigured, to the sound of brass cymbals, through this climate of impending catastrophe. Complacency, conformity: these are the futile umbrellas sailing like kites through *No Certain Weather*. Modern Ulysses is no longer hero, but unresting sleepwalker facing "the one-eyed monster in the neural cave." The mind becomes its own labyrinth. "Is there a Minotaur?" finds answer in "The Victims" with these worried words, "The fear itself becomes the Minotaur/ That gores our guts." As the Night of the Gods descends, the most valiant mortal is merely a "gentleman of wounds": "He stands bare-headed and his outshirt flaps./ Only a pebble fills his pocket now."

A driving seawind-whisper of death is in the air; strange bombers are in the air (no matter from where). This is a book of recognitions; it is not for sun bathers. Neither does the poet come as a healer. Punctured Mr. Average Man is left enlightened but still bleeding; while the poet, detached, alone but not suffering, not properly lonely at all, points and proclaims. He is largely "other," the divorcement proceeding from his history as a rebel, marked principally in "Rebellious Sonnets" and "Vicious Idol." Because of his Filipino father-the-god, stern-handed on bamboo lash, he lost faith in the love of God the father. Under a tipped icon, "I felt ant pellets leak on my shocked child's hands." Finally, from the oppressive commandments of a too-proper town, he fled to a lake where "I was a bronzed god bared against the brake."

Although in resisting authority Demetillo avoids the extreme narcissism of Jose Garcia Villa ("Cavalier and Priest"), yet his resistance is clear and adamant. He will not be stampeded into Nick Joaquin's backward flight to handy traditions ("Born in an Age of Lead"). He is his own man; or rather, he is still in a sense bronzed boy-god reveling in morning's lake. Myths which fail Mr. Average Man yet work magic for this poet; *his* rebel, unruffled, insists that he is different; therefore, invulnerable.

Such detachment makes for cameo rhetoric, a poetry often expository, gently ironic, almost decorous, not confounding or apocalyptic: since Mr. Average Man is too cocksure to be shaken, why get excited? The poet's bravest metaphors are never lost in ellipsis; his sentences ride even-keeled. But no poet can make a career of detachment. In *No Certain Weather* proudly secular ex-seminarian Demetillo thrives on uncertainty of himself, because it authorizes freedom. Yet a reactionary who insists on severing himself absolutely from precedent may well be unable to act. A man must participate, if only in his own life. The time comes for a rebel to write his constitution, form his government however provisional, however subject to amendment. Blind denial is complacency as surely as is blind faith.

Demetillo's ultimate direction may already have been foreseen in those early poems which look for a farther horizon ("Rock Sprouted Springs" and "Life and Death") where mortality makes even the poet tremble; or in "Longinus" and "Sand and the Lolling City," where suffering is meaningful in accord with philosophies older than print. First, however, Demetillo seemed compelled to write his long poem, *La Via: A Spiritual Journey* (1958), which is far less an authentic expedition in search of self than a rather boisterous (and boyish) pretense at cleansing, inside and out, in preparation for such a trip: a catharsis. Both the author's preface and the introduction by Leopoldo Yabes are misleading. In shrill tones, Yabes charges that the emphasis of Christian institutions on rigorous asceticism "could lead to crimes of lust and even of simony [*sic*]." Spiritual bliss, he argues, can best be approached through the "sanative mysteries" of the flesh, "the proper exercise of the psychosomatic functions of the body"; and, as if unaware of history, he suggests that mankind experiment with paganism in order to heal its ills. Demetillo, too, blames Christian discipline for sensuality, vulgarity, materialism, and hypocrisy and rebelliously offers each man's instincts as origin and sanction for personal behavior.

Such preliminary orientation is misleading because much of the morality behind the criticism, in the poem that follows, is not only orthodox but commonplace, and even paltry. The flaws and peccadilloes, for example, remarked in "Book One: Dissonances" are of the most self-evident, self-exposing sort. They are more often than not antithetical to church law and official practice, although the poem does not seem intimate with either of these. Similarly, examples of "depth psychology," which the author has promised to provide as a twentieth-century mode of perception, seem limited to the most ordinary, explicit dreams —more transparent than those in ancient legends. Only the most superficial understanding of Freud, and none at all of those who have modified his theories, is evident. Furthermore, the vignettes of sexual perversion—whether cause or effect of social restriction is not always made clear in the examples—do little to prove the inborn, incorruptible virtue of man on which Demetillo's "paganism" depends.

Book Two continues to incriminate the church for not ending war and other crimes until, disillusioned, the protagonist longs for the Wordsworthian rapture he felt as a child, in innocent rapport with river and birds. Momentarily, in "Book Three: Harmonies," he seems prepared (through phrases such as the one invoking "Christ in the groin's shrine") for the declaration of anarchy recommended in Yabes' preface. However, the preponderance of verses are dedicated to conventional husbandry, with erotic love carefully confined to the most decorous and custom-made marriages. Adam, renewed, celebrates the rule of the Lord within his body. Far from dismissing moral commandments, he codifies his own version of the Christian ethic: Law and Desire, two extremes long in contest, must be reconciled through Love.

Read selectively, *La Via* might seem passionately iconoclastic; nevertheless, taken in its entirety, it is often illogical and tasteless, but—surprisingly—far more conservative than outrageous. Its storm is artificial; its journey, one without genuine movement. The fact is that the Beatnik temperament—renunciation of all ethical standards and capacity for feeling guilty, the neutralizing of all desires in the "floating world" of relaxed instinct, the disassociation from all political or social creeds—does not fit Demetillo comfortably at all. What has distinguished his best poetry always, as well as the rationale implicit in "The Authentic Voice of Poetry," has been its urbane, critical tone, disciplined by a formal sense of function. *La Via* served, apparently, as a kind of catharsis for the poet, after which, in exhaustion, he slowly reformed his powers in *Daedalus and Other Poems* (1961), restoring poems twenty years old, while he revised his major work, the epic *Barter in Panay*.

One of the more lucid portions of *La Via* contrasts the modern Philistine with the high grandeur of the ancient Malays' mind and effort, which through courage and orderly labor created a legendary greatness in the Philippine archipelago long before the *conquistadores* arrived. With *Barter in Panay* (1961), Demetillo has released the first third of his free adaptation of the folk epic, *Maragtas*, which was recorded on bamboo barks by the ten *datu* groups which, in 1212, fled tyranny in Brunei and established settlements in the Visayas. Although the original *Maragtas* relates the histories of the entire pioneer venture (including the sacrificial return of Datu Puti to Brunei to avenge his dead wife) and contains the enlightened Code of Maragtas, undoubtedly the heart of that epic is the story of betrayal which Demetillo has borrowed. The twenty-one cantos of Book I explain the peaceful arrangement made between Datu Puti, and the pygmy Negrito inhabitants of Panay island, and begin to explore the lust of Guronggurong for Datu Sumakwel's young wife which was to test in an intimate way the new rule of law and justice. Book II will recount the justified killing of Guronggurong; Book III, the chastening of Kapinangan.

In its immediate plunge into events, its lengthy councils, its scenes of clairvoyance, Demetillo's adaptation may seem more responsive to Western than to Asian traditions of the epic. Propriety of conventions aside, however, his presentation of character is full-bodied, re-creative, authentic. Symbolic gesture and stream of thought converge to reveal motive in multidimension. Demetillo seems adequately aware of the importance of having the love-rivalry of Sumakwel exemplify, rather than distract from, the problems of social law and order. The proper alternative to tyranny is not anarchy, but such mutual fidelity as a marriage contract imposes. Demetillo is at home with personal-social virtues: *Barter in Panay* is the authentic journey to that truth of self-in-society which *La Via* counterfeits.

ALEJANDRINO G. HUFANA

Even closer than Demetillo to the modern Filipino's problem of multiple identity is Alejandrino Hufana's *Sickle Season* (1959), a search for all usable pasts. When Kronos with his sickle cleft his kingly father so cruelly that children still unborn were disinherited forever, he set the example for his own son's right to patricide and became grievous symbol for each generation's dispossession of the past. In *Sickle Season*, the edge of Alejandrino Hufana's poetic line and image has been ten years honed until it is as infinitesimally attuned as time; as cutting as the horizon's severance of earth/sky, night/day; as capable of challenging the loudest laureate claimant as ever Kronos was. The significant difference is that Hufana's protagonist does not demand discovery of himself at the expense of older poets. He admits mutual tolerance of faculties (imitation, accommodation, mutation) indicative of the poet's various relationships with the experience of others. Each predecessor worthy of competition is, instead, completed—by a Filipino voice as authentic as any and a comprehension of total tradition more generous than usual. Only whatever handicaps, encumbers, barricades, usurps, or interposes invites the mutineer's wind-sharp blade.

The pendulum of attack describes what is, after all, an in-

trinsically creative human arc, a movement toward definition
through balance. Every downward plunge swings to recovery
—a poise in motion: so that Kronos not under the aspect of
Destroyer, but as Sower and Reaper (since the swinging motion
in every instance is identical) is invoked.

Because so many human divisions are inward, so is the motion, often, of these poems. In some sequences (particularly the
13 *Kalisud*), there is an occurrence of image-clusters from the
undersea, from dreams of love and loss. Night-thoughts find
language scraped from the mind's tissues during the body's mon-
soon season. Things are said which the speaker seems to understand only later and, only later, to know to be true. Sounds from
the mass memory become speech in a liquid but solid, however
heaving, medium. The handsome sailor, Malayan Billy Budd—
lost wanderer ancient with the guilt of need—is a stranger in
the daylight world of direct communication of trivialities. Ship-
wrecked, he walks below language, seeking his own meaning in
a sea of rising and falling breath, in the tides of his own fisher
heart, in the used darkness where sharp constellations shine
inside the skull's planetarium.

Where is her shore? the lover's brittle gestures ask, in half-
words. Why, between flesh and flesh, is there always the hanging, heavy odor, touch, taste? Why are pores like caves? The
mind, in the midst of marriage, remains a function of body, of
the longing of loins and injured eyes and lungs. All past history,
from which he would play prodigal, claims recognition from
him of its consequences; yet he is required to be the future too:
their image, himself, and consummate husband and father. At
his wedding feast, the ancient mariner now young mutineer eats
not the consubstantial god but the lining of his own dissolving
stomach.

Through the upper dark of the soul, the wanderer is buoyed
toward wakefulness, and bitterness. Having returned from the
brink of self-recognition, he knows the weathering he must still
endure from history's totem and society's taboo. Daylight will
begin to measure distances for him, the perimeter of his private

confessed purgatory. That is the price of survival. Such explora-
tions and admissions are too intimate to be personal. And
Hufana's mastery of the generic persona is the very quality that
allows one to speak of his collective work as an epic (or, perhaps,
as several epics-in-progress), despite the distinctive predominance
of the brief narrative or intense lyrical fragment in that work.
No other Filipino poetry of this half-century is comparable
(Demetillo's *La Via* is a mock-epic only and shows none of
Sickle Season's virtuosity). "I had to go for singing where I grew,"
the poet says, not speaking parochially; and he accepts far less
eclectically than Nick Joaquin all usable pasts. Geron Munar,
both alter ego and ancestor for the protagonist, recurs as a kind
of Malayan culture hero, progenitor and proxy for all—a man
clothed in rags and courage; seeker, founder, pilgrim. He is that
epic pedigree each man-nation traces in search of kinship with
godhead and verifies in present performance. The poet's log
recapitulates stages in everyman's ascension: pursuits of divinity,
identity, happiness through life's liberty.

"Total tradition" embraces not only all of mankind in their
angelic-bestial range of natures, but also nonanonymous persons
from myth, legend, and other fames. Bernardo Carpio and Ur-
duja, here, are no less real than Balagtas, Father Burgos, Luna,
Mabini. And who would deny the likelihood of the sorrowing
pygmy mother, Salidom-ay dancing, Montemayor the burden-
some blacksmith, Nenita Flores untrusted wife, and a dozen
other apocalyptic personifications? Hufana's "Poro Point Anthology," although still in progress as it appears in *Sickle Season,*
is an impressive, incisive exercise in portraiture—as if on the
large mural forms of a Carlos Francisco were inscribed the in-
ternalized detail and *batik*-like emblems of a Hernando Ocampo.
Yet, immense as such dimensions are, they do not exhaust
Hufana's world.

At the time of the 1958 P.E.N. conference in Baguio, Francisco Arcellana wrote, "The only political action possible for the
writer is to remember. . . . He must remember that he is first
a human being before he is a national." The breadth of this

perception has its counterpart in the way that Hufana implicates every continent and condition in his concentric spheres of search. Lam-ang and Beowulf become analogues; Christ and Confucius cloister in the same womb; Bukaneg and Beethoven, Dewey and the *tinikling* dancers, Quiapo and Jerusalem, Hitler and Santissimo—nothing human is alien to the "folk intelligence," the instinctive acknowledgments of this poetry. Its major images, which set the whole work's motifs, are sustained by references that cross-index time and space. The Malayan mutineer, under other names and in other circumstances, is Henry the Navigator, Copernicus, Kepler, Magellan, Prometheus, Sisyphus—all who aspire and circumnavigate their own flesh, fall, fail, and still reach out. Munar's blade is the knife of circumcision, the imprint pattern made by the feet of Salidom-ay in her death dance, the arc of Tantalus' arm, the bone-seeking embrace of death, yes; but more often Ruth, gleaning among the *kasamás* in orient corn, catching the truth before it falls from the edge of the scythe, breathing the green future in the grain's fertile crescent. No, these poems are not parochial.

Yet extension is meaningless unless it proceeds from intensity. The substantial alone can sustain the consequential; the motion of the reaping blade is only as firm as the still foot of the reaper. What is true esthetically is true politically also: equality is not interchangeability, or loss of individuality. However broad a brotherhood, each member of it has his own identity, an assigned responsibility to be himself, his first truth. Hufana's terms are not transparent names dropped for effect but persons authenticated in characterized action, dramatically disposed. Each is available as personified flesh, participant in his own pedigree through the needs of this day and immediate hour. Each is a tangible presence, a firm integer first, however he may function in some ultimate calculus or grand equation.

So well is this initial identity established, that the cryptic language of many of the poems is plausible even while it puzzles. No critical reader will soon exhaust its meaning. It has, in fact, some of the grandeur of Enrico Fermi's first revelation, in code, that a nuclear chain reaction had been successfully controlled, in 1942: "The Italian navigator has landed in the new world." What distinguishes the poet, however, from the imaginative scientist is that the former has available language-symbols of diverse order, capable of recording not simply outcomes but whole processes of interim experience. The travail of seeking birth across amniotic seas has its successful conclusion, but not without lasting memory of the death of sperm in the competition for conception. *Sickle Season* knows, too thoroughly to invite complacent celebration, the dependence of life on death, in any world that man has yet imagined. But unless the seed dies, who will ever reap?

Several dramatic monologues in *Sickle Season* are the matrix for the vignettes in *Poro Point: An Anthology of Lives* (1961). Hufana, like F. Sionil Jose, has searched among his more immediate Ilocano ancestors and contemporaries, composite or imagined, for sustenance to the poet's anticipated high image of himself as heir. But most of the vignettes reveal lives of clamorous desperation—the ark-builder, church beggars, religious fanatics, driftwood hawkers, globe-trotters with rotting homes, the junk dealer in explosives. The language is lodged in tight linguistic forms reminiscent of primitive folk riddles: [3] commemorative, sacred indirections sometimes terrifying; and all more cryptically intense than the epitaph-clarity of Edgar Lee Masters' *Spoon River Anthology* with which the collection has sometimes been compared. They acknowledge the poet's acceptance of his dispossession in this century of any divine birthright once assigned him (there is a self-knowledge and fierce humility in Hufana not available in Villa's romantics). Now the poet's role is that of tragic clown, but certainly not of a hermit uninvolved. In the person of Geron Munar, Malayan wanderer, he takes on his back his family and the pilgrim passers-through and every citizen born

[3] For Christian-Philippine examples, see Donn V. Hart, *Riddles in Filipino Folklore: An Anthropological Analysis* (Syracuse: Syracuse University Press, 1964); but Hufana's cryptic quality resembles also Anglo-Saxon riddles, just as the monologue form he uses in analogous to the anonymous Anglo-Saxon "Seafarer."

of woman, penitentially, as if they have not failed the poet so much as the poet somehow, somewhere has failed them. Munar represents compassion with a conscience.

Since *Poro Point*, Hufana has turned his mind's craft more and more toward the epic. In the mid-sixties he put aside revisions of his monumental "Journey to Judgment" (a quest for identity among Europeans during the race pogroms of Hitler), in order to research a multisectional poem based on the figure of Kamel-ud-din and the Islamic heritage of Sulu. At the same time, realizing that creation of a modern epic has to be an experiment in humanizing a culture hero and in dramatizing the eventfulness of action, Hufana apprenticed himself to playwriting. The five one-act plays in his *Curtain-Raisers* (1964) are displays of language disciplined by rapidly developed familial relationships, threatened by some perversion in the natural order: the nymphomania of a professor's wife (*Gull in the Wind*); near-incest (*Honeymoon* and *Ivory Tower*); homoeroticism (*Ivory Tower*); the mad conspiracy of impotent mayor and eunuch (*Terra Firma*). His presentations could hardly be more violent if they were enactments of tribal taboos; but the language is so appropriately terse, yet heightened—form moves so quickly from folk lyric to surrealistic juxtaposition—that one is reminded instead of Federico Garcia Lorca's poetic-symbolic plays. Hufana's epics should benefit from such dramatic use of word as man, and of man as word.

Hufana still wrestles with his own virtuosity: the accumulation of sharply individualized and dramatized truths in *Poro Point* is nearly overpowering, whereas the plays retain human energy in embodied shapes which are permitted kinesthetic motion, performance. Throughout his development as a poet, Hufana has found it necessary to train his imagery to coalesce (eventually—in the retentive imagination—though not immediately), instead of each word's, each phrase's having its separate side show. And the coalescence has had to occur despite the fact that Hufana's poetic energy derives from the conflict of ideas and temporary contrast of symbols. As he restrains the delight he obviously takes in excessive alliteration and internal rhyme, and puts poetic consequence before his own pleasure at play, then paradoxically he achieves what after all is never a *donnée* but a destination, the illusion of personal admission into the object. The self denied in the act of objectifying experience is always restored when the experience attains universality. Realizing this truth from his playwriting especially, Hufana has been able to see the same process as a paradigm of the mutual definition and assimilation of self and society.

BIENVENIDO N. SANTOS

The imagery of return employed by Hufana has its counterpart in the fiction of Bienvenido Santos. Yet, how the sense of humaneness which is Santos' trademark elevates this return into ritual, without becoming sentimental, is in some ways best illustrated from his poetry. Some men carry their private pain into underground burrows and die nursing it without comprehension. Others like the wounded stag lie down "to die under the poplars flecked with morning," wide eyes refusing to release the world they have known. Not the death of beauty, but the beauty of beauty even in death, is the poet's burden. Appropriately, the voice of Bienvenido Santos' fifty poems, entitled *The Wounded Stag* (1956), is elegiac, scraped raw by havoc—yet heroic in its acceptance of the need to be responsive, to be responsible. It is the sound of endurance, denying that it must drop into silence unheard. Consequently, there is dawning vigor in each dying phrase.

In his introduction to this collection, Manuel A. Viray identifies three specific periods in Santos' life which correspond with the range of these poems: the Sulucan years of youth in Tondo slums; the wartime exile in America; and the return to a devastated native land. It is true that most of these poems are too heartfelt, too committed to human eventfulness not to have had long histories in the man's personal feelings. Yet it is a more important fact that the author himself has not attempted to arrange his work chronologically, according to those three "stages" in his life—perhaps to indicate that they were not stages at all, but rather replicas of one another. The earliness or lateness of Santos' poems cannot be distinguished, because evidently his life as poet has been marked not by development-in-time but by constancy-of-vision. The experiences of deprived youth, exile, and repatriate presumably were unitary, since the poetic theme now is seen to be singular. Over and over, whatever the changing circumstances (and sometimes these are made quite foreign and displaced, as if to test the personal vision), the feeling is that of human expenditure, waste, and the fatal wound, of weariness, of terror among the loveless and the lost, of spiritual drought.

Almost as a fugue, certainly as something more compelling than mere accompaniment, the imagery of physical corruption is pursued by imagery of the great betrayals of religion. Soul *and* body are disappearing from the human scene, leaving only the grease of cosmetic illusions. The poems are populated with frantic gods and with calvaries. But this very placing of one in the other's context—human and divine pain—instead of multiplying the feeling of depression, exhorts man to make of his exile a pilgrimage, to offer his suffering for his own redemption, to inspirit each otherwise meaningless daily gesture.

Nevertheless, such juxtaposition is not made from complacency: the Christian myth is not to be swallowed like some modern-day "happy pill," according to "Footnote to Wisdom." These poems are petitions, equivalents of prayer; they are a horizon of ripe, not naive hope, at the near margin of despair. Santos' knowledge of the depth of man's dilemma—he must sink to rise—is shown in "Father and Son":

> My father's wound was deep
> Stretched through the ends of earth
> Tortuous like many rivers
> Thus waited for my birth.

Here is man's moral heredity, the tracing of essential history. Like the other poems, this one is more than autobiographical.

In a world where survival itself keeps men occupied, belief in purpose is difficult. Each man, like the Tantalus of "In Fair Exchange" or the novitiate seen in the deserted terminal, is tempted to grow weary of trial. Christ at least knew that he was not forsaken; in "Brotherhood" the poet begs for equal reasurance:

> Tell me, as you softly cried in anguish
> O my God, why hast thou forsaken me,
> You heard an answer, did you not, promise
> Of life beyond, your own divinity.

And "Pilgrimage" speaks of sainthood as a thing of the past.

Yet "Apostleship"—and how many others?—accepts "April's captaincy" and the "true wound." Particularly the poet-as-magician of the imagination, although sometimes sidetracked like the wandering Magi in "Gift Bearers," is restless because he is dissatisfied with the sight of himself or any other man dying-alive spending his hours "blowing into swollen entrails." Beauty, uncloistered and experienced and nevertheless inviolated, dying intact, does not die. There is bitterness and cynicism in "The Eyeless Saying Yes," yet, however deep the sense of outrage, mankind is not confused with its own unkindness. There is no retreat, from the truth of evil—or from the truth of good. Faith is the good of the poet.

The same courage, the same confirmation through hardship revisited, springs from the images in *You Lovely People* (1955). In the moving histories of others—deprived youths, exiles, repatriates—Santos can see again his own varied selves revealed. In Emporia, an American college girl–wife of a Filipino said, "Now, I know why I love my husband." In Kentucky an overgrown farm boy carrying Ben's suitcases all the way to the station at four in the morning, explained, "You said something yesterday, sir, which I shall remember always." In Illinois, an old teacher, once in the islands, brought her mother "to see how the boys we taught in the Philippines had grown up to be."

What Bienvenido Santos, who served the Commonwealth government in exile when war caught him in America, said "with a little fervor, a little nostalgia" to these Americans about their best brothers-in-arms is not recorded in *You Lovely People*. But if he spoke as honestly, in uncoy conversation, about Filipinos at home as he has written about these others, like himself, the homeless ones, why his audiences were moved is clear. The wrenching power of the book lies in its understatement, acknowledging the quiet desperation and yet almost iron gentleness of these expatriates who, in crisis, felt welling in themselves the sentiments which made a Philippine nation, already independent in fact because independent at heart, inevitable.

German POWs in Kansas laughingly told Santos that he was as much a prisoner as they. Yet there was the daily bread of hope (as when one POW rescued a frozen goldfish from the wintry campus fountain) and of memory. These were hurt men whom Santos knew, lonely Filipinos whose American wives suffered as much as insanity, huddling near them in their second-rate run-down neighborhoods. A few exiles were simply "blonde crazy"; but more actually found in their wives the faithfulness that they would have expected only from their own kind. (The pregnant wife of an old Filipino farmer who was stricken with acute appendicitis warmed him with her own body while they waited in the snow for the rural mailman to come to take him to the hospital.) Others were betrayed over and over, by their wives and their in-laws, but sat out their lives with quiet courage on doorsteps or collapsed at last from t.b. behind the steering wheel of a taxi.

They were hurt men, confined as if in crypts. The war, the isolation they endured far from the land of their morning, the mutilation of people to whom they had never expected to return but whom, in a sense, they had never left—somehow these men wore their wounds with a kind of honor. The Filipino Dream only survived more passionately in them for its frustration. It is of this Filipino Dream, not of himself, that Santos has written: the character of the narrator is deliberately left incomplete. Sometimes the storytelling function passes over to men like poker-faced Ambo, of the trembling hands, or to others more anonymous, until a few sections of the book are even told from the omniscient point of view, that is, tell themselves. Withdrawal of the narrator actually permits the reader, suddenly naked and abandoned in a crowd, unmediated experience: the discovery of himself in the ghost and flesh, the dream and reality of others.

In his introduction, N. V. M. Gonzalez has contented himself with calling *You Lovely People* a book. At least half of its divisions are not self-contained, not short stories—although others are some of the country's best stories: "The Prisoners," "The Door," "Brown Coterie," "Scent of Apples," "Accept the Homage." It might, however, be considered a novel in the sense that Faulkner's four-quartered *The Hamlet* is a novel. Only a small part of *You Lovely People* has absolute continuity; unique rhythms, in pace and perspective, arranged through mobility of setting and the quick-change artistry of narrators, make a puzzling motion (fit for the wounded, the wondering); but the reverberating theme, which perhaps finds its finest symbol in Ambo—the trembling hands of need which idealizes memory, the poker face of realistic perception of the present—makes this a book with a singleness of voice, though a variety of echoes.

More than any other character, more than Ben himself, Ambo emerges monumental and memorable—but not separable from the rest. He embodies the Filipino Dream. He hovers over Ben, like an elder guardian angel, trying to keep the younger innocence uncorrupted. He collects money for forgotten Nanoy's funeral. His dream is muddled only in the Philippines, by his wife who has tired of wanting him and by his friend Doc whom easy money is corroding; and ironically, Ambo wants to return to the U.S., where the dream still makes sense.

Just as he makes understatement discipline his sentiment, in the end Santos cannot be false, cannot help showing what the Philippines was like to the returned prodigals, the expatriates who had loved well from a distance. Father Ocampo had warned, prophetically, of ruins in the spirits of those touched by war. A migration in reverse has already begun by the end of the book: the horizon, after all, was only a mirage. But there is an unwritten epilogue. Despite the clear, rare value of this book, Bienvenido Santos needed ten postwar years to find his publisher and his audience, ten years to be welcomed home. Yet he stayed, looked around, did not retreat back up the gangway, because he must have believed whatever it was that he had told Americans in Kentucky and Kansas; he must have had faith that the Philippines he pictured would, gradually, return.

The stories collected in *Brother, My Brother* (1960) are largely prewar stories; but just as wars epitomize whole periods which precede them, so too only slight changes in surfaces—mainly stylistic—distinguish these stories from *You Lovely People*. More significantly, both volumes are linked by the dramatized theme of homecoming. One day, naked, man notices that his birthmark is still there. However far from his origins he has traveled restlessly in the quest to overtake that cosmetic image of self dangling before his willing eyes, now he remembers yesterday—those days before the parading of pride. Whatever province of impostors he inhabits, having been elected to high office—when the sun is just right so that he feels big with shadow in that private part where no arteries, trafficking in change, trespass—he remembers, as does Santos in *Brother, My Brother*.

Then it is time for that painful journey back to his heritage: to acknowledge a father (how could he have been so presumptuous as to make life, who never took a diploma?), a family (the aunt who tried to cripple him so that she could be useful), his earlier selves (the boy whose nose bled when he dreamed rape). In recollection there is a pain beyond embarrassment: but who, faced with that unflinching nakedness, can honestly deny that he was born, into *this* world, subject to its dark lusts and frailties, however he glories in dreams of rebellion or flight to another?

We will not be what we could, except by admission of what we were.

"A few of my childhood friends are dead," Santos once wrote, "some are languishing in jails, others are coughing their lives out in these slums of Sulucan. They only look at me: they never approach. It's I who come to them, glib with platitudes, but all the time, some sort of apology—apology for what, I really don't know—trembles on my lips and remains unspoken."

The journey is not for the roast pig or cooled beer with which, remembering our failures, we console each other at the end. It is not for reputation, for the distribution of little gifts. It is to confront ourselves in others. After all, what can one do for his parents? What can a man do for friends or those who have envied or despised? He can only return and look them in the face and not deny them. Despite what he was or will become, he can take them as they are. In place of the disdainful silence that asks, "Are you now or have you ever been?" he can say simply, "I know you."

In *You Lovely People*, Santos commemorated those Pinoys who constructed an elaborate Filipino Dream which was shattered when they returned to postwar, mutilated Manila. Santos was one of the few who did not join the migration in reverse which then began. Perhaps he could not be disillusioned because, coming from Sulucan, he had never been given the right to expect otherwise; or perhaps faith founded on a habit of honesty, rather than of self-deception, is unshakable.

That so many of these earlier stories, in *Brother, My Brother*, are told from the point of view of the personal "I" indicates Santos' compassionate share in the experiences related. The identity of that "I" fluctuates; but such is the occupational hazard and glory of any author. Entering person after person, perhaps looking for himself, he finds and for awhile becomes them; for although self as essence must stand separate from others, self as existence depends on their company. This is the dialectic of human history, the drama of rejection and embrace, departure and return.

Homecomings which recognize this necessary interplay of different personalities, different times, not only serve to join these stories—otherwise ranging in space from Sulucan to Albay, in time from pre-war to occupation days—through thematic continuity; but also, in the first story and the last, provide a special comment on the human quest. After seven years the first protagonist finds his father living; after seven, the last discovers his is dead. Essentially these are the same person and no time has elapsed. Told in these tales are simply two versions of the same occasion; alternatives, in a sense—since how and when a man returns are partly his own responsibility. But in life timing is everything; human seasons are so indistinguishable that it is a wise man indeed who knows the moment of ripeness. Sometimes he is uncertain until his return whether the seven years of absence have been lean or fat; whether he has been captive in an alien land or has merely extended the boundaries of his first home; whether he will find a garden or a grave.

All of the stories are informed by knowledge of this dilemma and are disciplined by its dramatic counterforces. When, occasionally, a character wavers in thought toward sentimentality, event snatches him erect again. Here the control-through-irony that shaped *You Lovely People* is already visible. Again and again, therefore, the elements essential to tragedy are apparent, the merely pathetic is transcended: the forced bride, as symbolic of early death as the tiny coffin she accompanies downhill; the shrinking lawyer who can destroy what a volcano will not; the teacher whose favorite song is "Where is the land of joy?"; the old family friend who, trapped behind his broken eyes, is like the last man alive.

This sifting, winnowing technique of Santos as writer, his failure to be false, is authority for saying that the source of his deep and conscience-driven concern is not social in the schoolbook sense. If he were only being true to his society and times, these stories would smile until their gums showed, be rowdy as corner boys caught in a passion, or wear hangdog heads of clowns' self-pity. The world, as governments and as individuals, busies itself revising its history, today as always, ready to confess anyone's sins but its own. All around the writer—in the capital but also in the provinces—the sham goes on. Streets fill with the self-adulation of dancers; the guest chokes to satisfy the host's reputation for hospitality.

Santos as writer is no mere observer of custom; his theme of humble commemoration and charity owes nothing to the cold conventions of ancestor worship. Such gestures are put to shame by *Brother, My Brother*'s long-suffering patient style, which accepts even what it cannot admire, which does not make the stranger wash before letting him in through the gate. We are, flesh and spirit, what we are. The man who cannot help but turn and look, and will not smile, knows. This man who is a pilgrim not always to pleasure, who journeys footsore toward the very revelation every ambition in him hoped to forget, has a private resource of knowledge. For him, truth has become more important than desire: he is the person/nation in direct confrontation with himself.

This motif of return recurrent in his stories, this longing for homogeneity, reappears in Santos' first novel, *Villa Magdalena* (1965). The old mansion seems to be a death house to which two families have come for the final stages of their decay: the aristocratic Condes and the Medalladas, leather merchants to whom odors of the slaughterhouse and tannery cling. Nevertheless, as far across oceans and continents as flight takes the younger clan members, the place of least loneliness is their ancestral home. Elsewhere they feel as futile as the woman (in an early draft) who expects to save Filipinos from themselves by permanently changing their complexion. The stench they have fled is, after all, the stench of mortality, corruptibility; and only the perfume of mutual solicitude can wash that from the mind. Parts of *Villa Magdalena* were written at the same time as "The Day the Dancers Came." Both explore a variety of actual and symbolic deaths of the self, from which men are delivered only by a restored sense of community and camaraderie. The dramatic testing of this intuition has become Santos' signature.

LINDA TY-CASPER

The degradation of man by the very power structure proclaimed as his benefactor is a common irony in the history of all human relationships; and colonialism is simply one of its more available modern symbols. *The Peninsulars*, the first novel in a trilogy on the confusion of loyalties in the Philippines, is unique in that it recreates, with the exacting thoroughness of a Stendhal, conditions just prior to the British occupation of Manila in mid-eighteenth century. But it is powerful because it sees Peninsular abuse of the *indio* as macrocosmic mirror of human infirmities of such scope that this past panorama refracts images of the disturbed present. Although its particulars have been faithfully researched from Philippine historical sources, the prodigal ambitions and dilemmas it exposes could be any man's.

If the deputies of royal officialdom—governor general, royal fiscal, archbishop—are kept anonymous, the motive may be to permit composites from history; but the effect is to indict, by extension, all the hierarchic orders of authority represented by these exemplars. The English privateer, Falkener, is able to reduce Manila by hasty siege alone because its leaders, in all degree, have forfeited the personal citadels of their integrity, with a reckless overreaching in some instances, with a gradualness almost invisible in others. Single-minded Falkener is almost a welcome figure, in the morass of uncertain motives which "the ever loyal and noble city of Manila" has become; he is a satisfactory scourge.

Particularly the royal fiscal, frustrated and crafty crown prosecutor, comes to represent ruthless vainglory as he conspires to discredit still another governor general. Nevertheless, even the latter who wants to be immortalized as the defender of Filipinos finds himself violating obligations to those dependent on him: the Capitan Chino, leader of the city's minority; Carre, outcast

French inventor; Don Paco, honest entrepeneur forced to lie in order to win funds for construction of the governor's bastion ships; even Santistevan, his aide, whose *indio* friend he executes after Agbayani enlists in the uprising incited secretly by the fiscal.

The Peninsulars is a "book of the magistrates" which, at the same time, concedes the difficulty of keeping purity of human motive and means intact. The very longing of its figures for heroic proportions often exposes their imperfections and leaves them vulnerable to unforeseen contingencies. Santistevan tries to obscure his having betrayed Agbayani with Araceli, by blaming the unfortunate governor for the rebel's death and by deserting the governor's cause. His new father-image, perversely, becomes the privateer Segovia who resembles the self-seeking royal fiscal. During the fearful attack on Negros by Moro pirates, Santistevan's sense of guilt returns, overwhelmingly disproportionate and destructive of all his confidence. Later, on his return, when the rescue of Manila is placed in his custody, undirected, uncomforted, utterly anguished, he sees the city of the Virgin disintegrating before his eyes—as irrecoverable as Araceli's chastity; and his romantic dream of personal glory deteriorates (as it had earlier for Agbayani, the patriot-*manqué*) into a death-wish.

The novel gives no sentimental allegiance to one nationality or class against another. Something of magnitude miraculously is recovered in a Peninsular and is discovered in an *indio*. Having been transported safely out of the confusion which he has helped create, the governor general plans to make one final attempt at immortalizing himself by delivering the city from Falkener. Luckily, his fever of pride is purged—the governor becomes a proper tragically ennobled figure when, recognizing his *hubris*, he delegates deliverance to Santistevan, Carre, and Licaros. The first two have been like sons to him. Licaros, the *indio* priest who, refused a parish, has mortified and prepared himself equally through meditation and through battle with the infidels, recapitulates some of the governor's complex self-division. Far from having perfected himself, he is constantly worried that he may be a better *indio* than a priest. In the battle on Negros, Licaros contemplates the possibility that Moro raids in part may be justified as self-defense; and he cannot help admiring their refusal to submit to Spain. Later, he is slow to absolve Santistevan who, he fears, may be confessing his sins of deed and intent out of weakness and not out of true contrition. He himself can concede that Santistevan may have desired "not to defile Araceli but to be incarnated in her, to be protected forever from all change by her virginity—perhaps to be immaculately reconceived"—a folly perhaps, but only questionably a sin.

Licaros' broad-mindedness represents the breadth of the novel's vision, just as the governor general's ultimate purgation represents its inevitable thrust toward affirmation, through the slough of scruple and despond. Both men see that pursuit of personal honor, at another's expense, can be self-corrupting. The major relationships and countless devices in *The Peninsulars* imply acceptance of man's need to discover himself through others. The images of Araceli as saintly virgin and of the governor general as god-father help to define Santistevan to himself; but he reduces them to less than person, he permits the ideal no aspect of reality and therefore is mortally bewildered by each new casualty of circumstance. Similarly, the governor general, pretending to sacrifice himself for the defense of his people, uses them for his personal ends. Each inclines to make the other his "colony" in miniature, his store of ready resource.

Doña Gabriela, for example, is tempted to become the first woman ever to be *gobernadora* twice, so that she can manipulate her second husband as she failed to do her first. Consequently, she is disappointed with the governor general's physical decline. Then, at his sickbed, each is recalled by the other to his previous mate: and Doña Gabriela is reconciled thereafter to mothering the stricken man. The need for completion of self remains; but it is accommodated to the needs of others; it is humane. Precisely because man is defective and demands the presence of others, he dare not discount what he has proven precious. On one level, a social contract—on another, love; the only glory

—is required; mutual dependence, not mutual debauchery. So violently, however, flow the consequences of men's unrestrained will, explosive testimonials of their privilege, that few characters can see beyond the fugitive shape of onrushing event. Only gradually does the submerged structure, the interplay of dependencies dimly sensed, confirm the possibilities of exaltation in the midst of outrage.

The same emotion that marks the impulse to error and martyrdom in *The Peninsulars* also moves the characters, young and old, in *The Transparent Sun and Other Stories*. Each is seen at the moment of some grievous, threatened loss: of the last family heirloom; of a pension that would permit a dying grandeur; of successfully prolonged childhood innocence. The things man clings to which provide the comfort of self secured against surprise—these inevitably he one day fumbles. It is the fate of would-be heroes to become disenchanted; but the greatest illusion of all is despair. The stories are characterized by the quality of matured faith left in those (the boy in "The Longer Ritual"; the girl of "In Time of Moulting Doves") not permanently mutilated but transfigured beyond defacement.

NICK JOAQUIN

The work of Nick Joaquin, it is generally said, is nostalgic, repentant that the present cannot measure up to the past, that is, to the socioreligious ethic of Spanish times explored briefly in the title essay of his 1964 collection, *La Naval de Manila*. Whatever Joaquin's intention, however, in his selected *Prose and Poems* (1952), his achievement more closely approximates Alejandro Roces' reading of the text as "stories on a dying culture bearing the weight of a dead culture." The past which Joaquin has courted is an intermingling of Christian and pagan values.

Doña Lupeng, in one of Joaquin's most successful stories, "The Summer Solstice," is a terrifying if fascinating fertility symbol, a bitch-goddess who creates in order to possess. She is a kind of Salome raised to a sainthood beyond the Baptist's, whose religious festival she has appropriated. In "Three Generations," the lust of old Monzon is made to seem purer than the sadistic chastity of the father, through the would-be seminarian son's decision to let that lust be satisfied (an "either-or" proposition: naturally the son feels fated, because he fails to see the range of choices and attitudes open to him). In "After the Picnic," a similar lust in Dr. Chavez is frustrated only because he has a second vice—enormous pride—which intervenes.

The pagan element in the past revisited by Joaquin clearly has been of a special sort. Constantly there is an urge (particularly among older characters) for physical regeneration, renewal of their youth. Only rarely is this physically passionate nostalgia rendered symbolic of a longing for the cosmic order or, in terms of Spanish culture, medieval ways; and almost never does it strive for sublimation, never for spiritual consummation. In "La Naval de Manila" Joaquin asserts that "there is as great a gulf between the pre-Spanish drift of totem-and-taboo tribes and our present existence as one people as there is between protoplasm and a human creature. The *content* of our national destiny is ours to create, but the basic *form*, the *temper*, the *physiognomy*, Spain has created for us"; and he sharply distinguishes between "pagan fate and Christian freedom." Nevertheless, in his early work there is an apparently unconscious appeal that primitive attitudes and acts have for him.

The little legends of Joaquin are not Christian so much as fundamentally pagan in their devotion to superstition (as have been a small number of his articles, written for the *Philippines Free Press* under the anagrammatic pseudonym, Quijano de Manila.) "The Mass of St. Sylvestre" particularly is almost a parody of religious writing. These tales are written as if Joaquin believed what Angel Cabrera wrote in his *Journal* (in the story "It Was Later Than We Thought")—"World's best artist couldn't paint flood he was drowning in. Primary requirement is some point of vantage. Where shall that be found today? In Church, perhaps, but then artist knowingly cuts himself off from that portion of audience that's heathen. His work's bound to suffer by that much."

In other words, Joaquin's stories chiefly derive not from within the Mystical Body, with its multifold field of universals radiant, but within the shifting lore of folk not fully converted. However, what is most interesting for a critic to observe in Joaquin's work is that at times he is repelled by his own fascination with this brute world and its cults. "The Summer Solstice" is reminiscent of Euripides' *Bacchae*; and the limitations of Joaquin can best be seen, perhaps, by the contrast between these two works. During a blind bacchanalian orgy, King Pentheus' mother finds what she thinks is a lion's head in her hand; and only later does she realize it is the head of her intruding son, which she has torn off! Euripides was satirizing the devotion to such sensual gods as Dionysus, in whose honor the Greek theater itself had its start. Joaquin's story, on the other hand, seems undecided whether to run with priests or satyrs.

Of similar division are his thoughts on free will, as expressed in his stories. Despite editor Teodoro Locsin's twice-offered opinion, not freedom of the will but inevitable fate is the theme of "Guardia de Honor." Either it is a tour de force; or, if Joaquin is committed to the concept dramatized within, it is a fable of low superstition, in implication and amplitude unlike the Greek sense of nemesis. At least the recurrence of the same temptation (with variations) in "Three Generations" is credible: even aside from the doctrine of original sin, no man believes himself immaculate; sin is part of the human condition. But "Guardia de Honor" is almost as contrived as "May Day Eve," which is clearly a cleverly presented old wives' tale based on the evocation of one's prospective husband in an enchanted mirror; and "Guardia" is undramatic in the absence of successful human resistance to the drag of circumstance.

The very earliest stories of Joaquin prove to be much more at ease with translated Spanish idioms than with English. At other times, in the very act of satirizing them, he has written like those "boys in the latest loudest Hollywood styles, with American slang in their mouths and the crucifix on their breasts." The same early awkwardness with words and imprecision has made Joaquin's contribution to Philippine poetry minor. His literary strengths, in the days when he still wrote poetry, were structural, not textural. At one extreme, "Verde Yo Te Quiero Verde" tries to imitate the gypsy liberty of Federico Garcia Lorca's impressionistic poetry, but is too cool to be sensual. At the other, "The 14 Stations of the Cross" is equally startling because of the absence of religious passion, as the eye progresses by rote along the obscure wall of any church, hoping to be distracted. In between are those poems affecting colloquial speech, such as "O Death Be Proud" or "Ballade," which are not even interesting prose.

Only rarely does a poem tremble under Joaquin's touch— and such occasions are revealing: the cycle called "Stubbs Road Cantos," written in a Hong Kong seminary where the less-than-Anthony protagonist is tempted by the memory of his childhood tropical home, "waiting for the sun and the summer sunflowers"; or "The Innocence of Solomon," whose sensuous experience is so exciting as to overwhelm its temporary moralizing. It is the lost flesh incarnate in memory or wishful thought that satisfies Joaquin's early esthetics most, not the descent of God to human form. Yet biblical allusion, religious reference, serve his purpose by providing through formula and ritual the distance which his nature requires from the very object by which he hopes to be possessed. In his fiction one senses the overflow of a memory of what perhaps has never occurred outside the imagination. In poetry, Joaquin has not yet balanced this passion and restraint.

It is to Nick Joaquin's unforgettable play, A Portrait of the Artist as Filipino, that one must go to find theme and form made indivisible. Here, integrity locks together all acts and actors in a way that renders personal relevance indistinct from impersonal. Although the play ends during the Naval de Manila procession, the religious side of the ethic commemorated is almost totally absent. The excitement of the procession is used, rather, to transfigure the image of Don Lorenzo as father, protector, and progenitor which appears to the expectant Marasigan daughters at the curtain. Similarly, sensuality has been reduced by aging its victim Paula, the spinster most tempted by Javier. Thus one of the more interesting plot elements is kept credible: Candida, the elder sister, nearly destroys the younger one, as together they had nearly destroyed their father. Such an extreme test is necessary to shake them back to their senses—to that confirmation of inherited values and renunciation of the "easy life" which earns for them that final almost beatific vision of their restored father. Were Paula younger, the temptation might have been overwhelming; as it is, her character is so fixed that she is never really violated.

The labyrinth of right-turns and about-faces, which illustrate so well Joaquin's sense of ironic structure, is illuminated by the generationless fond remembrance of things past, clear in the allusions made by Don Lorenzo's contemporaries, the Marasigan spinsters, and Bitoy Camacho—whose imitation of his own childhood voice of wonder is so charming, almost literally enchanting, that the Manila (real or imaginary) of the past is ever-present, though invisible, as surely as in this play the father and the painting on the "fourth wall" are present.

For the public, this play is an elegy for lost virtues—childhood innocence; it is a reminder of the First Fall: its appeal therefore is to every man. For Joaquin himself, however, there seems to be more. His fixation with time and patterns of recurrence, noticeable in his best short stories, reappears here: several generations become involved in the attempted salvage and renewal of the past. (However, the desperate drive toward acts of lust, as if to compensate for or to replace the feared loss, has now subsided.) Victory for the spirit here (one cannot quite say the soul) is so nearly complete that, finally, there is no sense of loss. The past is carried into the future on the shoulders of the present, as in Marasigan's painting of Aeneas bearing from Troy on his shoulders an Anchises whose face is his own.

The physical destruction of Intramuros has not destroyed

the values the Marasigans held most dear. Bitoy says, standing on the ruins, "while I live, you live." The ultimate tone of the play, therefore, is not elegiac, not even backward-looking. Whatever was, still is: its value lies precisely in its indestructibility, its detachment from the changing physical surface. Whether Manila ever really was as Bitoy and Candida picture it is unimportant; even if it existed "only" in their minds, their visions of need, that becomes the more important realm of existence according to this play. The values—human consideration dignified by daily custom and ceremony—then become not past and gone but ever-present as a future compelling because desired.

Whatever made Joaquin look back and whether or not his memory is accurate (there may be as many pasts as there are interpretations provided for the painting in the play; or *the* past may remain as invisible as that painting), it is neither the looking backward nor the accuracy which makes his play memorable, but the evident love which he has felt for what was on his mind —things made so much more than things: Friday *tertulias*, sailor blouses, seawinds, October typhoons. It is this comprehensive love that opens one's eyes each moment to "morning all over the world"; it is this act of creation, justly performed re-creation, that completes the portrait of a Filipino as artist.

If his play uses religious reinforcement of values fundamentally cultural, there is a reversal of this strategy in Joaquin's *The Woman Who Had Two Navels* (1961). As a novelette, the work was one of the less romantic parts of his 1952 collection. As a novel, it is not only twice its original length but more richly ambiguous. Where the playwright relied primarily on a painting to serve as the conscience of his characters, the novel is more inventive. The dimensions of moral memory come to suggest not just the coexistence of the divinely oriented Spanish past and the pragmatic American-influenced present, but the intersection of time and eternity as well. Everyman's possession of two navels symbolizes just such dualities—as well as the coincidence of the diabolic and angelic in man. The Filipinos who recall their homeland from self-imposed exile in Hong Kong represent an impulse that includes, at the same time that it is larger than, nationalism. They seem to express a cosmic alienation, a yearning to return to some higher identity.

The division of the storytelling among a number of narrators indicates the difficulty of discerning truth from error, right from wrong. Even the judgment of young Father Tony is erratic and undependable. Nevertheless, Joaquin's reliance on a variety of mirror images symbolizes the capacity for individuals, out of a sense of responsibility both personal and communal, to progress toward the fullness of truth with one another's help. Band-leader Paco (who at one point is said to resemble his wife Mary as closely as a twin), is caught between the passions of the sister-sirens, Concha (Señora de Vidal) and her daughter Connie, who wants to rescue the older woman from this liaison. Similarly, but earlier, Macho—young plantation-owner and a former lover of Concha's—has been wished onto Connie as a husband. The grotesque doll Biliken has long been a substitute, for Connie, for all the security and love she has missed; and the idol in the Chinese temple becomes its later equivalent. The tissue of these lives and others tightens until Macho, who has come to love his wife Connie but has been rejected because his former letters to Concha were discovered, shoots Concha in futile revenge. In a sense, they have all contributed to her death—but she most of all; in the midst of her sinning, Concha never failed to feel guilty and to wait patiently for God's hand to strike her down. Furthermore, it is implied that her death may release Connie, who has chosen between suicide and elopement with Paco but, having finally found the courage to do wrong, may some day find courage to do what is right.

Irony is the blurred image of right wrestling, interlocked, with wrong; but even if the lives of these agonized characters are still knotted at the end, the decision of Father Tony to return to his duties at the priory after failing Connie so often that he had despaired, is instructive of Joaquin's faith in the divine mystery. Even more elaborately, the direction of life has been established just before Connie's elopement. In Chapter IV, "The Chinese Moon" (signifying a new year), a series of progressively advanced flashbacks is interlaced with flashes forward, hysterical anticipations by Connie of death through the four elements—earth, water, air, and fire, the last fortunately becoming a means of purging herself of all desires of self-destruction. Then, in the final chapter, both Connie and old *katipunero* Monson (who has lived in exile rather than face post-Revolutionary life at home), having confronted themselves in each other and having seen how obsessed they both have been with evasion, become recommitted to life. All the patterns in the novel, of children betraying their fathers and of parents betraying their children, are epitomized and at the same time resolved in this magnificent confrontation. Connie and Monson accept, wordlessly, the difference between dream and reality, and accept furthermore the necessity of both as springs of action.

Style and theme are perfectly adapted to each other's needs in this novel, proving that Joaquin is Faulkner/Dostoevsky to Gonzalez' Hemingway/Chekhov. Formerly, Joaquin has only talked about the splendor of Spanish times; here, in his flashbacks, for the first time he credibly recreates those days when "people like your father," as Concha says to young Monson, "were my conscience walking around in elegant clothes." Moreover, in his implied criticism of *katipunero* Monson's static view of history, Joaquin has come to terms with the realization that the future, too, is an active participant in tradition.

For all its elaborate order and symbolic engagement, there is a deliberate withholding of dogmatic denouement appropriate to the author's refusal to make any single character his or his novel's exclusive spokesman. The ultimate wisdom emergent from this very irresolution—after the most assured characters have unfixed their opinions several times—is acceptance of some portion of mystery in divine-human negotiations and an expression of the possibility that human error short of despair is forgivable and that good will moves man closer to salvation not only despite but sometimes through error. May punishment not be a blessing most welcome then, as Concha thinks? Here pagan and Christian attitudes may find common ground: if so, it is not wholly incongruous that Connie should seek a veterinarian to examine her mutilated soul.

GREGORIO BRILLANTES

Cosmic alienation—the incommensurability of God and man —is implied not only in Joaquin's novel but also in most of the stories in Gregorio Brillantes' collection, *The Distance to Andromeda and Other Stories* (1960). Structure and symbol establish an extraordinary awareness of human isolation at its most profound. Nevertheless, the separateness which moves Brillantes most—perhaps because it can be ameliorated—is that which persists owing to man's refusal to act or to speak. Probably it should be called the inarticulateness of inertia, or of silence self-imposed.

In five of the twenty stories, Brillantes uses a rotating point of view, not to investigate society in cross-section but to dramatize the irony of individuals' similarities which they conceal behind assumed separateness. In "The Years," for example, the De Leons are presented through this device less as a family than as a series of compartmentalized individuals occasionally sharing one roof. They hardly exchange the time of day, although the degree of assistance they could give each other's secret problem is suggested through the final scene. Chabeng finds her husband Carlos speechless in the bedroom after a severe heart attack and, calling out to him, moves to comfort him with a "fear as deep and overwhelming as love." The same kind of private barriers stand between family members in "The Living and the Dead," "The Exiles," and "A Wind over the Earth" (in which Tony, despairing that he and his dying father will never really know each other, pulls his wife close—only to have his gesture of need misunderstood). What in effect is rotation of point of view is employed for a somewhat different end when, in "The Light and the Shadow of Leaves," it signifies the abyss between generations, as the elders are betrayed by their successors.

The cleavage within man and between men finds its image in each of Brillantes' most significant stories. In "The Young Man," the narrator suffers a sense of his own lost identity when he discovers that no one remembers the smiling family friend whose calm was focal in a prewar photograph. The alienation of father and son in "Faith, Love, Time, and Dr. Lazaro" is reinforced by the sight of an infant dying of lockjaw and apparently "straining to express some terrible ancient wisdom," as well as by the suggestive title character's name. As Brillantes— a conscious, but rarely self-conscious, artist—has explained in the analysis printed in Father Miguel Bernad's *Bamboo and the Greenwood Tree*, "His name is at once ironic and symbolic, for the theme is the unresurrected Lazarus." The story begins and ends with "tomb-images." In "The World of the Moon," it is the secret dark side of man which is revealed by the permanence of mystery managed through containment of the experience presented within the half-light of a young boy's point of view. Perhaps isolation at its most frightful is epitomized by the smoking pit beneath the schoolhouse, scene of the anonymous boy's initiation in "What Shall We Do When We All Go Out?"

Nevertheless, other privacies are bright, even if their illumination is cast inward only. The narrator in "The Strangers" finds it impossible to convey to her aunt or her lover what grace pierced her side during her attendance at Mass in Quiapo; what remembrances now flood her of a virginal childhood which these others would defile. Moreover, it is characteristic of Brillantes that, if most of his stories depend on irony, his ironic vision is seldom grim. The image of space offered suggests empty, impassable distances less often than a cosmos filled with a divine love which, however "incomprehensible, a wordless thought" ("The Distance of Andromeda"), invites the pilgrimage of man. Scenes of oncoming despair open on the night sky flooded with moonlight, the flowing of grace toward a rendezvous with the startled eye or reaching fingertip. When the walls of pride fall, rescue is that close; in the meantime there are windows to watch. There are the vocations that overtake and fulfill character after character; there is the tremulous sense of adolescent yearning and growth in stories such as "The Rain": these are co-correlatives, and windows.

Similarly, the very fact that the "dream of the lost city" recurs ("The Exiles," "The Beautiful Gerrls") converts it into a commitment, the prompting of a future occasion, a wish-to-be-fulfilled; and into a consolation, therefore, and not merely a Wordsworthian memory of glory rapidly growing ever more remote. It is an authentic intimation of immortality; a compelling, if quiet, evocation not of a community that has crumbled beyond recovery but of a perpetual place of light and refreshment, a heavenly city beyond the encompass of Babylon's lofty gardens or Babel's towering confusion. As N. V. M. Gonzalez points out in his introduction to these stories, they are constructed around images of "arrivals and departures," of movement through the distances within man and between men, and between men and the transcendent; this is the ultimate consolation that life offers and that Brillantes sees.

However, the strength of the writer lies in more than consistency of insight or the ability to provide a paradigm of variations on a central theme. The same pattern of idea and image occurs in stories which seem minor when removed from the collective support of the others: "Blue Piano" (separateness is the theme, but the night club setting is formularistic, artificial); "Sunday" (the immanence of God is invoked, but only at the expense of reducing the divine to the level of carabao-buying and movie-going, rather than elevating man and event to meet the divine in its act of incarnation); "The Rice Fields" (the dream, realized, becomes more than mirage, but the climactic events seem to have an existence outside the central character, who is too transparently presented). There is a thinness about persons in such stories which is not typical of Brillantes' fiction. Many of his stories are richly textured, their details serving not simply to authenticate place or thing but to characterize those who occupy and possess these. Or where characterization has to be accomplished economically—whenever, for example, a rotating point of view is employed—Brillantes often manages this by the intense correctness of the few details allowed; by the perfection of scene, if the full drama is withheld. From such details-as-crux, theme emerges credibly, without contrivance.

Perhaps the difference between pattern emergent and pattern imposed can be accounted for, in part, by the apparently autobiographical element in several of the more successful short stories—although even in those cases, the use of personal history as point of departure rather than as destination would seem to be the cause of success. Tarlac, Brillantes' home town, recurs as place and matrix for several narrators who otherwise, occasionally, would be nearly anonymous, their character taken for granted as one might expect from an author unconsciously serving as his own point of view (a constant device for Estrella Alfon, for example). Even this circumstance, which normally would be considered a defect, is not inappropriate in stories which trace a pilgrimage to self-knowledge. The anonymity of the narrator does not remain, but diminishes as his identity is formed out of the substantial context of place and of other persons. The propriety of a narrator-in-transition is additionally justified by the concern of many of these stories with adolescence, a time of trial, of trying on. In turn, the tumultuous equivocations of adolescence mirror the sense of uneasiness provided by placement of event after event within war's shadow.

Such mutual reinforcement indicates not merely that Brillantes' adolescent years during war's upheavals must have been major formative years for him, but also that he has proven his ability to extend private experience, through the symbolic imagination, into what is more than simply the "record of a generation." He has objectified the philosophical implications of life through a careful negotiation of the philosophical implications of literary form. Personal history does not remain private in Brillantes; nor is it purged: but it is transfigured—and this is the signature of the writer as seer. It is also final demonstration that the capacity for vision which figures in Brillantes' stories does exist in fact. Here is no dream of a dead past, but an authentic intimation of the possibilities of regeneration, within the shadow of Armageddon. The season of grace is now—and here, as Brillantes implies.

When the Asian Writers Conference met in Manila, during the week following Christmas in 1962, Philippine writers were the hosts in more ways than customary hospitality required. Discussions had been organized around the conflict of supposed antitheses: tradition and modernity, science and art, change and stability. As the heir of multiple cultures, as one of the most westernized of all Asian countries, as the oldest of the new republics and independent nations, the Philippines was able to provide from its own experience models of the possibilities of synthesis. Especially the spokesmen from India and Taiwan and Indonesia seemed almost embarrassed—certainly encumbered— by the ways of the past, in such haste were they to be among the *avant-garde* in the electronics age. By contrast, the so-called age of revolution for the Filipino has extended, in stages throughout several centuries of his history. It is difficult for him, therefore, to distinguish it from evolution. He is likely to conceive of tradition as all particulars ever inherited and consequently, for better or for worse, inescapable even when most hotly denied. On the other hand, he translates modernity into the open, living end of organic tradition, the right to protest against conventionality and the reduction of meaning's momentum to routine.

Struggling to make purposeful the socioeconomic complexities of his heritage, the Filipino finds, is essentially not very different from his struggle to make his competing languages say something true and enduring. He has discovered that reliance on the vernacular is no sure guarantee of excellence when naturalness of idiom is counteracted by artificial conventions difficult to dislodge and by the reluctance of most periodicals and moviemakers to risk raising their literary standards. Even among those writers most dedicated (sometimes overdefensively) to sustaining whatever splendor in vernacular literature can be sensed, most avoid the special martyrdom which making a public appraisal in a personalized culture entails. Only the rare critic labors to find detailed textual support for his claims about craftsmanship, so that the subject's worth can be confirmed objectively and standards be defined.[4]

The circumstances of the writer in English are hardly more pleasant. Yet, as the quality of achievement indicated by Florentino's *Midcentury Guide to Philippine Literature in English* (1963) proves, the unpredictable keeps occurring. Although magazine space reserved for fiction diminishes; although organized theater is virtually nonexistent; although criticism is typically personal and eccentric, and contemporary literature has only grudgingly been recognized in Philippine schools; although there are financial distractions in other fields—still the pace and quality of publication constantly improves. All this, in spite of the great social and personal disorders recognized by what is written: revolution, agrarian riot, the horrors of war, and the terrors of freedom.

It might seem especially incredible that so much of this achievement has been managed in a language only recently assimilated. Yet N. V. M. Gonzalez suggested at the 1964 USIS symposium on "Literature and Society" that a writer, to be wakeful, must undergo self-laceration, and "it is in the work in English where the corresponding sacrificial effort seems to be indicated." Similarly, Father Bernad has acknowledged "A Twofold Renaissance in Philippine Literature," as his monograph's title suggests. He records how Mexican independence in 1821,

---

[4] See Teodoro A. Agoncillo, *Ang Maikling Kuwentong Tagalog* (1886–1948) (Manila: Inang Wika Publishing, 1954), pp. 11–65; Andres C. Cruz, "The Vernacular Writer," Panorama, XII (April, 1960), 28–36; E. San Juan, Jr., "Cultural Resurgence in Philippine Literature, II: In Tagalog," *Literature East and West* (March, 1965), pp. 16–23; E. San Juan, Jr., "The World of Abadilla," and Francisco Arcellana, "Introduction," pp. 1–14 and 47–8, respectively, in A. G. Abadilla, *Piniling Mga Tula ni AGA* (San Juan, Rizal: Abadilla, 1965).

introduction of the newspaper to the archipelago in 1822, the opening of the Suez Canal in 1869, the opulence of certain Filipinos which permitted study in Europe—all these circumstances promoted closer cultural ties with Spain and a cultural renaissance in the nineteenth century. Romances in Tagalog verse blossomed; but the novel in Spanish was a special flowering recognized even by the Peninsulars. Now the Filipino has struggled with still another language, and with a host of attitudes expressed in English. Creative adaptability rather than animal mimicry is involved; and its success can be explained only as the result of a profound impulse to know and to become.

Whatever the idiom of his effort, the Philippine writer is, simply, a representative man, for whom fiction and poetry are acts of faith to help make those long daily leaps into the unknown. They are the source of new beliefs, not the mere suspension of disbelief. The immediacy of art takes man's initial intuitions and shapes them into temporary working knowledge —because literature, like man, is experimental. Its revelations and admissions arrive, they are never brought; they emerge naturally, they are not made.

The attrition of the struggle has to be acknowledged; affirmation, earned. The fiction in *Kathá I* (1955) seems to reflect that loneliness which editor Juan Tuvera says is the bone of any author's bone: men who grow shrilly unmanned from loss of human touch, children on the curb of perversion, the adulterer who dulls his own lust, the aging aching bachelor unloved, the lost totem, the lost self, the wife for whom childbirth is unbearable, the girl who will not ransom her need. Human failure is common substance in life. It becomes fiction when it is felt through form; it becomes important, more than recognizable and informative, not for what is lost but for what is salvaged. In these stories, untouchable men and women are touched; here, the speechlessness of the trapped and isolated "I" is audible in violent silence; here, human loneliness is shared, like grafted skin.

Similarly, the *Palanca Prize Stories: 1950–1955* (edited by

Kerima Polotan-Tuvera, 1957) demonstrates the superiority of the prize story over the sentimental valentine, the chronicle of violence as unchallenged heroic deed, the narrative essay or expanded aphorism, the oratorical piece for propaganda's occasion. In the mature Philippine story, the drift of events often exceeds the events themselves in importance, reducing sensation to proper proportion. Direction of sudden growth, sometimes, is all: a sense of ripeness. The gentleness of such a story is deceptive, as exquisite as the pain from a wound being unbandaged but as yet unrevealed. By attending the tremulous, the nearly intangible, these stories prove human worth far better than did their predecessors' complacent assumptions.

This sense of drift, in turn, reinforces the Filipino's feeling for isolation and unfulfillment. The underlying theme of Asuncion David-Maramba's anthology, *Philippine Contemporary Literature* (1962), is the search for cultural continuity; and several of the most interesting stories in Francisco Arcellana's 1963 P.E.N. anthology dramatize this alienation through the Filipino's experience of dislocation overseas: not only in America (Santos' "The Day the Dancers Came"), but also in such Asian countries as Korea and Viet Nam, world battlefields for recognition; and, just as significantly, through the disorientation of Indians in Manila (Morli's "Dada").

Furthermore, as "Rice Wine" in the latter volume indicates, even the younger generation is painfully aware of man's incongruity, as well as of the occasions for its cause and revelation. Nolledo built his early reputation on stylized language and on action that was almost choreography. "Harana," for example, was a tour de force, an adagio for blue strings and a conventionalized tremolo, commemorating the impoverished poet mutilated for loving the landowner's unattainable daughter: a sophisticated version of an ancient folk lyric. "Rice Wine" trembles on the edge of that same excess, but becomes fable instead of artifice, becomes an expressionistic parable of the unfinished revolution, and the betrayal of the future by those who (like Hightower in Faulkner's *Light in August*) fall into the past as into a 'trance. Sacrifice then becomes a travesty; communion (rice/wine) a sacrilege. The passionate yearning to matter, to be assimilated, is shattered with all the explosiveness of a transplendent composition by Mexico's Jose Clemente Orozco.

In volumes such as these, occasions are encountered again and again for the characters' realization of personal incompleteness. Nor is the world wholly created in which they must seek and find themselves. These stories know the need for man to help make his world, and his self in that world. Culture is never a gift; it is in a complex process of constant ratification or rejection or modification. The *delicadeza*, the self-effacement of Philippine fiction is not only traditional, but also modern, in origin. A man, a people who labor long years for independence, political or economic, may well stagger from the sudden apprehension of the risks of self-reliance, the requirements of responsibility, when finally freed—just as sharecroppers resettled on EDCOR lands in Mindanao found themselves unaccustomed to making their own decisions. Liberation can feel like expulsion, under certain circumstances. The repressed mind, released, gropes back to its prison for orientation. It holds on to darkness, to measure the light. It finds that it cannot immediately and wholly reject past habit, customs which whatever their vice did relieve individual judgment. This is part of the Philippine contribution to world literature by and about man's awakening.

The fiction of Gonzalez, Joaquin, Santos, Cruz, Brillantes, and others—given the forcefulness of its persuasions and the honesty of its outcome—safeguards the Filipino from denying his identity in the very act of seeking its fulfillment. The journalist and the ambitious civil servant sometimes are tempted to define the national experience as if it had occurred outside history. They clamor for a sudden leap—forward?—into automation. But though the city novelist may be just as concerned with freeing the national economy from its role as dumping grounds for foreign manufactures, he cannot so totally despise an agrarian way of life, but recalls both evils and virtues of the *barrio* of his birth; and, without nostalgia, he touches again his

first and most-enduring flesh. That same honest acknowledgment, however painful its aftermath in the necessary reconciliation of apparent opposites, has begun to accommodate pre-
Spanish tribesmen, Peninsular Christian, Moro rebel, and American do-gooder in an image of common ancestry, with the same
ingathering generosity that made a nation out of seven thousand
islands.

Present history lies around and within the writer. He is time's
eye: he will be its record.

Anthology

Carlos P. Romulo

The Impact of Literature on Philippine Society: A Historical Perspective

To speak on the impact of literature on society is to accept —implicitly—a great many or a few assumptions, not only about the relationship of literature and society; or about the writer's dialectical relationship to his milieu or between imagination and the social reality; but also—and I think this is the primary assumption we ought to clarify—to accept that there *is* such a relationship; that it is actual, not merely inferential.

I raised this problem at once because I want to initiate some doubts and for a particular academic and critical strategy: it is my feeling that literature is best served by the liberal imagination; by the intellect that affirms and denies; that celebrates and condemns. Philippine literature is pervaded with precisely such an intelligence: it accounts for the strength of Balagtas; the continuing relevance and cogency of Rizal; the permanent cultural significance of S. P. Lopez's *Literature and Society*; for the novels of Laya; the importance of *Banaag at Sikat*, the poetry of Jose Garcia Villa, the short stories of N. V. M. Gonzalez, Rotor and Arguilla, and the works of Nick Joaquin. If I fail here to be inclusive in my mentionings, it is because of a great uneasiness on my part regarding the position I have to take as regards my subject. For in speaking about the relationship of literature and society and, more specially, on "the impact of literature on Philippine society," I wish to preserve the literary terms of the subject and to refer indirectly only to society and politics.

It is indeed true that some sort of relationship inheres between literature and society or, to pursue its philosophical implications, between the images of the writer and the social fact itself. Some such relationship inheres between, say, the virtual universe in the novels of Sir Walter Scott and the external, material context of his novels. This is also true of Jane Austen: the virtual life in her novels and the palpable life of the English boroughs. Or of Balzac and Zola. The very fact that Balzac bores us, in his attempt to represent the fate of Eugènie Grandet, with such details as the size of a possible inheritance; the appearance of houses; the number of pieces of furniture and how they look like in a particular room, does indicate, for us, the pressing claim of facts, of the material context of imagination, on the novel.

The claims of the factual or, conversely, the yearning of literature to approximate as closely as possible the solidity of fact, manifests itself even in Rizal. We all know Rizal's intention in *Noli Me Tangere*. We know it because we have not only read the novel, but because Rizal himself declared it. But in the course of his narrative, Rizal must pay attention to facts: besides enumerating the kinds and number of images in the *sala* of Capitan Tiago's house, he must also tell us the dimensions of the cockpit of San Diego—it consists of three parts: the entrance is rectangular: it is 20 meters long and 14 meters wide, etc. The same attention to facts is to be found in Arguilla: the Hacienda in "Elias" is 15 kilometers from the station; 25 yards separated the central female character from the boy narrator when "the tail of her skirt fell out of where she had tucked it in at the waist"; and, in "Epilogue to Revolt," the distance between the house of the *teniente del barrio* and the station is 500 meters; Quezon was 58 years old when he pardoned 31 Sakdalistas, "four of whom came from this village." And, in "The Socialists," the man who recited Markham's "The Man With the Hoe" has two front gold teeth. Arguilla's rendering of his English is even more precise:

> *Is dis da Ting de Lord God made and gabe*
> *To habe dominion ober sea and land*

One recalls the precision, too, with which Rizal indicates his character's stupidity: while on the subject of the Suez Canal, Doña Victorina de Espadaña inquires whether it was opened before or after Christ; and, on the problem of digging the Pasig river so that it would facilitate transportation, Don Custodio suggests that they should raise ducks because the ducks would eat the snails and therefore deepen the bottom of the river: which suggestion, of course, increased the worries of Doña Victorina: if the country were to raise more ducks, *balút* would become the primary industry and would disgrace the country!

But it is not only in the statistics of objects or of distance; nor is it on the precise indication of folly merely that literature aspires to be taken as true. In his unfinished novel, tentatively titled *The Tagalog Nobility*, Rizal indicates the context explicitly, before proceeding to the actual narrative; the year is 1635, sixty-four years after the arrival of the Spaniards at Manila; Spain is waging a series of wars with the Dutch and the natives of the South, "wars in which the Filipinos were playing the toughest and most painful part." Sporadic revolts, too, characterize the political situation of the country: the conspiracy alleged to have been plotted by Pampanga, Manila and Borneo in 1585 but which failed because of the betrayal of a soldier's Filipino wife; the Cagayan uprising in 1589, provoked by the *encomenderos'* demands for tribute and their other exactions; the recruitment for the expedition to Formosa in 1629. History itself becomes the necessary context of fiction, as it is in Tolstoy's *War and Peace*; in Stendhal's *The Red and the Black* and *The Charterhouse of Parma*; as it is, too, even in relatively recent fiction, in Hemingway's *For Whom the Bell Tolls* and *The Sun Also Rises*; in Koestler's *Darkness at Noon*; in Sartre's trilogy, *Roads to Freedom*; and in Pasternak's *Dr. Zhivago*.

All these facts, these details in fiction, not merely serve to reinforce the sense of reality we usually expect of literature, but also establish, I think, the rapport, or call it *empathy* if you wish, between the work of the imagination and the sources of its images which exist external to it—in the very context of life, of reality, in the appearances and qualities of the social fact.

Perhaps our most modern theorist on this aspect of literary criticism is S. P. Lopez, as he has defined its canons and articulated its implications in his book, *Literature and Society*. The Committee of the Commonwealth Literary Awards—of which I happened to be chairman—was aware of this when it awarded the book the first prize. In giving the award, we were also conscious that the book was significant, not merely for reasons of its stylistic excellence or the consistency with which Lopez presented his critical formulations. More significantly, the book was the first of its kind, and the only one up to the present time, to have interpreted the literary tradition of the Philippines with intelligence and perception. Or, perhaps, "interpret" is a misleading term: for Lopez, in *Literature and Society*, was also concerned with recalling, to the consciousness of the Filipino writer during the Commonwealth era, the canons that had been evolved and established by the previous literary tradition: the literary canons and direction of the national intellectual literary tradition, as it is to be found and/or perceived in the works of Balagtas, Paterno, Rizal, Lopez Jaena, Marcelo H. del Pilar, and Lope K. Santos. Indeed, I know of no other body of works in the Philippines that could compare to the achieved canons of this tradition. And when Lopez criticizes such preoccupation, in Philippine poetry, as could result in such lines as:

I waited, love. All nature waited, too.

one feels that he was merely making the burden of this tradition to bear upon the body of imaginative works in the Philippines in the latter part of the American regime. In giving the historical perspective of Philippine literature, we must, therefore, simply take into account the impact of this tradition on Philippine critical thought, on the literature that came to be written after 1898, and on the relationship that the works within this tradition had assumed to be social reality.

II

The established scholarship in this country recognizes Balagtas' *Florante at Laura* as an allegorical poem. In the context of this reading and interpretation, we are, therefore, expected to deal with its details as symbols—not as symbols of thematic meanings, but more directly as symbols of social facts. Here the poem would stand in direct relation to history rather than to cosmic significations: Albania, in the poem of Balagtas, is not the human situation in general, as perhaps we could say of Oran in Albert Camus' *The Plague* (*La Peste*). Rather Albania is a definite geography, a specific community—the Philippines—at a particular instance of history. It would follow from this reading, therefore, that the characters must also be interpreted as agents of the action of allegory: Florante and Laura; Alladin and Flerida; as against the villainous Laertes: the Christian and Moslem Filipino in dialectical relationship with an intruder, a perfidious force that stands against the idea of rightful sovereignty.

Rizal himself accepted this symbology. And when he came to write his first novel, Rizal said in a letter to Blumentritt that it was a "book about the life of the Tagalog. The Filipinos will find in it the history of the last ten years." Rizal, of course, was writing fiction and not reportage, but he meant it to insinuate facts: "The Filipinos," he said in the same letter to Blumentritt, "will note how different are my descriptions from those of other writers. The government and the friars will probably attack the work, but I trust in the God of truth and in the persons who have seen our sufferings at close range. Here I answer all that has been written about us . . . " Rizal, therefore, meant to exercise a corrective function through the novel—he meant to constitute the truth about the country; the quality of the Spanish political and religious administration; the errors of some Filipinos; the basis of the demands of those who wanted reforms.

The impact of Rizal's novels on the society of his time may

be indicated by the two kinds of sentiment—entirely opposed to each other—they elicited. The Filipinos, as Rizal had hoped, indeed noted the difference of his descriptions from "those of other writers." Rizal's contemporaries saw in his representations the correct image of the social truth. "I have not read anything more truthful nor more graphic referring to [Philippine] society as much calumniated as it is afflicted," said A. Rigor, of the *Noli*. Old Tasio recalled to him "two or three illustrious countrymen of ours." And Eduardo de Lete, writing to Rizal on June 20, 1887, thought that the descriptions of situations and characters in the book were true to type. And of the *Fili*, Pardo de Tavera becomes even more confiding and gossipy: of two characters in the novel, de Tavera states that they were real "countrymen of ours: one whom we knew in Barcelona, who was with us in Madrid, and now is in the Philippines; and the other we knew here during the Exposition." Then he asks: "Do you recognize them?"

The opposite sentiment was expressed by the colonial administration. The Rector of the University of Santo Tomas at the time (expressing the opinion of a committee of the faculty assigned to render judgment on the *Noli*) pronounced it "heretical, impious, and scandalous to the religious order, and unpatriotic and subversive to public order, libelous to the government of Spain and to its political policies in the Islands." These judgments may be right, but do not contradict the testimony of the Filipinos that the novel was suggestive of the social truth.

But the novels of Rizal were yet to find greater reverberation, not so much on the immediate milieu of the author, but on our present situation. So that the statement of Juan Luna on the *Fili* is even more accurate now than perhaps it was when Luna first expressed it. Writing to Rizal on September 23, 1891, Luna said: " . . . you are the creator of *our* novel and the one who will, with his writings, establish the freedom of thought."

Indeed, it was Rizal who created *the* Filipino novel. I think it was Flaubert who said that Madame Bovary was a spiritual cousin of Don Quixote: both were victims of their romantic imaginings and their own illusions. In the same way, the major characters of contemporary fiction in the Philippines are direct descendants of Rizal's creations: Martin in *His Native Soil* by Juan C. Laya is a spiritual cousin of Crisostomo Ibarra. The very title of the novel intones the central sentiment of Rizal, and Martin returning to the Philippines from America and finding the country parochial and squalid, attempts to introduce some reforms, not by donating a schoolhouse as Ibarra did, but by engaging in business, by encouraging private enterprise to hasten economic development. In Arguilla, "the voice of the hunted" in Rizal expresses itself through parliamentary procedures: Sakdalistas on a propaganda campaign in a village near Mount Arayat; whereas the underprivileged, the dispossessed and the exploited classes in the *Noli* and the *Fili* become the central object of the social conscience in Arguilla's stories: the proofreader, the "galley slave" Mr. Santos, in "Caps and Lower Case"; the villagers in "Hunger"; etc. In *Without Seeing the Dawn* (again the phrase is Rizal's) by Stevan Javellana, the nationalist student in *El Filibusterismo*—Isagani, probably—is transformed into a *guerrillero*, first a victim of economic contumely in the Hacienda where he works and later finding his conscience affirmed in patriotic resistance work. In *Watch in the Night* (has the title any reference to old Tasio's *no todos dormian en la noche de nuestro abuelos?*), the theme of withdrawal and participation in Rizal's fiction is treated. Social corruption is again the theme of Mr. Sionil Jose's *The Pretenders*. In Mr. Nick Joaquin's *The Woman Who Had Two Navels*, cultural and spiritual neurosis is adumbrated against a context of history: our experience with two cultures and the inability of political independence to resolve the conflicts that experience generated. The torment and irresolution of Connie Vidal in Mr. Joaquin's novel —isn't this already anticipated in the character of the Filipino woman in Rizal's? The claims of the pagan and the Christian ethos are precisely the forces symbolized by Maria Sinagtala and Maligaya in *Tagalog Nobility*. Then, there is Emma Gorrez in Kerima Polotan's *The Hand of the Enemy*: do we not see in her problem a faint reverberation of a compendium of complexes derived from the personal problems of Sisa, of Maria Clara and of Juli? Polotan is said to have once publicly declared that the enemy in the novel is life itself: life as the betrayal of a woman's dreams of personal liberation and happiness and also of her wish for security and love.

From this we can make a general observation of Philippine literature: that its preoccupation is in raising alternative images to the condition of the national reality. Rizal spoke of his novels as a diagnosis of the social cancer. The term is perhaps too medical, although Balzac and Zola would greatly approve of it. But the writers after him have precisely done that: to avail themselves of the social facts of their research into the national pathology. Señor Pasta has come to assume the significance of more than being such a character in fiction: to the national sentiment, his manifestation in society is an object of satire and innuendoes. The same can be said of any social manifestation of the mind of Capitan Tiago; of Doña Victorina de Espadaña; of evil priests; of fanaticism, etc. On the other hand, Ibarra and Elias, Tasio, the philosopher, Isagani, Cabesang Tales, too, have come to suggest modes of relating one's self to reality, political power, or to the social malady. As to Laya's Martin, Joaquin's Connie Vidal, Polotan's Emma Gorrez, or Sionil Jose's Antonio Samson, we can perhaps ask the rhetorical question that Pardo de Tavera addressed to Rizal: "Who does not recognize them?"

To say this is perhaps not really to express a literary judgment, but more to exercise a critical intelligence towards literature and society. But this is precisely my subject and I did no more than concur with Arnold and, since we are talking of Philippine literature, with the canons of the Filipino intelligentsia of the 19th century and with the formulations of S. P. Lopez that greater critical and cultural possibilities would indeed be perceived if we take literature as a criticism of life.

ARTURO B. ROTOR

Zila

Turong brought him from Pauambang in his little sailboat for the coastwise steamer did not stop at any little island of broken cliffs and coconut palms. It was almost midday; they had been standing in that white glare where the tiniest pebble and fluted conch had become points of light, piercing-bright—the municipal president, the parish priest, Don Eliodoro who owned almost all the coconuts, the herb doctor, the village character. Their mild surprise over when he spoke in their native dialect, they saw him more closely and his easy manner did not deceive them. His head was uncovered and he had a way of bringing the back of his hand to his brow or mouth. They read behind that too; it was not a gesture of protection. "An exile has come to Anayat . . . and he is so young, so young." So young and lonely and sufficient unto himself. There was no mistaking the stamp of an inflexible will on that brow, the brow of those who have to be cold and haughty, those shoulders stooped slightly, less from the burden that they bore than from a carefully cultivated air of unconcern; no common school teacher could dress so carelessly and not appear shoddy; no one could assume the detached, bored, uncongenial manner in a small village and not excite offense.

They had prepared a room for him in Don Eliodoro's house so that he would not have to walk far every morning, but he gave nothing more than a glance at the big stone building with its Spanish *azotea*, its arched doorways, its flagged courtyard. He chose Turong's home, a shaky hut near the sea. Was the sea rough and dangerous at times? He did not mind it. Was the place far from the church and the schoolhouse? The walk would do him good. Would he not feel lonely with nobody but an illiterate fisherman for a companion? He was used to living alone. And they let him do as he wanted, for the old men knew that it was not so much the nearness of the sea that he desired as its silence so that he might tell it secrets he could not tell anyone else.

They thought of nobody but him; they talked about him in the barber shop, in the cockpit, in the *sari-sari* store, the way he walked, the way he looked at you, his unruly hair. They dressed him in purple and linen, in myth and mystery, put him astride a black stallion, at the wheel of a blue automobile. Mr. Reteche? Mr. Reteche? The name was redolent of the glitter and fantasy of a place and people they would never see. He was the scion of a powerful family, a poet and artist, a prince.

That night, Don Eliodoro had the story from his daughter of his first day in the classroom; she perched wide-eyed, low-voiced, short of breath on his arm.

"He bowed as if we were his equals. He asked for the list of our names and as he read each one we looked at him long. When he came to my name, Father, the most surprising thing happened. He started pronouncing it and then he stopped as if he had forgotten something and just stared and stared at the paper in his hands. I heard my name repeated three times through his half-closed lips. 'Zita, Zita, Zita.'

" 'Yes, sir, I am Zita.'

"He looked uncomprehendingly, inarticulately, and it seemed to me, Father, it actually seemed that he was begging me to tell him that that was not my name, that I was deceiving him. He looked so miserable and sick I felt like sinking down or running away.

" 'Zita is not your name: it is just a pet name, no?'

" 'My father has always called me that, sir.'

" 'It can't be; maybe it is Pacita or Luisa or ——'

"His voice was scarcely above a whisper, Father, and all the while he looked at me begging, begging. I shook my head determinedly. My answer must have angered him, he must have thought I was so hard-headed for he said, 'A thousand miles, Mother of Mercy . . . It is not possible.' He kept on looking at me; he was so hurt perhaps that he should have such a stubborn pupil. But I am not really so, am I, Father?"

"Yes, you are, my dear. But you must try to please him, he is a gentleman, he comes from the City. I was thinking . . . Private lessons, perhaps, if he won't ask so much." Don Eliodoro had his dreams and she was his only daughter.

Turong had his own story to tell in the barber shop that night, a story so vividly etched as the lone coconut palm in front of the shop that shot up straight into the darkness of the night, as vaguely disturbing as the secrets that the sea whispered into the night.

"He did not sleep a wink, I am sure of it. When I came from the market the stars were already out and I saw that he had not touched the food I had prepared. I asked him to eat and he said he was not hungry. He sat by the window that faces the sea and just looked out hour after hour. I woke up three times during the night and saw that he had not so much as changed his position. I thought once that he was asleep and came near him, but he motioned me away. When I awoke at dawn to prepare the nets, he was still there."

"Maybe he wants to go home already." They looked up with concern.

"He is sick. You remember Father Fernando? He had a way of looking like that, into space, seeing nobody, just before he died."

Every month there was a letter that came for him, sometimes two or three large, blue envelopes with a gold design in the upper left hand corner and a broad, angular, sweeping handwriting. One time Turong brought it to him in the classroom. They were busy writing a composition on a subject that he had given, "The

Things That I Love Most." Carelessly he had opened it, carelessly read it, and carelessly tossed it aside. Zita was all aflutter when they handed in their work for he had promised that he would read aloud the best. He went over the piles two times, once again, absently, a deep frown on his brow, as if he was displeased with their works. Then he stopped and picked up one. Her heart sank when she saw that it was not hers; she hardly heard him reading:

"I did not know that the poise and pomp of wealth dies by itself, so quickly. Moths are not supposed to know; they only come to the light. And the light was decorated with diamonds and pearls, exquisitely perfumed, exquisitely tinted, it looked so inviting, there was no resisting it. Moths are not supposed to know; one does not even know one is a moth until one's wings are burned."

It was incomprehensible, no beginning, no end. It did not have unity, coherence, emphasis. Why did he choose that one? What did he see in it? And she had worked so hard, she had wanted to please, she had written about the flowers that she loved most. Who could have written it? She did not know that any of her classmates would write so, use such words, sentences, use a blue paper to write her lessons on.

But then there was little in him that they could understand. Even his words were so difficult, just like those dark and dismaying things that they came across in their readers, which took them hour after hour in the dictionary. She had learned like a good student to pick out the words she did not recognize, writing them down as she heard them but it was a thankless task. She had a whole notebook filled now, two columns to each page:

Esurient . . . greedy
amaranth . . . a flower that never fades
peacock . . . a large bird with lovely green feathers
mirash . . .
The word was not in the dictionary.
And what did such things as original sin, selfishness, insati-

able, actress of a thousand faces mean, and who were Sirce, Lorelay, other names she could not find anywhere? She meant to ask him someday, someday his eyes were more kind, someday he did not bite his hands so fiercely.

He never went to church, but then, that always went with learning and education, did it not? One night Bue saw him coming out of the dim doorway. He watched again and the following night he saw him again. They would not believe it, they must see it with their own eyes and so they came. He did not go in every night, but he could be seen at the most unusual hours, sometimes at dusk, sometimes at dawn, once when it was storming and the lightning stretched a ragged path from heaven to earth. Sometimes he stared for a few minutes, sometimes he came twice or thrice. They reported it to Father Cesario but it seemed that he already knew. "Let a peaceful man alone in his prayers." The answer surprised them.

The sky hangs over the Anayat, in the middle of Anayat Sea, like an inverted wineglass, a glass whose wine has been spilled, a purple wine of which Anayat was the last precious drop. For that is Anayat in the crepuscule, purple and mellow, sparkling and warm and effulgent, when there is a moon, cool and heady and sensuous when there is no moon. One may drink of it and forget what lies beyond a thousand miles, beyond a thousand years; one may sip it at the top of a jagged cliff, nearer peace, nearer God. Where one could see the ocean dashing against the rocks in eternal frustration, more moving, more terrible than man's; or touch it to his lips in the lush shadows of the *dama de noche*, its bubbles iridescent like a thousand fireflies, its bouquets the fragrance of flowers that know no fading.

Zita sat by her open window, half asleep, half dreaming. Francisco B. Reteche, what a name. What could his nickname be? Paking. Frank. Pa . . . The night lay silent and expectant, a fairy princess waiting for the whispered words of a lover. She was a bit sleepy. Already she had counted three stars that had fallen to earth, one almost directly into that bush of *dama de noche* at their garden gate, where it had lighted the lamps of a thousand fireflies. He was not so forbidding now; he spoke less frequently to himself, more frequently to her; his eyes were still unseeing, but now they rested on her. She loved to remember those moments when she had caught him looking, when he thought she did not know. The knowledge came keenly, bitingly, like the sea breeze at dawn, like the prick of the rose's thorn, or —yes, like the purple liquid that her father gave the visitors during *pintakasi,* which made them red and noisy. She had stolen a few drops one day, because she wanted to know, to taste, and that little sip had made her head whirl.

Suddenly she stiffened, a shadow had emerged from the shrubs and had been lost in the other shadows. Her pulses raced, she strained forward. Was she dreaming? Who was it? A lost soul, an unvoiced thought, the shadow of a shadow, the prince from his tryst with the fairy princess? What were the words that he whispered to her?

They who have been young once say that only youth can make it forget itself, that life is a river bed. The water passes in it, sometimes it encounters obstacles and cannot go on, sometimes it flows unencumbered with a song in every bubble and ripple, but always it goes forward. When its way is obstructed it burrows deeply or swerves aside and leaves its impression, and whether the impress will be shallow and transient, or deep and searing, only God determines. They remembered the day when he went up Don Eliodoro's house, and, the light of a great decision in his eyes, finally accepted the father's offer to teach his daughter "To be a lady."

"We are going to the City soon, after the next harvest perhaps. I want her not to feel like a *provinciana* when we get there."

They remembered the time when his walks by the seashore became less frequent at night, less solitary, for now of afternoons he would draw the whole crowd of village boys from their game of leapfrog or *patintero* and bring them with him. And they would go home hours after sunset with the wonderful things that Mr. Reteche had told them, why the sea was green, the sky blue, what one who was strong and fearless might find at that exact place where the sky met the sea. They would be flushed and happy and bright-eyed, for he could stand on his head longer than any of them, dig for crabs faster, send a pebble skimming over the breast of Anayat Bay farthest.

Turong still remembered, though dimly, those ominous terrifying nights when he had got up cold and trembling to listen to the aching groan of the bamboo floor, as somebody in the other room restlessly paced to and fro. And his pupils now remembered those mornings he received their flowers, the *camia* which had fainted away at her own fragrance, the *kampupot*, with the night dew still trembling in its heart, received them with a smile and forgot the lessons of the day and told them all about those princesses and fairies who dwelt in flowers, why the *dama de noche* must have the darkness of the night to set off its fragrance, how the petal of the *ilang-ilang*, crushed and soaked in some liquid, would one day touch the lips of some wondrous creature in some faraway land whose eyes were blue and hair golden.

Those were days of surprise for Zita. Box after box came in Turong's sailboat and each time they were things that took the words from her lips. Silk as sheen and perishable as gossamer, or heavy and sheeny and tinted like the sunset sky, slippers studded with bright stones which tinkled with the least movement of her feet, a necklace of green, flat, polished mineral, whose feel against her throat sent a curious choking sensation there, perfume that she must touch her lips with. If only there would always be these in Turong's sailboat, none of those horrid blue envelopes that he always brought. And yet—the Virgin have pity on her selfish soul—suppose Turong brought not only these letters one day but their owner as well? She shuddered, not because she feared it but because she knew it would be.

"Why are these dresses so tight fitting?" Her father wanted to know.

"In society, women use clothes to reveal, not to hide." Was that a sneer or a smile in his eyes? The gown showed her arms and shoulders and she had never known how round and fair they were, how they could express so many things.

"Why do they have such bright colors?"

"Because the peacock has bright feathers."

"They paint their lips . . . "

"So that they can smile when they do not want to."

"And their eyelashes are long."

"To hide deception."

He was not pleased like her father, she saw it, he had turned his face toward the window. And as she came nearer, swaying like a lily atop its stalk, she heard the harsh, muttered words:

"One would think she'd feel shy or uncomfortable, but no . . . oh no . . . not a bit . . . all alike . . . comes naturally."

There were books to read, pictures, names to learn, lessons in everything, how to polish the nails, how to use a fan, how to walk. How did these days come, how did they go? What does one do when one is so happy, so breathless? Sometimes they were a memory, sometimes a dream.

"Look, Zita, a society girl does not smile so openly; her eyes don't seek one's so—that reveals your true feeling."

"But if I am glad and happy and I want to show it?"

"Don't. If you must show it by smiling, let your eyes be mocking; if you would invite with your eyes, repulse with your lips."

That was a memory.

She was in a great drawing room whose floor was so polished it reflected the myriad red and green and blue lights above, the arches of flowers and ribbons and streamers. All the great names of the capital were there, stately ladies in wonderful gowns who walked so, waved their fans so, who said one thing with their eyes and another with their lips. And she was among them and every good-looking young man wanted to dance with her. They were all so clever and charming but she answered: "Please, I am tired." For beyond them she had seen him alone, he whose eyes were dark and brooding and disapproving and she was waiting for him to take her.

That was a dream. Sometimes though, she could not tell so easily which was the dream and which the memory.

If only those letters would not bother him now, he seemed so happy and at peace. True, he thought less of them now, never answered them, but every time Turong brought him one, he would become thoughtful and distracted. Like that time he was teaching her a dance, a Spanish dance, he said, and he had told her to dress accordingly. Her heavy hair hung in a big, carelessly tied knot that always threatened to get loose but never did, its dark, deep shadows showing off in startling vividness how red a rose can be, how like velvet its petals. Her earrings—two circlets of precious stones, red like the pigeon's blood—almost touched her shoulders. The heavy Spanish shawl gave her the most trouble—she had nothing to help her but some pictures and magazines—she could not put it on just as she wanted. Like this it revealed her shoulder too much, that way it hampered the free movement of the legs. But she had done her best, for hours she had stood before her mirror and for hours it had told her that she was beautiful, that red lips and tragic eyes were becoming to her.

She'd never forget that look in his face when she came out. It was not surprise, joy, admiration. It was as if he saw somebody there whom he was expecting, for whom he had waited, prayed.

"Zita!" It was a cry of recognition.

She blushed even under her rouge when he took her in his arms and taught her to step this way, glide so, turn about; she looked half questioningly at her father for disapproval, but she saw that there was nothing there but admiration too. Mr. Reteche seemed so serious and intent that she should learn quickly, but he did not deceive her, for once she happened to lean close and she felt how wildly his heart was beating. It had frightened her and she had drawn away but when she saw how unconcerned he was, as if he did not even know that she was in his arms, she smiled knowingly and drew close again. Dreamily she closed her eyes and dimly wondered if his were shut too. Was he thinking the same thoughts, breathing the same prayer?

Turong came up and after his respectful "Good evening" he handed an envelope to the school teacher. It was large and blue and had a gold design in one corner, the handwriting was broad, angular, sweeping.

"Thank you, Turong." His voice was drawling, heavy, the voice of one who had just awakened. With one movement he tore the unopened envelope, slowly, unconsciously, it seemed to her.

"I thought I had forgotten," he murmured dully.

That changed the whole evening. His eyes lost their sparkle, his gaze wandered from time to time. Something powerful and dark had come in between them, something which shut out the light, brought in a chill. The tears came to her eyes for she felt utterly powerless. When her sight cleared she saw that he was sitting down and trying to piece together the letter.

"Why do you tear letters if you must put them together again?" she asked rebelliously.

He looked at her kindly. "Some day, Zita, you will do it, also, and then you will understand."

One day Turong came from Pauambang and this time he brought a stranger. They knew at once that he came from where the teacher came—his clothes, his features, his politeness—and that he had come for the teacher. This one did not speak their dialect, as he was ever wiping his face, gazing at the wobbly, thatched huts and muttering short, vehement phrases to himself. Zita heard his knock before Mr. Reteche did and she knew it was he and for what he had come. She must have been as pale as her teacher, as shaken, as rebellious. And yet the stranger was so cordial, there was nothing but gladness in his greeting, gladness at meeting an old friend. How strong he was; even at that moment he did not forget himself; he turned to his class and dismissed it for the day.

The door was thick and she did not dare lean against the jamb too much, so something of their voices floated away before they reached her.

" . . . like children . . . making yourselves . . . so unhappy."

" . . . happiness? Her idea of happiness . . . "

Mr. Reteche's voice was more low-pitched, hoarse, so that it didn't carry at all. She shuddered as he laughed: it was that way when he first came.

"She's been . . . did not mean . . . understand."

" . . . learning to forget . . . "

There were periods when they both became excited and talked fast and hard. She heard somebody's restless pacing, somebody sitting down heavily, the sharp intake of breaths.

"I never realize what she meant to me until I begin trying to seek from others what she cannot give me."

She knew what was coming now, knew it before the stranger asked the question:

"Tomorrow?"

She fled. She could not wait for the answer.

He did not sleep that night. She knew he did not, she told herself fiercely. And it was not only his preparations that kept him awake: she knew it, she knew it. With the first flicker of light she ran to the mirror. She must not show her feeling, it was not in good form, she must manage somehow. If her lips quivered, her eyes must smile, if in her eyes there were tears . . . She heard her father go out, but she did not go, although she knew his purpose. She had more important things to do. Little boys came up to their house and she wiped away their tears and told them that he was coming back—coming back, soon, soon.

The minutes flew. She was almost done now. Her lips were red and her eyebrows penciled; the crimson shawl wrapped on just right. Everything must be like that day he had first seen her in a Spanish dress. Still he did not come; he must be bidding farewell now to Father Cesario, now he was in Doña Ramona's house, now he was shaking the barber's hands. He would soon be through and retrace his steps back to their house. She glanced at the mirror and decided that her lips were not enough, and she put on more color. The rose in her hair had too long a stem; she tried to trim it with her fingers and a thorn dug deeply into her flesh.

Who knows? Perhaps they would soon meet again in the city. She wondered if she could not wheedle her father into going earlier. But she must know now. What were the words he wanted to whisper that night under the *dama de noche?* What did he want to say that day he held her in his arms? Other things, questions whose answers she knew. How well she knew them!

The big house was silent as death; the little village seemed deserted. Everybody had gone to the seashore. Again she looked at the mirror. She was too pale; she must put on more rouge. She tried to keep from counting the minutes, the seconds, from getting up and pacing. But she was getting chilly and she must do it to keep warm.

The steps creaked. She bit her lips to stifle a wild cry. The door opened.

"Turong!"

"Mr. Reteche bade me to give this. He said you would understand."

In one bound she had reached the open window. But dimly, for the sun was too bright—or was her sight failing?—she saw a blur of white moving this way, moving that way, turning around so that she could not follow it, and clearly against a horizon suddenly drawn out of perspective, Mr. Reteche, tall, lean, brooding, looking at her with eyes that told her somebody had hurt him. It was like that when he first came, and now he was gone. The tears came freely now. What matter, what matter? There was nobody to see and criticize her breeding. They came down unchecked and when she tried to brush them off with her hand, the color came away from her cheeks, leaving them bloodless, cold. Sometimes they got into her mouth and they tasted bitter.

Her hands worked convulsively; there was a sound of tearing paper, once, twice. She became suddenly aware of what she had done when she looked at the pieces, wet and brightly stained with uneven streaks of red. Slowly, painfully, she tried to put the pieces together and as she did so a sob escaped deep from her breast—a great understanding had come to her.

So

One nice thing about all this is that they were neighbors—
he living in the house on the other side of the *estero* spanned by
a small wooden bridge that had its one end lying firmly on the
wide cement edge of the *estero* on his side, and she living, with
her mother and aunt and brothers and elder sisters, who were all
married and had had their own secret affairs with the men they
were going to marry and had married and were now having their
own children, in the house with the backstairs that went down
directly on the other end of the wooden bridge under which
flowed *estero*-water with its daily load of scum and waterlogged
floating refuse—their houses with their backs to each other but
connected to each other's lot by the bridge which she would
soon cross on her way to the street several blocks away from the
place.

The twin-tone will indicate exactly nine-fifteen a.m. Manila
time, the radio announcer in the *sala* announced. She paused
to listen. Ding-dong meant she had fifteen minutes more and
she wished her elder sister Ka Puring would stop looking now
and then at her outside the door of her room so she could look
out of the window and see if he had gone ahead of her. She felt
uneasy as Ka Puring watched her combing her long thick, dark-
brown hair. Your hair makes such a soft pillow, Pin, she remembered him saying.

A nicer thing about all this is that they have never considered
themselves as friends although they knew each other when they
happened to meet, smile, greet, pass each other several years ago
when she was still studying in the high school, where he was also
studying in the same year as she was but in a higher section. The

only time we got to see each other more often was since we moved to the vacant lot on the other side, at the back of your house. She knew him then the way she had always thought he knew her—a cousin, third or fourth. And as such she would come to him to their house and help him type his research papers in the afternoons he would come home very early from the university, and it was during those times she got to know him more and enjoyed being with him not because he was teaching her now and then the things he had learned from his professors and also not because she was feeling she was learning higher college things but . . . I really didn't know why, Cris, I just had the desire to see you, hear you, I always wanted to be with you often, and now I know why . . . because you were feeling the same way too.

And the nicest thing about all this is that she was going out with him again after almost three weeks now since the last time they spent a whole day together when she was supposed to be out with her best friend Tessie, and her mother always let her go out as long as it was with Tessie she was going, but it was always with him that she spent the day each time she told her mother she was going out with Tessie.

Tessie is sick, am going to visit her, she answered her elder sister. She wished Ka Puring would go out so she could look out of the window to see if the window of his room was closed. He closed the window every time he was going out with her.

In the *sala* the smooth-voiced man in the radio said: And finally the same song is dedicated to Marcia, Ellen, and Joan for their listening pleasure from Carmen, here now is the song Always, Always. She listened to the song. The last three nights she had sung the song with him, she washing plates in the kitchen and he taking his nightly bath. The song in her mind. Ka Puring went out of the room and turned off the radio. She looked at herself in the mirror. By the time I get there it'll be nine-thirty, she thought. She looked out of the door. Ka Puring was putting her baby to sleep. She went out of the room to the backdoor. She made the sign of the cross as she went down the rungs of the backstair. Am going, Inay, she told her mother who was washing clothes under the stair. Her legs felt a little shaky. She steadied herself on the end of the bridge. She looked up behind her. Ka Puring was coming down the stair.

She looked at his window as she crossed the bridge. His window was closed, she knew that in two minutes and a half she would be out on the sidewalk of the street, where a bus would stop for her without her giving any sign for the driver to stop, she would get into the bus to a backseat where he would be sitting.

Her Ka Puring followed behind her. She passed through the small passage at one side of his house. She crossed the small street in front of his house and hurried out of the corner of the small chapel, out of Ka Puring's now suspicious eyes. She gave herself a pat on the cheek, she walked fast. He liked punctuality. She was anxious all over to be with him. She crossed the central street where a bus would stop for her with him in it. Two buses passed her. When the street cleared itself of passing jeeps and cars and other vehicles she saw him crossing the street.

Ka Puring will get angry, she said when he stood beside her on the sidewalk, your window was closed. She stopped a passenger jeep.

He helped her into the front seat. There is Ka Puring, he said pointing in the direction of their place which could be seen from the street. She looked to where he was pointing. Ka Puring was standing akimbo on the sidewalk across the Canlapan house. Am sure she'll follow, but I don't care any more, let her, let your elders know about us, he said. The jeep was running away from the place.

Am going to see Tessie, she said leaning back on the seat to rest herself on his arm across her shoulders. Ben said she's sick although I know Tessie just don't want to see Ben. She's fed up with him.

And you, are you fed up with me too? he asked.

She answered, no! no! grasping and pressing his hand between their thighs pressing against each other.

Don't go to Tes then, he said, let's spend the day together.

She didn't answer, but moved closer to his side . . .

They sat beside each other in a private curtained booth of a snack bar looking across the boulevard to the sea. She drank her glass of milk. She loved the way he always reminded her of her health, the way he always patted her cheek saying, be a good girl, or I want you to be strong and enduring forever, or, that's my girl, when she said something nice or witty extemporaneously, or when she reminded him to finish his studies, get a job, save . . . then we'll settle, nothing can stop me from doing what I like . . .

What do you want? he said, when they were resting, locked in a small world so big enough to contain all of themselves without fear, unseparate, without time, undying. And she answered: You.

It was already raining hard outside. The sky above her poured its wild song through the ceiling. She felt her pores opening to the spasms and gusts outside, her softness in a sweet ache as it welled with the rhythm of the hard long song sinking into her. She closed her eyes to the scattering song, to its crashing and bursting of her tenderness. It said, Pin, Pin. And she released her Cris, Cris, as the adagio of the rain came deeply drawn out.

If they should find out about us, she said after a long while, about this, never mind, it's you and I. On her side, a little below her waist, was a wet gash of rain that had seeped through the line of crevice between two boards of the wall on her side. He reached across her and slowly wiped the purplish gash of wetness with his three middle fingers making the sign of the cross on it. She took up his wet fingers and rubbed each of them with her fingers in the goldish light of the bulb hanging down the ceiling.

It was already mid-afternoon when they went down to the boulevard along the sea. The wide street smelled fresh and clean and it lay shining under a full sun. The boulevard trees were still wet and dripping, and from their branches buds and leaves fell spiralling to the grass and the asphalt.

Do not walk fast now, he told her as they went across the street, we still have three hours, walk normally, can't you?

She nodded, murmuring: I'll try, I'll try. She walked slowly, keeping herself from dragging her feet, leaning on his shoulder and smiling at her successful effort. She felt his hand on her waist pressing encouragements.

They found a seat on the breakwater. There were a few couples away from them. You're heavy, he told her as she leaned on his shoulder.

You were heavy, she answered, and I'll be heavier some day.

She watched him crinkling the skin on the bridge of his nose and under his eyes as he made her favorite funny-face. She imitated him. They laughed together, the waves rolling and dashing against the large boulders a little below them on the foot of the breakwater. She watched the sea with him. The waves repeatedly formed, rolled, closed in and under each other on the bouldered margin of the sea. The deep blue sea would gather itself far out into long curved shutters, then each shutter would open foaming on its emerged end as another shutter would close under it. The endless sound and force and wind was a nude view of perfection in opening and closing in each other in the creation of another like themselves. She watched and listened and felt the sea with him whose hands she held, a long dark husk of her hair blowing against his cheek, a deep crevice between two leg-shaped boulders in front of her releasing a steady flowage with sticky-looking foam. She released his hands and pressed herself down on her front. She felt tired. She felt like vomiting and she told him. He placed a rubbing hand on her back as she leaned out beyond her legs. She opened her mouth. Nothing came out. In her throat was a line of sour and bitter liquid which she tried to gurgle out. Her eyes smarted, the sharp tears hazed her eyes as she shook her head to take out the liquid in her throat. She heard him say: Tickle it out with a finger. She crooked her left index finger in her mouth and her fingertip tickled her throat, her tongue pulled itself up on its sides and jerked back deep into her throat, she drew out her finger quickly. Still no mess came out. She swallowed hard. His hand on her back kept rubbing and patting. She straightened up from her waist and said: Let's go, Cris. He helped her down the breakwater, saying: Nothing can really part us now. And she answered: Forever . . .

It was beginning to dark when she arrived on the wooden bridge across the *estero*. Ka Puring was at the backdoor. The black scummy water of the *estero* was beginning to rise in, she walked up fast on the backstair. Ka Puring pulled her up viciously into the kitchen and said: So! Ka Puring left her in her room to call up their mother.

So. It contained all the things she knew would soon be said to her harshly without her having a chance to be understood. Even before she was left alone in her room where she had put on and was now taking off the rust-brown dress she had worn the first time she secretly spent a day with him, she knew that it would take a long time, weeks, months, a year or two, before she would wear it again for him, before she could be able to go out with him again. Nothing can really part us now. And she knew that what she had taken into herself out of his being would outlast all the painful things that would be done, said, thought of her by those who would not understand her much less him to whom she had given all of herself as he had given all of himself to her who was now in her houseclothes she had worn that afternoon she, for the first time in her life, gave her answer: Yes, forever, Cris . . . to him to whose allness her allness responded in suffering and joy, to whom she was related even before they found themselves, the one and the other like lock and key to a door that held in its room their one identity before a holy knowledge of a fountainhead to perfection—Life, out of their sowing into each other, perfect into and out of each other like the waves.

Cris, Cris, she called him in her being as she tried to press back in her closed eyes the sudden teasing that had rushed up from her breast to her face and now out of her opened eyes that saw the dim outline of her mother's old but big bulk blocking the light of the living room outside her silently waiting bedroom where she was caught full by her mother's shadow. She bent over the edge of her bed, pulled up the hem of her dress and wiped her eyes with it. She heard the sharp, tearing *traidores* of her mother's voice that was now hating and hateful. She raised her face bravely to her mother who blocked the light of the living room where she heard her elder sister Puring's I suspected, and went to Tessie, and your angel of a sister was not there, to her eldest brother Nayong, and her brother's I'll talk to him, with as much hate in his voice as in her sister's.

I forbid you ever to see him again, her mother said, don't you people know you're cousins, you were both blinded by your youth. You deceived me, Tessie, Tessie, all the time it was really with him you were going out, the foulness of a rot could never be hidden. What will people say, I am a *consentidora*. No! no! you must part from each other.

She stayed in her room while her brothers and sisters and their husbands and the children ate silently. They were suddenly strangers to each other. I will kill myself, she repeated what she had told her mother, she repeated the words to herself in her mind. She lay in bed. Her mother had closed and locked the only window of her room.

It was late in the night when she heard him singing in his room on the other side of the *estero*. She could not sing now the way she used to.

His song caught her. His voice came through the darkness, came over the mud and flowing filth of the *estero*. She remembered the afternoon, the long lovely hours when she was most alone with him; she saw him again sitting beside her and watching and feeling the sun with him; she saw themselves in the full light of the sun, heard themselves; she felt him now as he sang song after song of promise and love and yearning, of remembering.

She heard the mating sounds of lizards somewhere on the ceiling. She heard Ka Puring's baby Lita crying in the room next to hers. She heard her brother-in-law Tony saying, my child. She heard her Ka Tony and Ka Puring teasing each other about having another child.

She breathed quietly. The darkness in her room seemed to

be breathing a song into her. And the song seemed to heave with her body. She imagined the stars outside. Her wakefulness in the darkness as she recalled him eased into her body. She pressed herself below her bosom throbbing. He was still singing in his room on the other side of the *estero*. She was still listening in her room on the other side. And between them she saw in her mind the black water flowing in the *estero*. She smiled as she imagined him coming on the bridge, bravely coming into her room. She felt him now singing into her.

Her hands on her bosom she counted months on her fingers. She was now a woman. Forever. So.

Rice Wine

When Santiago saw her in the mirror, comb in hand, he knew it was time for him. It was time to leave the hut. For it was the time of the crescent moon, and if there were people he knew in the corner store, it was time for a cup.

Though his limbs were still numb, Santiago rose. He went to the basin with the fresh water and washed his face. His remaining life was measured: the uniform in the trunk; the medal under his pillow; the kiss of his daughter on the cheek. The day was made for waiting, and the night, for wine. Nothing was missing.

When he looked at her once more, she had put on her beige skirt, a sheath.

"Are you going out?" he asked, as was his wont.

"Yes, father," she replied automatically. There was a ribbon in her hair.

He went back to his cot near the window. The moon was out. The street shimmering below like a lake drifted evenly toward the mountains in the east while mad traffic droned into the dolorous hum of the beggars, kinsmen all, stretched in a column on the sidewalk, banging their pails, sleeping resignedly on the cold cement, yelling at God. From a distance, in a yard, the smell of rice fermenting in earthen jars oozed from the depths of the earth. Earlier, the sun had aged it into essence and at the rising of the moon, the wind carried it, sweet, sourish, the dead aroma of beans—the wine of rice that the shriveled people on the sidewalk, drunk with its flavor, inhaled and swallowed greedily in their slumber.

186

Now Santiago leaned on the wall, trying not to look at her, trying not to ask her again.

"Where are you going after the piano lesson, Elena?" he asked.

"To my mother's grave," she said.

He turned to the moon, and sighed. In the old days, they had attended the *misa de gallo* under the sweet *dama de noche*, the scent sending them frolicking to the church in the *barrio* where already gathered the last flirtations of the fiesta. It was their own Binondo, though their prayers pleaded crosswise to the altar and to all the womenfolk that ever swayed in their *camisa*.

"How is the pupil doing in his lessons?"

"Father, he is only seven. He cannot even put sugar in his milk."

"That is a strange child—learning to play the piano at night."

"He plays in the sun all morning."

He sighed.

"What are they raising now?"

She took out a tube of lipstick and began to work on her lips.

"They are quiet tonight," she said, indicating the window where outside lay the world.

"If they are quiet, they are dead."

She was now pulling out her hair-pins.

"Is it not time for the corner store? I pressed your other *barò* this afternoon."

"In a moment."

"Perhaps De Palma will sing again," she said cheerfully.

Santiago grinned.

"It is a truth. He sings every night. There he will come, coughing, epileptic, climbing out of a fit, holding *sampaguitas* he has not sold, a guitar slung across his shoulder as though it were a hump on his back—a birthright. The songs he sings are straight out of the *kaingin*, like arrows from the vows of our beloved. Nobody understands us, we two. We are the irredeemable fragments of the veranda, reuniting on the pass, swimming in the ravine where the star apples fell from the siege and where only memory can hurt us. Sing, De Palma, old goat! There is new grass in every song."

"Is he still in good voice?"

"Cracking, but still there."

"And still ill."

"Ill? The man is dying, even as I am. Do you not know? He was the lamplighter of the Old Manila and he still cannot believe the new city has no more need of him."

"Poor old De Palma. Poor old warrior . . ."

Santiago wiped his forehead with the back of his arm.

"And Ruben?" This, her back to him.

"Ah, that one. He is a sponge. What are you doing to him, daughter? He works hard in the daytime and has school in the evening, but he comes to the corner store and reminisces with us. What has happened between you two?"

She stood up from the mirror.

"I have my pride," she snapped, combing her hair.

"Of course. That is what Ruben is trying to reach at the bottom of the cup. But I suppose the well runs deep."

She turned to him, eyes flashing.

"It is my life, father."

She made ready to leave, her things neatly arranged on the rattan table as they had been every night for a year now. On her ears, hung her only pair of earrings, ornaments of blue, none the less bluer than her way with them, for she wore everything elegantly, even the cheap leather belt, the high-heeled shoes, the purse she had bought in a fire sale. Once more arrayed for her evening, she loomed before him, erect, radiant, a product from the solicitude of the cracked mirror in the room—a jewel cast in nerve and mulatto. As Santiago studied her, wondering where the year had deposited itself, he realized that she was altered. When she spoke, she was not as passive as she had been before her change of clothes.

"Tell De Palma to sing a little louder that I may hear him, where I will be."

Santiago grimaced. "Do not worry. The wine will do that."

"The wine is a good guitar. Better than that wood he strums on."

"The wine understands."

"Yes. Well, I have to go."

"And is this why Ruben is so sad?"

"Please. Let us not speak of him. He is just a boy."

"He is drinking himself old before he is twenty."

"That is not my doing."

"How brave we all are."

"The wine is braver. Go to it, father. I am no comfort to you."

She lingered by his side, fidgeting, uncertain.

"Fetch your mother's umbrella," he commanded. "It might rain tonight."

"Yes. It always rains at night."

"I will light a candle while you are gone," he said, going to the cabinet where she kept their things.

She unhooked the red umbrella from its post.

"Father . . ."

"Yes, daughter?"

"Please. Don't lose The Revolution tonight."

Before he could answer, she had hurried down the stairway and he heard her footfalls on the gravel road. He settled back in the cot, listening to the injury of rice on the pavements, thinking of wine.

De Palma was deep in his cups when Santiago, a medal conspicuous on his breast, arrived in the store. The old *sampaguita* vender was heavy with drink and oratory, aging with every sip. He cut a ridiculous figure on the bamboo bench as he imposed upon his wine-mates a visage of whiskers and a rambling, ranting talk of another century. The minor drunkards avoided him passionately, this ragged creature who lavished the small change he earned from his garlands on a morose old veteran who received the wine and returned the wildness. Illustrious, dazzling in their era, the twin patricians maintained, among the stevedores, a stern, traditional front.

"How now, my courier of Malolos? Still compiling the evils of the 10,000 pieces of silver from the battle?" De Palma taunted.

Santiago sneered. "I see the vintage is on your tongue already."

"Why not? It is my legacy."

"Speak with caution then. I am not well disposed."

"You have no spirit."

"Leave that to the wine."

"With edge, as always, my courier, my Malolos—lost to a congress in the bushes."

Santiago took the tin cup Fermin the proprietor offered him, gulping down the liquid hungrily, feeling it warm the pit of his stomach. He exhaled and licked the drops on his lips.

"They do not make wine like they used to, in my home town."

De Palma gurgled noisily. "They do not know how to age these days. These distilleries . . . they are a crime."

They sat there, (*"los grandes"*), the *aficionados* of the Lost Republic, both flaming in their piety, burning the marble epitaphs, correcting history, fumbling, precise, rigid, restless, whole, divided: the future of the past.

"Remember how we used to read Carlyle?" sighed De Palma.

"Remember the Mayorca?" chorused Santiago.

"The *ayuntamiento?*"

"The Fort?"

"The mauser hidden in the mind?"

"The Treaty?"

"The Domecq?"

"The Zorilla?"

"The Pasig?"

"The Yanqui?"

"The carriages?"

"The Binondo?"

"The theater?"

"The opera?"

"The assignations?"

"The Cause?"

"The secret literature?"

"The parks?"

"The *puñal?*"

"The rogues?"

"The women of salt?"

"The fandango?"

De Palma sniffed, spanning his arms at the swelling sidewalk.

"Now watch the calamity spread like an epidemic over the rice terraces."

Now Santiago saw the mothers and their children filling the sidewalk, swaying in rhythm, swinging their baskets in the dust, their moan, one call only: rice! It was the talk and terror of the town; a topic boiled and fried or taken raw with a grain of salt. And even at the weddings, nobody ever threw it any more.

Santiago saw the embankment bear the weight of the line stretching from the fire hydrant to the granary and he heard the pedestrians talk about The Bomb.

"There was no bomb in our time, eh, *caballero?*" he said to his friend.

The flower man smiled patiently.

"But there has always been a bomb, Santiago. There will always be a bomb."

"Where is that Ruben?" Santiago protested, searching for an ally.

"You cannot change progress. That is the will of Our Father and the scientists."

"Someday, I shall free the people."

"Sit down, *caballero*. Drink your wine and let it happen. The Bomb will fall whatever you do. Ask the people there, living for their *ganta*. Ask the mothers. Ask the children. The Bomb is in their bellies. The Bomb is in the market. The Bomb is in the pawn shop."

"No!"

"Yes! The Bomb is God Who will not come."

"Have you abandoned the faith, too, *viejo?*"

"I am two months younger than you," complained De Palma.

"Do not change the subject, old man!"

"Faith?"

"That is what we fought for!"

"The Man was what we fought for."

"And is that not faith—was he not, is he not—religion?"

De Palma spat. "He whistles in the dark, incumbent in a hospital, mended by young doctors who exhaust their scholarships reviving the loneliness of the past. There he reigns in a wheelchair, waiting for *the day*, longing for the night. You and I, we have forfeited him. He is nothing but the weakness in my limbs and the whiteness of my hair."

"The greatness!"

"And the failure. They embalm him there; The Promise, sheltered, shuttered, analyzed, anesthetized; a relic in a museum that has forsaken its heritage. This"—and he pointed to the line on the asphalt—"is our heritage. This is what we fought for in the mountains: a retailer's bin that has squeezed the rice out of our land to bleed our people. Are you blind? Do you not see the hunger? Are you deaf? Do you not hear the thunder? And you sit there moaning about The Man whose blunder has led to this! Is this your grandeur?"

Santiago threw his cup away.

"Traitor!" he bellowed. "If The Man goes, every flower withers. Do you hear me, spawn of the *sampaguita?*"

De Palma glared at him.

"Man, why do we always quarrel?" boomed Santiago.

"Because that is all we have left, brother. We keep the dates accurate, the facts intact, though we destroy their meaning. The Man must suffer his mistake over and over and over, lest he vanish from our affection. Build him again, Santiago. Build him again. I thirst for *our day* once more when you drank from the brook where his gray mare stood like a dragon as he surveyed the forest range and traced a vision of the enemy in every acacia.

Build him for me, *caballero*. He is my life too. They do not know him *there*; no one will ever know. But we do, we, the last chips of the monument; we know him. And it is a knowledge that is my breath."

A young man, lean and disheveled, suddenly clambered on the bamboo bench, scraping his shoes, flinging his books disdainfully on the dirty counter.

"You are late, Ruben," Santiago greeted gladly, delighted at this intrusion in the debate.

Ruben motioned cryptically to the proprietor who immediately poured wine in a large glass and gave it to the new arrival. The glass was full to the brim.

"Yesterday," the young man began hoarsely, "I presented my fraternity pin to Elena, and she would not accept it. I asked her why and she said she loved me like a brother."

De Palma howled. Santiago colored.

"I just hate everybody," Ruben said, sulking over his wine.

"Do you not love anyone?" Santiago asked irritably.

The young man guffawed.

"Look around you and see the inequality of love. Love your wife and she runs away with another man. Love your best friend and he was that *other man*. Love your industry and it retires you to the gutter. Love your dog and it bites you. Love your God and there is a flood."

Bristling, Santiago wagged an imperious finger.

"Love your son, and he grows up."

"Don't feel like Job. The prophets deserted the Bible long ago."

"Just because you are an underpaid clerk in the backroom of some terminal, does that give you the gall to dislocate the anatomy of this government?"

"The government?" Ruben hissed. "The government is a brat that cannot even feed the malnourished child outside the door. The government is blind when it cannot see the blind dying like flies in front of the Quiapo church. The government is lame when it cannot walk to the cripple on Avenida and lead him away. Not that I care for the masses, personally. But they must be removed from the wound."

"But do you not see, Ruben, that the wound is you?"

"Poetry! Three hundred years of losing our corn to The West and we celebrate a man and his two novels written in Europe. You cannot liberate the slave with a metaphor! So dance the *zarzuela*; I will take my rice in a mug, not in the harvest!"

"I do not know what you are talking about," Santiago mocked. "But in my time, there was Spain, there was The Treaty, there was The Man. And that was enough. In my heart, there is a statue of him so tall only my love can reach it; so soft only the guitar can speak to it. *Por Dios*, young man of today, you with your present that has no future, only journalism, you are trampling on the last petal of the garden. You are adding to the water when you should be turning the sea into the bridge of the armada! Oh, country that never was, that was to me, my name, my sword, my armor, my pendant and my memory, I am surrounded by absence! By a worship that has descended into a whore! By the voice, not of my *harana*, but of the jukebox! *Adiós* . . ."

De Palma applauded.

Santiago ignored him and continued addressing the sullen young man.

"I look at you and I drown in Candaba; I look at you and I see a crack in the mirror at Malolos where I held the reins of his horse and touched the tip of his saber. All this, desecrated in your face forever, a face I would never have fought for had the gypsies told me it was such I was fighting for."

A toothless wheeze issued from the flower man.

"Another cup, *patrón*," he rasped.

Still, Santiago raved, and the bench rattled with his wrath.

"When they captured him in Palanan, it was as though my own identity had stopped; reason stopped. There was no longer any island without The Man; without him, there was no longer anything, only turncoats who bartered their allegiances for a puff of occidental tobacco. We were not beaten; we were betrayed."

"*Arriba!*" De Palma hooted.

Santiago was undaunted. "Nowadays, all you see is the tattoo in everybody's eyes."

Ruben, piqued, toasted his glass.

"That is in effigy of all the things that could have been— the synthesis of illusion."

"Is that your poetry on the walls? The charcoal scrawlings that say BEWARE OF MAN?"

"Put on your spectacles, old man. That's nothing but a detour. The sign actually says BEWARE OF VICIOUS GOD."

The proprietor flung up his hands helplessly. "This could go on forever," he moaned.

"And it will!" snarled Santiago. "For such a race as you! For such a disgrace as you!"

The young man picked up his books.

"I think I'll attend Political Science after all."

But De Palma pulled him back.

"Stay," he mumbled drunkenly. "I want to sing to you."

"Lunatics!"

Both of them studied Santiago contemptuously. Unable to stand the sting, De Palma sprang up, confronting his friend toe to toe. Retaliating fiercely, his words were clear and they did not pronounce the wine.

"The Bomb is in that house where your Elena—she that your shrunken hag of a wife danced into life one summer—lies naked waiting for the possession of the world!"

"Hold your tongue, old man!" Santiago blurted.

"Naked in that tall house with a balcony, I tell you, and I should have told you but you are so stupid!"

Santiago slapped him across the mouth.

"My Elena teaches the son of a rich man to play the piano!"

"Your Elena teaches the son of lightning to play on her body!"

Santiago slapped him again. "You have no honor!"

"Ask the boy here why he drinks!" De Palma whined.

Santiago whirled at the boy.

"I have my pride," Ruben whispered.

"Ask the store here where she passes every night," said De Palma. "Ask the beasts on the corner who whistle at her. It seems the earth knew the fragrance of your daughter before she ever touched the keys of a piano. She is no ivory, Santiago." With this, purged and remorseful, the old *sampaguita* man fell back limply on the bench. Santiago was running now, and behind, De Palma was beginning to pluck on his guitar.

Santiago moved among the brief lives in the tenements, inspecting the other insects big enough to leave a mark on the gravel as they moaned their rice; moved among the flow in the garbage cans and among the ardors in the alleys releasing their anguish. He stumbled among the hollow men and women on their rags and newspapers, breathing an apology, swearing to lead them out of the famine.

He inched his way into the avenue, picking up a trail through the city, boring a hole into the inlets shrieking its commerce in his ears. His pulse was beating as it had on the eve of The Battle when they heard the cannon as it blasted a tunnel through the lumber in the swamps and the bugles echoed and the horses neighed. He had blazed an escape route into the thicket, though he was only a courier, for his tender years had responded to the speeches of The Man on his mount as he preached a decade of reforms when he returned to rule.

Cannon and hoof in his ear, Santiago wended his way street after street, looking for a tall house with an *azotea* where his daughter played the piano to a child not old enough to sweeten his milk. The darkness chilled his sight, weed caked about his ankles, the sweet chant of De Palma caressed him with hymns that always spoke of the mountains and the stars and the stream that guarded the plateau where their leader stood, dreaming on his mount, looking to the east while The West advanced with Arkansas farm boys who washed their cotton socks in the ponds of Bacolor.

In half an hour, as though peering into hedges rich with Americans, Santiago had thrust his head into swinging doors where purple lights beckoned and the eyelashes of hostesses flapped like miniature bat-wings, as though, as he stood there, they were asleep and were having nightmares about a man of the revolution, glistening with a medal. In this half hour, frantic with a labor that thumped furiously in his chest, he collided into their figures, coiled and scented, a weary old man upon whose face hung a tear. Seeing this, they would giggle, rock, shake their heads knowingly, disappear into their florid spaces— an island so terrible to behold the old man eluded it as if a bullet had nicked his temples. There was no way of knowing where the tall house with the *azotea* might be, and he wished they would play their lesson louder, Elena and the retarded boy, that he might hear everything was well. But there was no sound of music, only the wind with the message of wine that transported him, head thrust in doorways, women laughing, not believing, then calling to him, a customer, to come, break bread with them before the hour of twelve when perforce he must retire the bones of his body. Finally, exhausted, he rested on the pavement under an awning, gasping sweat and tears washing his medal. As he stroked his face, burning with his heart, he saw it: the house, like a monastery, rising majestically out of a hill, the tallest tree of all, a castle winking its neon in the north. Slowly, his mind dancing in the rice wine, his cheeks flushed, he bolted from his resting place, heading directly toward this eagle of a house that leaned on a passage of leaves, a phantom, a windmill glowing ugly in the moon. When he knocked on the massive iron door, something like a thunder rumbled inside. No one answered. He knocked again. Still no one. Then he saw it, the balcony. Up there, in one of the rooms—for it was a big house—he felt the presence of people; heard a woman's quick tread; a man's thick voice, and what Santiago knew to be the creaking of a bed.

"Open this door!" he screamed.

Upstairs, someone lighted a cigarette.

Santiago gazed up, not so much at the window but at Whatever Man watched this spectacle from above. He leaped, caught hold of a vine, but his hand slipped and he felt the earth mothering his face. Rising, he leaped again, this time not even catching the vine, and slipping again.

He could not climb the balcony.

Looking around, he saw this house, which, a decade ago, was used as a chapel, was interlaced by a park. Fronting it was untended shrubbery with a stone bench. A fountain lay at the far right, facing the main street. A hero's stone monument held up its arms in salute of the dawn, though in the morning the sun normally rose on its back.

Santiago dragged himself to the bench, nursing his wounded fists. By now, the upstairs window had remained serene, untouched by his fury, a sinister chamber clinging to the silence of the city. Santiago looked up, seeing nothing but his pain, and he pushed himself down to the ground where he bit at pebble and scratched at rock and his loins ached and tore out at him in their own mute rebellion. The wine washed every part of him, every sense that could remember his story, stabbing at the coil of years curled like a snake in his throat. He was pounding on the earth with all his age, but not a sound came from him, for he was striking all the citizens now asleep in the city while he endured—ever loyal to the silence—the agony in the park.

He lay as he had lain in the green fields of the wild young country in the days of The Dream, looking into the eyes of The Man who told them about the coming of The Time. Lying in the sweet air, eating nothing but praise in the sudden doubling of a fist in the heart that now lived only in the memory of the loveliness, the bread was not stale, nor the water salty . . .

(Aguinaldo!) Like the terrible strength of all beginnings; the wine of his dream dancing wildly in his eyes, now a dried old man, a wraith in a rocking chair, sick, convalescent, a trophy honored once a year, a patriarch of the tomb, alone with revolution, transfixed in the twilight, a poet whose poetry rushed like pearls in the landscape.

Prostrate on the ground, twisting, writhing, he saw the moon, a circle in the heavens, repeating its aura, revering its own beauty, at random in the atmosphere: a destiny. Then a cloud, like a swift and ominous wing, touched it and the cloud sparkled and the moon darkened and he who lay on his back struggled up and went to the door, hammering with his knuckles at the silence.

The door opened. An old couple holding out a lamp, holding each other, questioned the dark together.

"What do you want?" asked the two.

Santiago's lips quivered.

"I want a woman."

The old man stared at his woman; held the lamp closer upon this shivering white man who would be a lover.

"Enter," the old man said.

Santiago followed the lamp and when it illuminated the interior, he found that the house was indeed a castle and must have been the home a governor-general once bequeathed to his *querida.*

"Is this a harem?" Santiago snickered, though he shook so.

"Follow, old one," the old man ordered harshly. The old woman had not spoken.

The couple and the lamp led Santiago into a maze of rooms, one dungeon succeeding another, each one unlocked ceremoniously by a key that swung from a chain the old woman encouraged to dangle by her side. As the old man introduced the caves, the old woman opened them, exposing women and children of all ages undoing packages and bundles, some sleeping, others disrobing, many just staring vacantly, and Santiago asked where the others were, for he was told that there were the new ones, just off the interisland ships. The old man with the lamp studied his customer maliciously and began scratching his bald head.

"We don't have your age right now, if you can wait . . ."

Santiago was going to answer when he tripped over some obstruction. "Pardon me," he said sincerely, and then he saw them. They were all lying on what appeared to be a huge mat, each covered with respective blankets; a tarpaulin here; a canvas there, a coat, even a towel. The women were strewn about like cattle.

"They are not prepared," the old man explained politely. "But go ahead. Choose one."

Santiago went around, lifting their covers, blinking in the oil lamp that followed, pulling out a leg, brushing aside a concealing arm, a lock of hair. A woman with pimples bit his hand and Santiago withdrew, pale. Out of nowhere, the old woman who had hovered perfectly still by the doorway, lunged with the agility of a cat, and with what looked like an animal's dried tail converted into a whip, struck the pimpled one twice in the face and thigh. A sob was stifled. The pimpled one cowered, covering herself with her end of the tarpaulin. The old woman, baring gold teeth in the lamp's glow, smiled apologetically at Santiago.

"They get listless sometimes," she said.

The guided tour was finished. The old woman restored her keys; the turnkey had done her duty. The master of the manor now mentioned a roster and a price. Going over their names, Santiago noticed there were thirty in all.

"Are they all here?"

"All present and accounted for," the old man announced, sweeping back a curtain with a flourish. "'Sorry, they are still resting. We didn't expect business . . . the late hour. But since you are a rare case . . .'"

Santiago smiled happily. "Then I must be———"

"There's that one upstairs," the old woman said naughtily, biting at a strand of her whip. "Special."

The wine stirred in Santiago. And without speaking, seeing the stairway, he ran up quietly, the old man stepping lightly behind him.

"If you can wait," he was saying.

But Santiago did not hear him. There, outside the middle door by a landing, stood a piano, a weird box with a mantle; and leaning on one of its legs, was a red umbrella. Santiago snatched it, and running downstairs, fell on top of the woman with the whip, sending her careening to the floor. Santiago slipped out of the curtain, ran out of the caves, still unlocked, fled out of the castle, chased by the couple; the old woman, just temporarily halted, lashing out blindly with her whip. And into the night Santiago fled, carrying a heart and its beating and a red umbrella clasped to his chest.

Half of the candle had melted when she returned. She was shivering, breathless.

"Was there wine tonight, father?"

He nodded. "There is always wine."

"Did De Palma speak of his bomb?"

"He has nothing else."

"Yes. He loves his misery. It is his only luxury. But tomorrow, we shall have rice and you can invite him for a change. There will be shrimps too."

"And will you fish the canals of the Pasig?"

She smiled indulgently, rubbing her hair with a towel. "No, father. Just the market by the way. I shall have money."

And then they were quiet.

When it seemed they would not speak at all, when there would always be this silence between them, he reached out, his hand full, and when she stooped to accept it, whatever it was, she found that this was a small wreath, a crown that he was giving her: flowers for the dead.

"I saw you in the graveyard," he said, his voice not rising.

Wet from the rain, she shuddered. She gripped the crown, still trembling, and now, she saw the red umbrella, dripping, as though drying its grief. At last, she understood and she flung herself at him.

"Father!"

". . . Forgive them!" he cried. "For she knows not what she is doing!"

Together, they sobbed out the sin of the house on the boulevard, their pain mingling, young and old, veil and uniform, sword and sheath.

"She danced for you, Elena, child," he stammered, "danced

her soles worn, her lungs torn. I saw her thin every day that she was childless; thinner while she danced, clapping her tiny palms, cursing the barrenness and chanting the glory in the *barrios* where we went with the Virgin's image in her missal . . .''

"Father . . ."

"I would pray too, for I could not father a child and your mother was bent from the old love of an old man ancient with revolution. And then one day, burning a taper in front of San Pascual, she danced in Obando, for some relative had told her of the miracle and there we went, carrying her wooden shoes and the rosaries and my guitar whose fifth string was the necklace of my mother; a string heavy with the music of her country. So one night in Obando, I played for my wife; I played in the crook of my arm, the splendor of your face while she danced her bounty, danced you into her belly. In that night wild with omens, she danced you, Elena, on the earth that summoned the substances of providence. That body you now sell every night and that you cut for my meal each day—she danced every morsel of it in that rain in Obando when I played to her the songs of my father. Obando bore you, my daughter, on the heels of your mother's love!"

And Elena, weeping, dropped on her knees to clutch at his feet.

"No more! No more!" she begged.

"I have been a monster, eating the nights of my daughter. The visitations of my child to the grave were nothing but license. And I thought it was rice, rice! Oh, I was feeding on you, my daughter! Eating your flesh day and night, your body, piece by piece, on the table while you surrendered it on the bed! Daughter!"

She shook violently.

He looked at the room, wincing at its every object. Her limbs made the steps of the hut strong; the cot, the stools, the spoons —her beauty. Perhaps the lantern shone because her mouth had loved sufficiently. Even the trunk she bought him could be a part of her, a mortgage to the men in her life. Everything in the house belonged to her body, everything. He was only a shadow in the womb burning out his candles, aging his wine.

Santiago buckled on his belt. Armed with his mission, he paced the floor; austere, elegiac, a Don Quixote in his cups.

Alarmed, she cried: "Where are you going?"

"I must free the people!" he said.

"No!"

And pulling out his sword from the sheath. "You are a prisoner in my belly while I eat!"

"I won't let you go!"

"I must perform the operation!"

"You cannot do anything!"

She blocked his way.

"Do you think you can hold back my conscience?"

And he swept her aside with a strength he had not known since the last hierarchy. Elena sank into a swoon.

He was rushing down the stairway, into the street, around the corner, still hearing the plaintive cry of De Palma, and was gone in the direction of the rice store, rousing the rice beggars, inciting them to the victory.

A truck loaded with cereal sped by, but Santiago, like a warrior, speared the point of his sword, once, twice, and a burst of rice flowed down the dirt and a burst of people swooped down, scooped up grain and ground, screeching grotesquely, drunkenly, like cannibals. The truck bumped on a garbage can, swerved and smashed on its side, rice spilling out like white blood, exploding from the seams, inundating the sidewalk where haggard mothers suckled their infants still groaning from cockroaches, lice and vaccination. An old woman broke from the throng, a sack of rice twice her size saddled on her back. Santiago roared with sword and wine, charging, rallying the people to the compound.

Before the guard could see him, Santiago had hurled himself into the barbed wire, and with a length of it sticking to his temples, he ran to the sacks in the nook where the dogs of the owner were fed with fish in the morning. And then, sword held tightly in his fist, cutting, slashing, crying, grabbing, he had clawed one sack open with his fingernails, and still clawing, he bled the rice out even as his fingers stained the grains and his people swarmed the fence. He crushed a handful of rice in his palm, scratching, moaning, swearing at the loot that ran like wine down his veins. When the guard called to him, who was obviously their leader, Santiago was running, leaving the butchered sack, running with rice in his hands. When the guard called again imploring and the old man fleeing did not answer, would not answer, the wind howling in the land—when calling again, the guard did not reach the thief running away, something like wind blew at Santiago, for the guard who was only a boy who had never held a gun before, had fired his rifle, dispersing the storm, leaving an old man resplendent with his medal.

And when Santiago fell—falling like a tear from a man's grief—he fell not on a pile of jute sacks in a sawdust yard above the *estero*, but on a cool moonscape of grass in a long ago September, in the hallow of belief, in the pool of all their blood, in the mountains. Like a sigh, like an old coin, gleaming, that would soon roll, lost, in a hole, he fell, as fallen he was part of the city's mountains whose loneliness became his fall; whose loveliness became his absence. So still he died, the bullet that took him almost seemed a gift, once given seemed absolute, seemed somehow a god of peace, a feast to God. Then alone, in a quiver of rice, he lay there with no one, save a sword and the sequins in the sky.

The Socialists

On a windless, white-hot day in May, a man stood upon the western slope of Mount Arayat, under the broiling sun, and recited Edwin Markham's "The Man with the Hoe."

The chocolate-brown woolen suit that the man wore fairly smoked with the heat; in a moment tiny streams of perspiration ran crookedly from behind his large ears down his thin, red neck.

Near him, a little farther up the slope, another man leaned on a hoe, eyes fixed on the dry brown sod at his feet. A piece of red cloth bound his shaggy head, leaving the top exposed. The ragged homespun shirt on his bony shoulders appeared ready to fall in pieces. One leg of his bright-red cotton trousers was rolled up to the knee, the other sagging loosely to his ankle. He gripped the bamboo handle of the hoe with both hands, and the emptiness of ages was on his face, and on his back the burden of the world.

> "Is dis da Ting da Lord God made and gabe
> To habe dominion ober sea and land;
> To trace da stars and sirch da hibens for poweh,
> To feel da passion ob eternitee?
> Is dis da dream He dreamt who shaped da suns
> And markt der ways upon de ancient deep?
> Down all da caberns ob Hell to der last gulf
> Der is no shape more ter-rible dan dis—
> More tongued wid cries against da world's blind greed—
> More filled wid signs and portents for da soul—
> More pakt wid dangeh to da uniberse."

205

The reciter's voice was bad and his pronunciation worse. But he made up for these obvious defects by a great deal of sincerity. Coming to the last three lines of the stanza, he swung around dramatically to face the sun, throwing wide his arms, and at the top of his voice shrieked out the words. From two front gold teeth, the sun's rays struck lurid flashes; the man with the hoe, bowed down with the weight of centuries, sweltered mutely in the baking heat.

There was also a third man on the slope, a dark man, powerfully built, pock-marked, blind. He sat on a rock, mindless of the heat, and on an ancient-looking guitar made accompaniment to the recitation. His short-cropped, rounded head swung jerkily to his strumming, and his eyes, bluish-white, glared sightlessly at the burning sun.

Below the three men on the heat-flooded slope, under a tall and leafy *camachilé* tree, was gathered a motley crowd. There were young women in the country costume of thin, gauzy *camisa* with gay silk *panuelo* tied around the head or draped over the shoulders, and bright-coloured skirt under brighter-hued *tapiz*. They were mostly dark-brown, looking more so because of the sharp contrast of their sunburned skin to the brightness of their apparel.

There were older women, fat and heavy around the hips, with breasts that sagged opulently against loose white bodice; or thin as sticks, withered, sapless, wrinkled—lips smeared blood-red with *buyò* stains. Some of these women wore on their heads the *salacót*, large, wide-brimmed hats of *anahaw* leaves.

There were mothers with babies astride their hips suckling well-filled breasts. There were children in various stages of undress, dark, wiry creatures, full of shrill noise and restless movement.

The majority of the men wore homespun *barong Tagalog* with pants that bagged easily at the knees since every man sooner or later squatted on his heels, tired from standing. Some of the younger men wore cheap Japanese-made polo shirts that revealed their thick, brawny arms and chunkily-muscled chests.

Scattered among the crowd were a few in white drill coats and one or two in woolen suits. These had the look of office workers on their faces—pale, pasty brown, pimpled, and two showed around the eyes traces of having heavily powdered themselves.

At the foot of the camachilé tree was an isolated group of some ten or twelve persons about whom more anon.

As the reciter came to the end of the poem, while he shook aloft a clenched fist and strained his shrill voice against the midday silence of Arayat, three women with baskets on their heads came down the path that lay between the crowd and the performers upon the slope of the mountain. They filed one behind the other, the shuffling of their bare feet and the rustling of their skirts audible beneath the impassioned recitation of Markham's masterpiece.

The three women were lost in a clump of dry reeds into which the narrow path vanished. The reciter reached the end of his piece. From the crowd arose a prolonged cheering in Tagalog, Pampango, and English. They clapped their hands and raised their voices against the blue sky.

From the towering brown dome of Arayat not an echo was awakened. The enervating heat seemed to have all things bound under its spell. But as the people's shouting died down and the heat-ridden silence closed in again, there was suddenly heard, incredibly cool and sweet, the purling of the little stream that circled the base of the mountain, its clear waters lapping the great roots of the camachilé tree that spread its branches over the crowd.

Wiping his flushed, sweaty face with a red handkerchief, the reciter descended from the slope.

A young man, immaculate in perfectly creased white wool trousers and glossy double-breasted alpaca coat, a gleaming straw hat on his head, now detached himself from the group seated on two long wooden benches near the foot of the camachilé tree, behind a small square table.

Throwing away a half-smoked cigaret, the young man sauntered over to meet the reciter. Held against his chest under his left arm, he carried a thick red book the title of which in bold black letters could plainly be seen: DAS KAPITAL, by Karl

Marx. An expensive German-made camera in a brown leather case hung by its strap across his left shoulder and rested on his right hip.

The persons composing the group at the foot of the *camachilé* tree were twelve in all, including the young man with the double-breasted coat. There were five girls—two unmarried, tall slender *mestizas*, with fine, well-bred features, thin, shapely lips rouged blood-red. They looked unbelievably chic. The third was an American, a round-faced, blue-eyed blonde with a good shape but rather thick ankles. She sat beside a handsome Jewish boy who was moodily staring at the ground between his widespread knees. The two other girls were the wives of two of the young men in the group. One, the smallest, thin, brown and pretty, wearing a sports suit of English wool, was married to the young man now shaking hands with the reciter of the poem.

"Congratulations, Comrade," the young man was saying, offering his hand, smiling graciously.

The other clutched the hand within his own and smiled gratefully, continuing to wipe his neck with the red handkerchief.

"Tank you, Mr. Lirios," he said, his voice harshened by his recent exertions. "Tank you—, Comrade," he repeated, shyly. His two front gold teeth flashed brightly. He drew the young man under a banana tree, saying: "Let's get in da shade. Let's get in da shade. It is bery hot out dere."

"Yeah, hot, isn't it?" the young man said, lifting his straw hat, fanning his face. He replaced the hat on his head, taking care to tilt it so that it shaded his face from the sun.

From where they stood, they could see over the heads of the people under the camachile tree. Comrade Lirios, the well-dressed young man, caught his wife's eye, and he raised the book, *Das Kapital*, to her. She smiled affectionately, dimpling the right cheek. Her name was Luisa.

"I wish to meet the man with the hoe," said Comrade Lirios, turning to Comrade Bautista, for that was the name of the reciter. "He is a good actor."

"Ah, Comrade Esteban. I'll call him. Wait here. I'll call him here."

Left alone, Comrade Lirios watched the proceedings below him. A barrel-chested individual with round prominent eyes, a bullet-head scarred whitely on the sides, was announcing the next number of the program. He spoke in Pampango. His voice was pugnacious and his round eyes bulged fiercely. Comrade Lirios, not understanding the words, felt an irresistible desire to laugh. He opened *Das Kapital*, ransacked its pages feverishly. The sun's ray striking the smooth white paper threw a glare upon his eyes. He desisted and listened once more, the impulse to laugh gone.

When Comrade Bautista returned, he had in tow besides the impersonator of the man with the hoe that was Comrade Esteban, another, a slight, sparsely-mustached person wearing a white, closed coat that emphasized his narrow shoulders and hollow chest. He was introduced as Comrade Manacis, legal adviser to the *Frente Popular*, as the gathering called itself.

There were now four of them in the scanty shade of the banana tree. Comrade Lirios turned his back to the sun, and, pressing close to his neck the straw hat, pretended not to mind the heat. However, since in that position he could not see his wife, he turned around now and then to give her a quick glance. She was chatting animatedly with the other married woman in the party. The two very chic *mestizas* sat at one end of the bench with long legs gracefully crossed, red-nailed fingers putting cigarets to red mouths, the while thick-lashed eyes were turned up interestedly toward the four other males of their party now engaged in what looked like a heated debate. Betty, the American girl, smoked a cigaret, chin in hand, elbow on knee. The Jewish lad hadn't changed his position.

Meanwhile, a young, dark-looking girl, dressed in pale-green skirt and *camisa* with red-stripped *panuelo*, had been helped atop the little square table by the muscular toastmaster. Followed a clapping of hands, then silence. The girl who had large, extraordinarily alive eyes, darted swift, flashing glances over the crowd, then with a quick lift of her head, starting singing the *Internationale!* The people joined her, and those who were sitting hurriedly rose to their feet.

Unbelievingly, Comrade Lirios stared, his straw hat in his

hand. His temples began to throb with a dull ache from the heat of the sun. He raised *Das Kapital* and shaded his head with it.

The song finished, the girl in the very next breath burst out into a rush of words that tumbled out of her mouth like angry waters through a break in a dike during the rainy season. Repeatedly the crowd interrupted her with enthusiastic clapping of hand and shouts of approbation.

Comrade Bautista, the reciter, clapped vigorously with the rest, a proud light in his eyes that never left the figure of the girl. Comrade Lirios remembered that during the singing of the *Internationale*, Comrade Bautista's voice had shrilled to the breaking point, and he had had a glimpse of the man's flushed and sweaty face uplifted to the blue sky, the gold teeth in his open mouth flashing in the sun. He turned to him saying: "I do not understand Pampango. What is she talking about?"

"She is discussing about da ims ob da *Frente Popular*——"

"Ah, and what does she say are the aims of the party?"

"She says why do we work and work and habe no mooney? Why do we slabe in da fields under da sun and habe notting to eat?"

"Is it as bad as all that? These people look quite robust and well-fed."

"You do not know what you are talking about, Comrade Lirios," Comrade Bautista said, forgetting to smile. "Dis peepul are suffering much dat you do not see."

"That is true," put in Comrade Esteban in a doleful tone, shifting his hold on the bamboo handle of the hoe.

"We know, Comrade Lirios," said Comrade Manacis, the lawyer, "we know, we know," nodding his big head on its scrawny neck emphatically.

There was another outburst of clapping and voices raised in a shout, "*Mabuhay*—long live!"

"And what did she say just now?"

"She said, 'Why do rich peepul become richer and da poor peepul poorer? Why do we see dem growing fatter and fatter as dey ride by in beautiful automobiles? Why do dey wear beautiful clodes and eat eggspensive foods when we are in rags and dying of starbation? Dis is all wrong. It should be changed. Away wid da present order. We must habe a goberment where ebbribody is rich and happy.'"

Comrade Lirios adjusted his straw hat carefully on the nape of his neck. His back felt smoking hot. His head was bursting. He unbuttoned his coat and, holding the lapels, tried to cool himself by waving the sides of the coat back and forth. But he only began to sweat more copiously from the effort. Besides, the book, *Das Kapital*, kept slipping; it was quite a job holding it under his armpit, and the camera-strap was in the way. He fixed his eyes on the sparse mustache of the lawyer and wanted to say that the socialism expounded so passionately by the girl was all wrong.

But Comrade Bautista was speaking again.

"We are so glad you came to dis meeting. When we sent da inbiteetion to da Socialist Club of Manila to come to da province to see der comrades here ——"

With sudden animation, Comrade Lirios turned to Comrade Bautista and said, "You know, I am glad I came. This is all a complete revelation to me—a complete revelation, I tell you. I am glad I came. Frankly, I did not think you people here ——"

A voice interrupted him, a complaining, disagreeable voice.

"Hey, why the hell did we ever come to this God-forsaken place? These people do not even know the ABC of socialism. It is treason they are proposing."

Comrade Lirios in turning to face the intruder, dislodged the straw hat from his neck and while retrieving it from the dusty earth, he was aware of an uncomfortable silence that seemed to double the heat until he felt he would suffocate.

"Oh, it is you," he said, affecting surprise, when he was upright again and faced the newcomer. "Comrades, may I introduce Comrade San Diego. He is as you know the Secretary of the Socialist Club of Manila."

Comrade Bautista flashed his gold teeth and shook hands

with Comrade San Diego. The lawyer, Comrade Manacis, shook hands with a slight bow. Comrade Esteban detached one bony hand from the handle of his hoe and shook the hand of Comrade San Diego. That done he gripped the end of the bamboo handle with both hands, rested his sharp chin on them, and was once more wrapped in doleful silence.

Comrade San Diego, who had a fair, yellowish complexion, with a wide expanse of forehead and small, quick-moving eyes above a large bulbous nose, now sent darting glances at each of the four. The immaculate Comrade Lirios was carefully wiping with a white silk handkerchief he had pulled out of his breast pocket, minute specks of dust clinging to the band of his straw hat.

"Hell," said Comrade San Deigo, "I am roasting." He looked back at the group he had left under the *camachilé* tree seated on the benches.

"I am glad you came, Comrade San Diego," said Comrade Bautista, with another flash of gold teeth.

Comrade San Diego turned his sharp gaze upon the speaker, but said nothing.

"I was just telling our comrades here," said the immaculate Lirios, "how glad I am to have come. This is all a complete revelation to me—a complete revelation. I wouldn't have missed it for the world."

"Hell," said Comrade San Diego, moving his shoulders under his coat. "The whole thing is a farce. I am going back under the *camachileé* tree."

"No, stay a while," said Comrade Lirios with his gracious smile. "Our comrades here are dying to hear the principles of socialism correctly expounded ——"

"In this heat? In all this sun? Hell!" Comrade San Diego turned to go, but Comrade Lirios held his arm.

"The trouble with you is that you are all talk. When you are face to face with the real thing, you refuse to come to grips with it. You would rather sit in the shade and split hairs."

"Hell," said Comrade San Diego, wrenching free his arm. "When it comes to fighting for what I think is right, I am as ready as the next man." He reached into the waist of his trousers and brought out a seven-inch knife. With a flip of his fingers, he exposed a gleaming, dagger-like blade. He darted quick glances at the four, the opened knife in his hand catching the sun on the middle of its blade and sending out a myriad of fine rays in every direction. "Hell," said Comrade San Diego, closing the knife with a snap and pushing it inside his waistband again. "Under the new sedition law these people could all be sent to prison."

"And being present at this meeting, don't forget that you are also liable to imprisonment," said Comrade Lirios quietly.

"Hell," said Comrade San Diego, turning away. "I shall tell my wife we are going home."

Comrade Lirios allowed his glance to wander toward the group on the benches at the foot of the *camachilé* tree. He caught his wife's eye and waved *Das Kapital* at her. She smiled and he thought he could see the dimple in her cheek.

A man, probably about fifty years old, with a long tapering face—broad, shapely forehead, thick graying hair, firm cheeks marked with tiny brown moles around the eyes and down in front of the ears—had been introduced by the belligerent toastmaster. This man stood beside the small square table with a hand on its edge. With the other hand he held the lapel of his white drill coat. He kept that pose throughout his speech. He was a tall man, thick-shouldered, erect, commanding. He spoke in low, measured tones, his words plain, without the usual flowery expressions that had characterized the speeches of the previous speakers. Everyone listened attentively and forgot to applaud. He spoke in Pampango and once more Comrade Lirios asked, "What is he saying? Who is he?"

"He is Laroco, the *Sakdal Supremo*," Comrade Bautista whispered. "He does not belong to our party, but we invited him to speak."

"He is an extraordinary-looking man," Comrade Lirios found

himself whispering back. "I know him. He sat beside me in the truck coming from Manila. I never dreamed he was the *Sakdal Supremo*. He dozed most of the way."

"He is like that," said the lawyer. "Quiet. Sleepy. No words."

"Like dynamite," supplied the man with the hoe. He was watching the speaker with great interest, his chin for the moment raised from the back of his hands that held the handle of the hoe.

"He is now telling about da way how he was imprisoned in Manila," translated Comrade Bautista. "He says da Constabulary soldiers put handcuffs on him and he has neber forgotten da feel of da cold iron around his wrists."

"I remember him," said Comrade Lirios. "Yes, I remember him now. But he was pardoned by the President, wasn't he?"

"Yes, dat's right," said Comrade Bautista, eagerly, smiling, his gold teeth flashing. "Dat's right. He was pardoned by da President——"

"Ah . . . and what is he saying now?"

"He says da Sakdals do not faboh force as a means ob getting what dey want."

"Ah," said Comrade Lirios, "so they do not favor the use of force." In another moment he knew his head would split. If only a breeze would start up. The shadows of the trees and shrubs were grotesque cut-outs pasted on the brown earth. The scorched ground underfoot sent up a strong musty reek that he could almost taste. Only the little stream purled on sweetly, maddeningly clear and cool . .

"No, but he says dey are forced to use force because——"

"Because of what?" This is foolish, Comrade Lirios told himself. It isn't so simple as all this——

"Many ob da followers are impatient. Dey cannot wait."

"Wait for what?"

"For da help ob Jesus Christ."

"Jesus Christ? What has Jesus Christ to do with Sakdalism?"

"He is da hope of da Sakdals. Dey are told by der leaders to depend upon His help to get what dey want. Dere is where we

are different from da Sakdals. We Socialists beleeb in coopera-
tion. We beleeb dat dere should be no separate societies. No
Sakdals. No Communists. We should all unite under da Red
Flag and den go after what we want."

"And if they should join you, the Sakdals, what then?" What
then? What then? Comrade Lirios felt a tightening in his chest.

"We shall see what we shall see," said the man with the hoe,
very quietly. His half-shut eyes met those of Comrade Bautista,
slid sideways to intercept the lawyer's, and silence fell upon
the three.

Comrade Lirios found the sudden silence of his companions
disconcerting, and he let his eyes wander to where his wife still
chatted with the other married woman under the cool shade of
the *camachilé* tree. Failing to catch her eye, he spread his gaze
westward. Just across the little stream were fields green with
young rice plants. Farther away were flat dun-coloured stretches,
untilled, the grass burned up by the sun. To the right and left as
far as the eye could reach were dark-green areas planted to cane
sugar. Not a soul was abroad. He thought he could discern the
heat raining down like arrows upon the plain.

The Sakdal leader finished his speech amidst loud applause.
And now the next number of the program was a quartet singing
the primary school song, "Planting Rice Is Never Fun," in
English.

A strange sensation of being transported out of himself possessed Comrade Lirios. In his ears rang the untutored voices
of the four girls singing, "Planting rice is nay-ber fu-un . . . "
He looked at them, at their upturned faces on which the sun cast
immobile leaf-shadows; at the blind guitarist swinging his round
head to his own accompaniment. How earnest they were! His
eyes encompassed the crowd of listeners caught in varied poses
of attention. They, too, were dead earnest. Not in a thousand
years could it have occurred to any one of them that they were
—comic. Comic? Comrade Lirios had a sudden vision of 16,-
000,000 people of the same cast and mold, capable of the same
direct, unself-conscious, child-like simplicity and earnestness.

They till the soil and plant rice and they know the quality of rain and sun. The feel of pure honest earth is in their work-hardened hands; they stand on it with bare feet, toes spread apart. What then if they sang the *Internationale* and recited Edwin Markham's poem upon a burning hillside under the midday sun?

Comrade Lirios now saw himself and his friends pouring beer down their throats in air-conditioned rooms in the City, biting into liverwurst sandwiches the size of shoeheels and costing 25 centavos apiece. He heard his voice and their voices smoothly juggling with words and phrases: planned economy, Marxian dialectics, labor and capital, society of the free and equal, et cetera, et cetera.

There now under the *camachile* tree was San Diego munching a sandwich he had taken out of a basket at his feet. They were all munching sandwiches and drinking beer from small cylindrical cans: the fat Morales, his heavy jowls working busily, and the lanky Espiritu shaking a finger under the nose of the squat, baldish Cruz. Only Levi, the Jewish boy, wasn't eating anything. He sat with hands clasped loosely between his knees. Handsome dog, that Jew. Was there anything between him and Betty? He thought of them a brief instant, remembering a glimpse he once had of the fair breasts of the American girl when they were out bathing in Sunset Beach . . . His wife turned and saw him, waved a sandwich pertly, and he merely stared at her unseeingly, for in his mind had arisen a picture of himself standing there in the sun in all his finery, his shining immaculate-ness! For a moment Comrade Lirios stood very still. Then his shoulders shaking with silent laughter, he walked over to his wife: "Give me a sandwich," he said. He fished in the basket in the nest of a crumpled newspapers and brought out a can of beer. He punched a hole into it with San Diego's knife.

As he bit into the flat triangle of white bread, there rang in his ears the words of the song, "planting rice is nay-ber fu-un . . . " The beer tasted flat; it was warm.

N. V. M. Gonzalez

The Sea Beyond

The *Adela*, the reconverted minesweeper that had become
the mainstay of commerce and progress in Sipolog Oriental, was
on her way to San Roque. As Horacio Arenas, our new assistant,
wanted to put it, the *Adela* was "expected" at San Roque, which
was the provincial capital, "in seven hours." He spoke at some
length of this particular voyage, looking worn-out instead of
refreshed after the two-week vacation we had hoped he would
enjoy.

There he was, he said, one of the hundred odd impatient
passengers that shivered under the low canvas awning of the
upper deck. A choppy sea met the ship as she approached Punta
Dumadáli, and the rise and fall of the deck suggested the labored
breathing of an already much-abused beast of burden. Her
hatches were in fact quite full, Arenas said. Hundreds of sacks
of copra had filled her hold at Dias. Piled all over the lower deck
were thousands of pieces of lauan boards from the mills of San
Tomé. The passageways alongside the engine room were blocked
by enormous baskets of cassava and bananas. A dozen wild-eyed
Simara cows, shoulder to shoulder in their makeshift corral at
stern, mooed intermittently as though the moon-drenched sea
were their pasture.

For the moon had risen over the Maniwala Ranges three
miles to the starboard. As more and more the *Adela* rounded the
Punta Dumadáli, the wind sent the ship buckling wildly. An
hour before, all this would have been understandable; it was
puzzling, if not thoroughly incomprehensible now. This kind of
sea was unusual for the reason that the Dumadáli headland was
known to mariners to throw off, especially this time of the year

if at no other, the full force of the *noroeste*. If some explanation were to be sought, it would be in some circumstance peculiar only to this voyage. This was the consensus, which made possible the next thought: that some presence was about, some evil force perhaps—so the talk went on board—which, until propitiated, might yet bring the ship to some foul end. The cows, so insistent in their lowing before, were markedly quiet now. The ship continued to pitch about; whenever the wind managed to tear at the awnings and cause loose ends of the canvas to beat savagely at the wire-mesh that covered the railings, small unreal patches of sea glimmered outside in the moonlight.

It was no secret that there was a dying man on board. He was out there in the third-class section. Whatever relation his presence had to the unpleasantness in the weather no one could explain, but the captain did do something. He had the man moved over to the first-class section, where there were fewer passengers and possibly more comfort.

The transfer was accomplished by two members of the crew. They carried the cot in which the man lay, and two women, the man's wife and her mother, followed them. Ample space was cleared for the cot; the two women helped push the heavy canvas beds and chairs out of the way. Finally the two men brought the canvas cot down. The ship listed to the starboard suddenly; and it seemed that from all quarters of the deck the hundred odd passengers of the *Adela* let out a wild scream.

Then the ship steadied somehow. For a moment it seemed as if her engines had stopped. Then there was a gentle splashing sound as though the bow had clipped neatly through the last of those treacherous waves. Either superior seamanship or luck held sway, but the ship might have entered then an estuary, perhaps the very mouth of a river.

The excitement had roused the passengers and, in the first-class section at least, everyone had sat up to talk, to make real all over again the danger they had just been through. The steaming-hot coffee which the steward began serving in thick blue-rimmed cups encouraged conversation. The presence of the two women and the man in the extra cot in their midst was hardly to be overlooked. A thick grey woolen blanket covered the man all over, except about the face. His groans underscored by the faint tapping of the wind on the canvas awnings were becoming all too familiar. The mother attracted some notice, although for a different reason; she had a particularly sharp-edged face—brow and nose and chin had a honed look to them. The wife, who had more pleasing features, evoked respect and compassion. It was touching to see her sit on the edge of the empty cot beside her husband's and tuck in the hem of her skirt under her knees. She could not have been more than twenty, and already she wore the sadness of her widowhood. The glare of the naked electric bulb that hung from the ridgepole of the deck's canvas roof accentuated it, revealed that she was about six months gone with child, and called attention to her already full breasts, under a rust-colored *camisa*, that soon would be nourishing yet another life.

It was four hours before, at Dias, where the accident had occurred. Although Dias was a rich port, no wharf had been constructed either by the government or the local association of copra and rice merchants. The old method of ferrying cargo in small outriggered *paráos* was less costly perhaps; it was even picturesque. But it was only possible in good weather. And already the *noroeste* had come. The same waves that pounded at the side of the *Adela* at anchor lashed at the frail *paráos* that were rowed over toward the ship and were brought into position for hauling up the copra. The man, one of the *cargadores*, had fallen off the ship's side.

He would have gone to the bottom had he not let go of the copra sack that he had held aloft, and more so had he not been caught across the hips by the outriggers of his *paráo*. Nevertheless, the next wave that lifted the ship and gathered strength from under her keel it seemed flung him headling toward the prow of the boat. The blunt end of this dugout pressed his body against the black, tar-coated side of the *Adela*. The crew pulled him out with difficulty, for the sea kept rising and falling and caused the prow's head to scrape continuously against the ship's side. The crew had expected to find a mass of broken flesh and bones, but in actuality the man came through quite intact. He did not start moaning and writhing until his wet undershirt and shorts had been changed and he had been laid out on the cot. There was nothing that could be done further except to keep him on board. Something after all had broken or had burst open somewhere inside him.

His family was sent for. The wife, accompanied by her mother, clambered up the ship's side thirty minutes later, to the jocose shouts of "Now you can see San Roque!" from innocent well-wishers in the *paráos*. The shippers, the Dias Development Co., had sent a telegram to the provincial doctor at San Roque, and an agent of the company had come on board and personally commended the *cargador* to the captain. When at last the fifty-ton copra shipment was on board, the *Adela* weighed anchor.

Now for having transferred the man from the third-class to the first-class section, the captain earned some praise and the connection between this act and the pleasant change in the weather elicited much speculation. If only the man did not groan so pitifully, if only he kept his misery to himself; if only the two women were less preoccupied too by some bitter and long-unresolved conflict between them. "Don't you think he is hungry?" the mother once asked; to which the wife answered, "He does not like food. You know that." And then the mother asked, "How about water? He will be thirsty perhaps"; and the wife's reply was, "I shall go down and fetch some water." The matter could have stopped there, but the mother wanted to have the last word. "That's better than just standing or sitting around."

The wife got up and walked away, only to return about ten minutes later with a pitcher and a drinking cup from the mess room below. The mother had the pitcher and drinking cup placed at the foot of the sick man's bed, for, as she explained, "He will ask for water any time and you won't be near enough to help me." The mother waited to see what her daughter would make of this; and the latter did have her say: "I'll be right here, Mother, if that's all you're worried about."

The man grew restless. His wife's assurance (she said again and again, "You will be all right!") drew nothing but interminable sighs ("O, God of mine!"). Between the man and his wife, some inexplicable source of irritation had begun to fester. "It is in your trying to move about that the pain comes," the wife chided him gently. "We are getting there soon. It will not be long now." Whereupon the man tried to raise his knee and twist his hips under the blanket. The blanket made a hump like one of the Maniwala mountains in the distance, and he let out a wail, followed by "But this boat is so very slow, God of mine! Why can't we go faster? Let the captain make the boat go faster. Tell him. Will someone go and tell him?"

Almost breathless after this exertion, he lay still. The mother, this time as if her son-in-law were an ally, took it upon herself to comfort him. "Better keep quiet and don't tire yourself. The captain will make the boat go faster, surely." And by putting down his knee carefully, the hump that the blanket had made before leveled off now into foothills instead of those high ranges of the Maniwala.

The business of the telegram came after this lull. It was preceded by a prolonged groan, and then the question was there before them: "And did they send the telegram?" "They" meant the Company of course, in whose service the man had enlisted as a *cargador*. If the answer to this was in the affirmative, then there was reason to say that the doctor would attend to him and put him together again and return him to his work. His wife assured him that the telegram had gone. "So now be quiet," she added. "The other people here would not want to be disturbed now. They want to sleep, no doubt," she said, looking round her, seeking the faces of some twenty or twenty-five passengers— which included merchants, students, and at least three public schoolteachers on some Christmas holiday jaunt.

The mother asked about food—a proper question, although

under the circumstances perhaps a tactless one. "I am not hungry, Mother," was what the daughter said, firmly. "I'll sit here," the mother offered, in a less authoritative tone than she had been accustomed to use. "I'll do that myself if you are hungry," countered the daughter. "I don't care for food," the mother assured her. "And did I tell you I wanted to eat?" Whereupon the daughter declared that she was not hungry, "——let me tell you that, Mother." The mother alleged that her most loving daughter was no doubt "too choosy" about food, "that's why." She ought to "go down below and ask for anything to eat." "Eat whatever you can find," was her solemn injunction, as if to overwhelm her daughter's claim that she was not hungry at all. "Don't worry about me, Mother," the wife added, pointedly. "I don't get hungry that easily." And then to round off this phase of their quarrel, the mother said, loud enough for anyone who cared to hear: "Maybe, it's sitting at the captain's table that you've been waiting for all this time."

The daughter said nothing in reply and the mother did not press her advantage either. It was clear, though, that the meaning of the remark, its insinuation, was not to be easily dismissed. What the mother had so expressed was a little out of the ordinary; the air, as Arenas put it, was rife with conjectures. It was not difficult to remember, he said, that ship officers, or sailors in general, had never been known to endow women their highest value. What remained to be understood was why the mother thought of her daughter in some such awful connection as this.

Five hours later, Arenas said, after the *Adela* had docked at the San Roque pier and the discharging of some of her cargo had begun, the subject came up again. Perhaps the first person to disembark had been the captain himself, to infer from the fact that somebody, possibly one of the mates, had shouted to someone standing on the wharf: "Duty before pleasure, captain!" A jeep of the Southern Star Navigation Co. had rolled up the ramp and then hurried off the mile-long seaside road toward the town, into San Roque *población* itself. The town was brightly lighted, particularly the section along the seaside.

"Now he's gone and we have not even thanked him," said the mother. "And the doctor has not come. How can we leave this ship? Answer that," she demanded. "You are too proud, that's what. All that you needed to say was a word or two, a word of thanks, surely." The wife remained silent through all this. "And he could have taken you in the jeep, to fetch the doctor; if there was that telegram, and it has been received—" She did not go further. The wife assured **her** calmly that the telegram was sent. "So what harm could it have done to have spoken to the captain, to have reminded him, since he would be riding into town anyway?" the mother said; and to this the daughter's reply was the kind of serenity, Arenas said, that can come only from knowledge: "All men know is to take advantage of us, Mother," she said.

Taken aback by these words, the mother searched the faces of people round her for help. She got nothing and she said nothing. The passengers had crowded at the railing to watch the lumber being unloaded. A gang of *cargadores* tossed pieces of lumber from over the ship's side to the wharf ten feet away while someone chanted: "A hundred and fifty-three—and fifty-four— and fifty-five. . . . " and the wood cluttered askew on the fast-mounting pile. The cows lowed again from their corral at the stern of the ship. This blended afresh with the man's groans and with the chant and the clatter of the boards. Meanwhile, the wife talked on softly: "We have arrived, and it's the doctor's jeep we're waiting for and nothing more," wiping her husband's brow with a handkerchief. "Two hundred and three—and four —and five. . . . " chanted the counter, over down below. "This is San Roque now," the wife continued. "A big town it is, with many lights. And with many people." Her husband's brow sweated profusely and it was all she could do with her handkerchief. "And the lights are bright, and so many. Rest now and tomorrow we can see the town," she said softly, folding her handkerchief this way and that so as not to get any section of it too damp with sweat.

It was at this point, Arenas said, that a motor sounded from down the road, followed by the blare of a jeep's horn and the swing of its headlights. The lights caught the man who was chanting his count of the lumber being unloaded, and they held him transfixed. He shouted out the numbers louder. The jeep stopped in the middle of the now cluttered up wharf, for what with the stacked rows of copra and the lauan boards from San Tomé there was no space for the jeep to move in. The driver, having gone no farther than possible, turned off his engine and slid off his seat awkwardly, and then approaching the man who was doing the counting, he demanded: "How much longer?" And the other replied, "Possibly until two o'clock—what with the men we have. You know how it is, sir." To which the other said, sternly: "Stop calling me 'sir.' And to think that the captain just told me he'll pull out in two hours, not a second later."

Words, Arenas said, which, although intended for somebody else did make the wife say to her husband: "They'll first move you over there, to the wharf—that will be solid ground at least —and there we shall wait for the doctor." She had dropped her voice to a whisper.

Across the ten feet of water to the edge of the wharf, lights fell harshly on the piles, on the heads and arms of the *cargadores* who slid up and down the gangplank with the copra sacks on their shoulders, looking like so many over-sized ants. To the right was the driver in his jeep; he had not turned off his lights and it flooded the first-class section with a garish glare. "What shamelessness," cried the wife. The jeep's lights singled her out. The driver had got stuck between the wall of copra to his left and a new pile of lumber to his right. He was trying to turn the jeep about but did not have the room. The man who had addressed him "Sir" had stopped his work, and the clatter of the boards had ceased. Up on the deck, Arenas said, the wife shouted: "What does he want of me? What does he want me to do now?" The mother pulled her away. "She's overwrought. Forgive her," she begged. "And as you've observed, I've been hard on her myself. I don't know why. Why must God punish us so?"

Once more the driver tried to maneuver his jeep and all the time his lights seemed to fix themselves forever on the wife, who, to meet this challenge, sprang away from the ship's railing and rushed down to the lower deck, shouting: "Here, here I am. Take me. What can you want of me?"

It was that way, Arenas said. Two hours later, the man was moved to the wharf, and there behind a pile of copra and another pile of lauan lumber the wife and the mother waited. Word was abroad that the captain, who had returned from town, had said that he had contacted the doctor. Contacted, Arenas said, was the very word. And wasn't that so revealing?

We didn't know at first what he meant, we told him. Did he want to remind us about the war, the same one during which the *Adela* had swept the mine-strewn sea in behalf of progress and civilization? The word Arenas had used belonged to that time, and he seemed to say, All this because it had been that way at that time. You must understand, you might forgive, even.

But we didn't want him to be apologetic like the mother-in-law he had described; and so, afterward, when he talked again about the subject, wearing that worried look on his face with which we had become familiar, we had to urge him: "Better not think about it any more."

GREGORIO C. BRILLANTES

*Our knowledge, our prophecy, are only
glimpses of the truth. . . . Now, we see
through a glass, darkly; then, we shall
see face to face.*

—ST. PAUL TO THE CORINTHIANS

A Wind Over the Earth

It was two o'clock in the afternoon when they drove over the bridge and passed the signboard that said they were now entering the Province of Tarlac, drive carefully, ten persons have been killed here, on this rain-dark highway slanting through the sudden angular hills. Then the road was straight again, level and fading ahead into the October horizon, where the rain was falling now, far away to the west; but he didn't resume his former nervous speed, and he breathed in the cool wind, and acknowledged his tiredness after the long dry miles of sun-glare and the fear that his father had died, was already dead, before they could speak, before they could touch one another with a final word.

"We'll be there in twenty minutes," he said.

He glanced at her beside him, and was grateful for the reassuring pats of her hand. She sat rather stiffly, because of the ripening swelling curve of her body; he wondered now, with a new solicitude, if it would have been wiser to have come alone, without her. The tires swished over the cement road wet from the rain that had preceded them, and the green-yellow fields of rice rushed by on either side of the road, and the wind funneled into the car with the far hollowness of strange voices.

From the highway approaching the town in a wide arc he saw the tin-sheet roofs of houses among the trees, washed sharp

226

against the mountains of Luzon, in the white sunless day; he felt no stir of recognition, only a resentful dread that his father might not be able to speak to him. He felt there was something his father had to tell him, something tremendously important left unsaid through the years; but even as they came into the town, driving under a sagging, rain-soaked arch for the Blessed Virgin (for this was the month of the rosary), past the first acacias and the coconut trees, he didn't hurry. A dark nameless quality in the clear air touched his heart; the almost palpable smell of earth and leaves pressed against him. Somebody he didn't recognize waved a greeting: perhaps a childhood playmate, he thought; a friend in high school . . . The wind rustled the trees over the cobbled streets and spattered collected rain-drops on the windshield.

The gate was open and he maneuvered the Chevrolet into the driveway. In the stillness after the last hum of the engine, he waited for the outcries of mourning women, the wind murmured in the trees around his father's house. He helped Teresa out of the car, and together they stood on the crushed gravel, waiting. A dog began to bark behind the house. All the windows were closed against the wind; no one came out to meet them. He guided her through the portico and was about to try the door when his brother, Luis, opened it. His brother was unshaven, and there were circles around his eyes.

He and Teresa followed Luis into the *sala*, their steps seeming loud in the high dim room.

"What happened?" he asked Luis.

"It's his heart. And complications. I can't say what exactly."

He thought there were people sitting in the enforced dusk of the living room; the chairs were bare, inanimate. They went up the stairs as the grandfather clock on the landing chimed two-thirty, the musical tones melting liquidly into the ancient wood of the walls.

He said, "But only last month, Mama wrote that he was already well."

"Something did happen," his brother said. "You remember Mr. Ramos?"

"What about him?"

"Papa almost killed him. With a revolver. They had a fight. Something about money, and honor . . . "

A nurse emerged from the sick room as they ascended on to the hallway; she brushed past them, carrying a basin pungent with alcohol. His mother met them at the door, calling his name as though blindly. He bent to kiss her wrinkled forehead; Teresa embraced her, and for a second, the women looked at each other, pensively, before his mother led them all into the room.

The windows were closed and the room was thick with the odors of illness and medicine; candles flamed before a crucifix. In the uncertain light his father lay on the poster-bed, breathing through his mouth, his chest rising, falling slowly; his eyes, catching the candle-light, burned with a silent fever.

"Papa," he said. "We're here, Teresa and I. It's me, Tony."

The eyes stared up into the canopy of the bed, burning intensely. He heard his father's slow exhalation, soft like a sigh.

"Papa," he said, "I'm Tony—your son, Tony . . . " His heart began to pound thickly in his throat. "Papa . . . "

"He can't talk," Luis said. "He hasn't said a word since the last stroke."

He straightened up and looked down at his father, the wide and rigid eyes, the slack mouth that couldn't speak; he stood there, tensely, and remembered the old man's pride, his passionate violence, and his vision blurred in tears. He felt Teresa edge closer, holding on to his arm. The nurse returned with a be-spectacled man fumbling with a stethoscope in a kind of bewilderment.

"You go and rest," his mother said. "It's all right—I have the nurse with me. You and Tony have come a long way."

"I'll stay with you, Mama," said Teresa.

"No," she said. "You're tired . . . You need to lie down . . . "

When they had left the room Doña Pilar sat down on the rocking-chair beside the bed. The nurse rearranged the bottles on the table. The windowpanes quivered in their grooves, pushed by the wind. She watched her husband fight for each breath of air. It was a sight no longer strange and terrible to her; she loved him, but she had also learned to care for the sick with a deliberate and efficient hardness; one must be courageous before the things one cannot change. But still there were times when she was assailed by a loneliness, an isolation of old age: one's husband becomes a stranger; the children go away and find their loves and are no longer truly one's own.

The candle-flames flickered despite the stillness in the room, as if aware of the wind outside. She had been saying the rosary when Teresa and Tony arrived; now she prayed the remaining decade, the Crucifixion. She tried to compose herself mentally. Think of the body supported by the nails piercing the hands and feet, think of the thirst, the bleeding, broken face of God-made-man. It was useless: she prayed distractedly, harried by innumerable images. She thought of Manuel, lost and unheard from in America: would he see in a dream his father dying? Teresa will give birth in January. Tony should be gentle with her. Manuel, Luis, Tony; and the girls, Nena, and Perla, who was now a nun.

Now in the dimness Doña Pilar reclined in the chair and closed her eyes. Tony and Teresa had come; she relaxed the tension of her waiting. She heard the nurse go into the hall. The wind outside seemed to be telling her: time lost, far away. Gradually a weakness came upon her like a drifting sleep. As in a dream she saw herself as a young girl, long ago, dancing. She was flushed and tireless and laughing, she was dancing to the waltzes that went on and on through the night, dancing around the kiosk of the town square under the bright streamers of a New Year's Eve with the young men who called her Pili and begged for her love. For they didn't know that she had already promised it to the sullen young man who couldn't dance, and who watched her jealously, dangerously, as she laughed and danced with all the young men who were in love with her. And when the dance was over and the tropical stars were pale in the sky, the sullen young man wouldn't let her go home but carried her into his car (the black, obsolescent Buick was commandeered by the army in the last war), and he kissed the outraged protests from her mouth and she wept as they drove to Manila in the dawn-light, knowing more than ever that she loved this violent young man who was to be her husband, and years later, mayor of the town, then the governor, the father of five children, the boys fearless and impetuous like their father but unashamed of tenderness, the girls beautiful with a fragile loveliness but honest and capable with their hands, helping her in the kitchen when her husband had guests for dinner (in 1939 the President himself, passing through on a country tour), or playing for her on the piano in the high wide living room in the summer evenings the waltzes she had danced to when she was a young girl long ago, when she was the tireless and laughing Pili of all the young men who were in love with her, and oh so many long years yet before she was to become the white-haired Doña Pilar struggling to Mass in the blue cold mornings that chilled her bones. . . .

She roused herself with a start and trembled with the guilt of her remembering, as if it were an unforgivable dereliction of duty. The final echo of her dream's music disappeared into the distance of an obscure landscape she could only sense and not understand. It was dark in the room now; in the town electricity was a luxury that came only after six o'clock. Her heart was tired, drained, empty. The nurse leaned against the foot-board of the bed, waiting.

The man on the bed stirred. The nurse sprang forward and felt for his pulse. Doña Pilar lighted a candle. She peered at her husband, the candle in her hand: his eyes moved at last and met hers in a stare of speechless terror.

She turned to the nurse. "Miss Corpus, please send for the priest," she said, and her voice was steady and calm.

He came to the house after the tolling of the Angelus. He was a tall young priest with a crew-cut and a shy smile and he walked with a slight limp. He was the new coadjutor of the parish, his first assignment after the seminary: there was a certain self-consciousness in his movements as he donned his surplice in the diffused light of candles and electric bulb.

Doña Pilar said, "Father Santos, I'm afraid it is impossible for him to confess. He cannot speak."

The priest massaged his chin, seemingly fingering the defects of his shave. "It's all right," he said, and his voice was surprisingly low and rounded. "He can make an act of will." He placed a small silver case, the chrism, on the table, before the crucifix and the candles.

He bent over Don Ricardo on the bed and blessed him with the Sign of the Cross. "You are sorry for all your sins," he began. "You are sorry for having offended God . . . " The eyes burned with their mute terror. "Tell God you are sorry. I am a priest . . . Make a sign," he pleaded. Sweat broke out on his brow and glistened on his earnest, boyish face. "Tell God you are deeply sorry . . . " He recited the Latin absolution rapidly, as if to spare the others in the room the mystic strangeness of the language.

After the *Indulgentiam*, the priest took the silver box from the table and proceeded to anoint the man on the bed with the consecrated oil. He finished the unction and knelt beside the bed and read the concluding prayers, while sweat shone on his face and a woman in the room cried softly and Don Ricardo's eyes burned with their wordless fire.

In the hall a tangle of children, curious and subdued, gaped at the priest. The son who was called Tony accompanied him down the stairs, across the *sala*, to the door. For the first time he realized the spaciousness of the house, its history; portraits of ancestors hung on the mellowed walls, and the shell-windows were of an antique design. He would have liked to stay awhile and smoke and talk before going back to the rectory, through the dark storm wind, but Tony had opened the door for him. He retrieved his jacket from the umbrella-stand.

"Who asked you to come, Father?"

"Your mother sent for me," the priest said, startled by the question. He thought he detected a breath of whisky on the other man, but then he wasn't sure. "You are Tony, aren't you?" he asked quietly, with a smile.

"Didn't you know that the slightest shock could kill him? Didn't you know that, Father?"

"No," he said. "I came because——"

"It didn't do him any good, did it? He gave no sign. I guess he didn't even know you were there."

"God is good and merciful."

The priest turned away from the slammed door and walked through the gate and down the street, under the trees of the evening. The wind was cold now and he wished he had a heavier coat. From the earth rose the smell of rain and decaying leaves. He stopped by a tree-trunk to light a cigarette, inhaling the warm soothing smoke gratefully.

He walked under the tossing trees, and he remembered his own father, dying long ago in drunkenness. How many of us die, never knowing in this life the infinite love of God? How many of us die in the shadow of hell, choked by our contradictory hungers? He quickened his strides, limping slightly; the street-lights stippled leaf-shadows on the wet and glimmering street.

Above the plaza the skies had cleared in part, with a few stars, sharp and brittle as glass. Mother of Christ, comforter of the afflicted, intercede for us . . . The cold wind swept over the town toward the mountains and the darkness beyond; it lashed at the date palms along the path beaten on the grass and flapped the hem of his cassock about his trouser-legs as he hurried on to the rectory, to a warm supper, and afterwards, a book to read in his safe well-lighted room.

The clock in the stairwell struck the first hour of morning, and Don Ricardo hadn't died, although his eyes were closed now, and he breathed in weak, even puffs, only asleep, it seemed, without pain. They sat about the carved bed, Tony and his mother and Luis, awaiting the perhaps forceful, awe-inspiring transfiguration of death.

"I think he'll be like this for a long while yet," Luis said. "What do you think, Tony?"

He unclenched his fingers then and stood up, scraping his chair in a spasm of repugnance at the odors in the enclosed air, his brother's harassed expression, the drag of the night's waiting. At once he was contrite, avoiding his mother's gaze. He thought of going out for a smoke, hesitated, swallowed dryly, then went down the hall to another bedroom.

Light through the lattices checkered the ceiling and part of a wall with tiny, indistinct trapezoids. He found his cigarettes in the pocket of a shirt draped on a chair, lit one, and pushed open a window. The wind rushed in, moist and cold, slapping his face, instantly filling the room and ballooning the mosquito net. He shut the window, cursing.

"Tony ... "

"Did I wake you up?"

"No," his wife said. "I haven't slept ... Tony, is Papa——"

"No, nothing's happened. Now I wish that goddamned priest would——"

"Please—please don't swear, Tony."

Teresa got up out of the mosquito net and sat on the edge of the bed, beside him. Somewhere in the house a child began to cry and complain, and he heard his sister Nena scold sharply before the crying stopped and he could only hear the wind. With his slipper he ground his cigarette out on the floor. He thought, with an odd sympathy, of his work in the city, the usual clutter of papers on his desk, the monotonous clicking of typewriters around him. The wind blew in lengthening waves through the trees. His father, who beat his sons with an ivory cane, mercilessly ... Discipline! he could hear his father shouting now down the dark corridors of his memory: that, and the obsessions they never shared, would be all that he would ever remember of him, his father: he was dying, speechless forever, and they would never know one another.

He reached for Teresa's hand, pulsing and warm, alive.

"Manuel and I used to sleep in this room," he said, recalling his other brother, the rebellious one who had dared to defy and strike their father; remembering the nights of boyhood in this room, their conversations, the clarity of all their impossible dreams.

A spell of memory and bitterness brooded in him like the pain of a huge defeat. His father would die, his friends and his enemies would come to pay their last respects; the ruined body would be buried in a ceremony befitting a noble citizen, a former governor of the province; perhaps with speeches even and a band, in the midday sun or in the rain. The road to the cemetery would be muddy this time of year, the season of the rains, littered with horse-dung, the pigs wallowing in the black waters of the canals. The unknown, unknowable end of this love and hate, this joy and despair; the brief time of man upon the earth. He felt Teresa's hand, real and immediate, stroking his tired shoulder, in the half-darkness, and she was saying his name, over and over, "Tony, oh Tony," as if it were a lament.

He pulled her blindly against him and held her tight in a desolation of grief and anger, hiding his face in the thick mass of her hair, twisting the swell of her body against him. He called her name with an inward sobbing, seeking only the living warmth of her body away and above the moment now, away from the house and all other transient things. But she fought to escape his grasp and she freed herself, tearing the sleeve of her night-gown, and she backed away against the wall.

"You—you don't have any respect. You are a beast! You are *heartless* . . . "

The loud ferocity of her whispers surprised him, stunned him like a blow. They stood facing each other, breathing hard in the pale darkness.

"Is that *all* you ever——" She faltered. "Oh Tony," she said, "why must you be this way? *This* night?"

Something confused and lonely and cruel in his heart burned brightly for a moment, then crumbled into ash. "I'm sorry," he said. "I didn't mean to—Teresa, I'm sorry. . . . "

Luis was calling him. He remained standing still in his numbness, before he turned about and walked to the other room, un-hurriedly, with the incredible slowness of the motions in a dream, knowing already that his father was dead. Teresa followed close after him, searching for him. His mother was praying the Litany of the Dead, her voice small and brave through the wind blowing in the vast skies of dawn with the sound of mysterious wings; and he knelt, not so much in sorrow for his father as for all the living and the unborn.

Dada

As he went up the stairs he felt the old fear return. There was a dryness in his throat and his hand sliding along the banister left wet imprints on the polished wood.

He had not wanted to come. There was that leaden weight within him when his mother had said he was well enough now to meet his uncle. He had thought up evasions, had put up various subterfuges, and when these did not avail him, had pitted a stolid stubborn front against his mother's nagging insistence. But she had been equally stubborn. Through the years, he did not remember a time when she had not had her way with him. However headstrong he might have been, she always won her point, always routed his resistance, so that in the end, his will broken, and the fortress of his desire battered down, a cold shuddering sensation would force him to say the one conciliatory word that stopped his torment. Such scenes with his mother left him shaken. That cold shuddering sensation would be the precursor to a strangling fit that turned him in one staggering moment into a mute. And when under such a fit the need to speak arose because his mother, unaware of his anguish, had spoken to him and he must needs answer her, the words would come limping out of his mouth in the gaspy stuttering whine of an imbecile. At such times his mother's eyes narrowed to a steely glare and with her strong thin arms akimbo, she would taunt him with her strident: "Idiot! Can't you talk straight?" And she would bring about his utter annihilation with her grotesque mimicry of his splintered speech: "Ah-ah-ah-ah . . . !" until hatred for her would so well up in him that the explosive desire to wreak violence would stir his hands to trembling.

"Don't be a baby," his mother whispered to him as she followed him up the stairs. "Speak up to him and tell him outright the things I told you to say. Make him listen to you. You're old enough now to demand his attention. Talk straight and don't be a baby."

At the top of the stairs he wiped his sweating hands, moistened his lips. Behind him he felt his mother's hand straighten his shirt collar, heard her emphatic whisper in his ear: "Do as I told you."

From where she was playing with her paper dolls on the Persian rug, his cousin Silawahnti looked up at them in calm wonder, her round eyes black buttons on the thin fabric of her face.

"Mummee-e-e, Mummee-e-e-e," the little girl rose and ran into the kitchen. "Luisa is here with Rama."

His aunt Jhamna came out of the kitchen wiping her floury hands on a towel. Among the Hindu women he had known, she was the most nearly Caucasian in color and features. She was tall, slender, upright as a reed, had auburn hair which she wore in fat twin plaits behind her head; and she had hazel eyes and a spray of freckles on her face and arms which deepened her complexion to a most becoming beige. Draped around her shoulders and trailing to the floor was a large white cambric stole (which when the moment called for it became the characteristic veil, the symbol of reverence all Hindu women wore in the presence of their menfolk). One side of her beak-like nose was pierced. The tiny eyelet was at the moment bared of its diamond stud which, were she dressed up, would lie embedded there, small and glittering. On her wrists she wore a loose cluster of thin gold bangles.

She bade them be seated on the low capacious chairs grouped around the glass-topped table on the center of the huge red Persian carpet that covered the living room floor. When his aunt Jhamna sat down, she drew up a trousered leg, rested the ball of her foot on the edge of the chair, leaned an elbow on the apex of her drawn-up knee, and in the course of their conversation, gently swung her sandal that hung by a thong on her big right toe.

He noticed that his aunt Jhamna drew up her veil over her head as she sat opposite him, and the full import of her action as it swiftly dawned on him caused a sharp flicker of shyness, inferiority, self-consciousness, to clutch at his already suffering ego so that he felt constrained to lower his eyes and fix his gaze vacantly on the folded newspaper at the glass-topped table. She had never before covered her head solely in his presence, had never before looked at him with this new intentness, this utterly confusing attention, this new respect as from one adult to another and she had never before addressed him by his full name Ramchand as she did now. So that there was that one second of stupefied awareness when his aunt Jhamna in her high hoarsey voice said: "Aré, Ramchand, how are you?"

He shifted his gaze from the table to his aunt's smiling face now framed like a madonna's in the thin white veil, swallowed and gave her a sly, lank smile. "Fine," he said.

His aunt Jhamna turned to his mother. There was a gently teasing humor in her cold-husky voice when she spoke, "Aré, Luisa, now you have a big boy. Soon he marry, then what you do? You like him marry Indian girl? Or you like him marry Filipino girl? What you like?"

His mother suggested that his aunt Jhamna ask him the question herself and determine his preference.

His aunt Jhamna turned to him again, and in the scant English she had learned from her husband, his uncle Vassanmal, she said, her gold bangles jingling thinly as she swept her arm out in a large gesture of admonition: "Filipino girl no good. Talk too much. Go out alone. Maybe fight with mother-in-law. Maybe fight with husband. But Indian girl good. She no talk too much. No fight mother-in-law. No fight husband. Can sew. Can cook. She bring you big dowry. Then you have money to open store. What you say?"

Both his aunt Jhamna and his mother turned on him the combined barrage of their appraisal, awaiting his answer; his aunt's, with that new attention and respect he found so disturbing; his mother's, with her possessive proprietary air that always made him squirm and which always loosed within him a hot swift tide of resentment against her.

"I don't know," he finally said, flushing under their probing stares.

His aunt Jhamna's freckles stood out clearly in the tiny mounds of her cheeks now raised in a smile of amusement suddenly widening and breaking into a gale of wheezy mirth. The little girl, Silawahnti, barefoot and in red silk trousers and yellow tunic, leaned inside the parenthesis of his aunt Jhamna's thighs, looking at him with dark wondering eyes, her lips convolved about a dirty thumb. Amused tolerance softened his mother's eyes but there lingered about her firmly set mouth the taint of smug triumph.

Then his mother snapped her fan open and while she employed it she launched, in broken English so his aunt would readily understand, into a spirited account of his recent, almost fatal bout with pneumonia. His mother was a large spare-boned woman with small restless eyes and a firmly set mouth sharp like an old knife grown thin with use. Her face had gone slack with the encroachment of age, and her neck was long and flabby like the pitiable obscene throat of an unfledged bird. She wore her hair bobbed, allowed herself the illusion of make-up which somehow was not incongruous with her thighs and legs which were well-preserved and had remained through the years firm and rounded and virginal.

His aunt Jhamna listened, asked questions, from time to time glanced at him. Meanwhile, he had opened the folded newspaper on the glass-topped table and had desperately tried to engross himself in its contents.

"You no more sick?" his aunt asked him, her hazel eyes soft like a doe's.

He was startled when his mother jarred with her fan the paper he was reading and in dialect snapped at him. "Pay attention when you're spoken to!"

He lowered his paper and hastily smoothed out the consternation from his face.

His aunt Jhamna's hazel eyes slanted, crinkled in their corners as she laughingly repeated her question.

"I'm all right now," he said, the words coming out low, depleted of their vocal force from squeezing past a parched, constricted throat. Catching the grim look in his mother's eyes, he lowered his gaze to the paper on his lap.

His mother snapped her fan in a weary, impatient gesture of disgust and said, her voice shrill with held-back anger: "He's very stubborn. Very hard-headed. Only likes reading. Always, always reading." Her face worked with exasperation and folding her fan with a snap, exclaimed: "I don't know what more to do with him."

His aunt Jhamna lowered her foot from the edge of her chair and discovering that Silawahnti was sucking her thumb, slapped the child's hand away and hoarsely chided her daughter: "How many times I told you no put finger in mouth? You also hard-headed like Ramchand? *Halá*, go! Go take bath now! Tell Felisa give you bath!"

Silawahnti wriggled her toes on the Persian rug and made no move to go.

"If you no take bath," his aunt continued, "Dada get angry and Dada no take you in auto to Luneta this afternoon."

Silawahnti considered this, then quickly turning on her heels, she scampered to the kitchen shouting as she ran: "Felisa, you give me bath now. I go Luneta this afternoon."

"Foolish child!" His aunt Jhamna told his mother. "Also very hard-headed. Even I beat her sometimes she still hard-headed."

"Beating is good for children." His mother's tone was firmly authoritative. "They never behave unless you beat them. Look at Rama. When he makes me very angry I still beat him."

"Yes?" A husky chuckle gurgled in his aunt Jhamna's throat. "Suppose he have wife, you still beat him?"

"Why not?" His mother's tone bristled with righteousness. "Even if he has wife, he's still my son."

"Oh yes." Then leaning toward him, her bangles again jingling thinly in her series of admonitory gestures, his aunt Jhamna said: "Aré, Ramchand! You always obey mother. You be good boy. Mother make sacrifice for you. Many sacrifice she make. When your father die she no marry again because she afraid maybe new husband no love you same like true son. She afraid maybe new husband beat you. Always happen. Even in India. So your mother make sacrifice . . . no more marry . . . always take good care of you . . . make many sacrifice when you sick . . ."

"That's true." His mother's voice went crumbly with tears. "He never will know all the suffering I've gone through bringing him up after his father died . . . when he was barely six months old. I always tell him: Even if his body were cut into a thousand pieces he never will be able to repay what it cost me to bear him and raise him into a decent boy."

"So you must love mother. You always be good boy," his aunt Jhamna said. Then as an afterthought, she asked, "You love mother?"

He was acutely ill at ease. His stomach was hot, tight with embarrassment. It was all he could do to manage a soft "Of course" from a throat and mouth arid with shame.

As his mother further related the details of his illness, her voice became by turns whining with self-pity, petulant with grief, somber with martyrdom.

Try as he would he could not avoid hearing all that was said, and what he heard brought a faint roaring in his ears, hot flushes racing through his body. He was sick with shame at his mother's volubly remembered instances of his obstinacy and her consequent distress on their account. He raised the newspaper he was reading so that it hid him from the two women in the room.

"Now, he's well." His mother's voice contained a contrary note of hopeless resignation as if his being well were not at all what she had wished. "Doctor said give him special kind of food. To make him strong. He is thin, you see. And still he takes injections. And that cost money. We have not as yet paid the doctor. And the hospital." Over the rim of his paper, he saw his mother; the turned-down corners of her sharp mouth gave her care-worn face a tragic cast.

His aunt Jhamna became bothered with her sniffles and searching for a corner of her cambric stole, blew her nose on it.

"What time will Dada come?"

"Maybe twelve. Maybe one o'clock. Today Sunday. They fixing store, putting new *estante*. Maybe new goods come this afternoon."

His aunt Jhamna rose from her chair, adjusted the cambric stole about her shoulders, hunted for one sandal that had somehow wedged itself under her chair. She pulled it out with her foot, slipped it on, and turning to his mother said, "Better I finish making *pan* now. By and by Dada come. If *pan* not yet make, he angry." Her hazel eyes took on a glint of mischief. "Maybe he beat me also, no, Ramchand?" She arched her neck back, snuffling out her rustling laughter at him. "Come, Luisa. I have buttermilk in ice box. I give you for Ramchand." She approached him at the same time pulling the veil over her head so that when, feeling her close presence, he looked up at her, he saw her head entirely covered with that symbol of reverence as if he were a man fully grown and in accordance with strict dictates of her caste she must needs defer to his superior position. "You like buttermilk, Ramchand?"

Slightly flushing, he met her gaze, softly said, "Yes, Jhamna."

She turned and while she walked to the kitchen she said, "You wait and Luisa bring you buttermilk. You be big boy now. You be good. No make mother angry. She make many sacrifice for you," she added, her voice coming to him, remote, from the kitchen.

He had drunk his buttermilk, eaten *pakhorra* and drunk ice water copiously to relieve his mouth of its peppery sting, read and yawned many times through the one newspaper on the glass-topped table when at precisely a quarter of two o'clock he heard the car arrive, heard the metallic slam of its door, the noisy babel in Sindhi floating up the stairwell, the leathery scrape of shoes on the stair treads.

He had a moment of quick terror until he remembered to hold the newspaper before his panic-stricken face and spare himself the cold impact of greeting any of the arrivals. He felt them enter the room, felt their actual bodily nearness slap at his senses, felt the room saturated with their oily pungent foreign talk.

Over the top of his newspaper he discerned his uncle Vassanmal's swarthy round head pass by, and, remembering his mother's stern injunctions, he manfully surmounted his panic and threw in his uncle's direction what he intended to be a casually affectionate "Hello, Dada," but what instead came out as an inaudible, abortive croak-like mumble. Almost at once he saw himself impaled on the spear of his terror, felt his stomach contract in a series of shuddery tremors.

"Aré, Mr. Ramchand, how are you?"

The voice was deep, throaty, bland with the spurious geniality of the subtly obsequious Indian salesman who comes to a customer with a silky smile and a "What can I do for you, Miss? Is there anything I can show you in the way of rayon, silk, satin?" The boy looked up into the droll beaming face of Mr. Krishinchand Lalchand seated beside Mr. Sehwani Bhagwani on the sofa opposite him, the two of them accompanied by their wives, having come with his uncle Vassanmal obviously for Sunday dinner. They were large, portly men with paunchy middles; dark-visaged, thick-necked, and their wives, big handsome women swathed in yards and yards of silk *sari*, were likewise sleek and fat. The two men visitors owned the two Indian bazars adjoining his Uncle's "Taj Mahal Silk Emporium" on the Escolta. The arrivals, aside from the two couples who were guests, included the three Indian salesmen apprenticed to his uncle's store, his cousin Shewakram who was a young man of twenty, and Arjhani, his uncle Vassanmal's only son, age five.

He knew them all and they in turn remembered him from the small chubby boy they had seen through the years lagging behind the heels of a large spare-boned dour-faced woman who jerked him out front whenever he had the tendency in the presence of strangers to disappear behind her skirt. They had twitted the small boy with the round dark eyes that looked at you as if he might at any moment burst into tears, had tweaked his nose, waggled his cheeks, balanced bits of a broken toothpick on his long upcurving lashes, swung him up in the air by his armpits until he fairly shrieked with terror, stuffed him with candies, a bit of money, and mechanical toys during Christmas, inveigled him to stay with them (*Aré, Rami! Better you stay with us. No more go home to Luisa. You stay and we take you to India. You like go India?*), teased his mother by hiding him behind show cases, behind bales of goods inside empty crates, until he gave himself away by bawling out loud, "Mama! Mama!"

He could feel them all looking at him, seeing a pale thin slat of a boy, his dark eyes rounder than ever but no longer seeming at any moment to burst into tears, now inscrutable rather and deep with only a trace of his boyhood chubbiness remaining on his lean hard cheeks now blotched with the eruptions of adolescent acne.

"What you do? You big boy now. You open store or you study more? Maybe you have sweetheart now, ha? When you marry?" Mr. Krishinchand Lalchand enjoyed his joke hugely, and the fat smirk across his shiny face gave him the aspect of a coarse billiken. The others in the room snickered deliciously like a pack of dark horses whinnying.

At dinner the two men visitors continued to discuss him with his uncle Vassanmal. As was customary, the men sat down to dinner first, his uncle at the head of the table, the two men visitors next, then the three Indian salesmen, his uncle's nephew Shewakram, himself, and at the foot of the table, the little boy Arjhani (perched on his high chair) whom his mother was trying to feed. His aunt Jhamna with the maid Felisa in her wake shuttled back and forth between the kitchen and the table, ladling out platters of the spice-fragrant thick-gravied foods, passing around bottles of ice water, replenishing the rapidly emptied bread platters with stacks of piping-hot *pan* wet with lard.

He watched the diners tear small chunks of *pan*, shape these into tiny cornucopias, dip these into the gravy saucers before them, scoop up gravy and pieces of goat meat and chuck the succulent morsels into their mouths; and the moist tongue-lapping sounds of their eating—*ptak-ptchak, ptak-ptchak, ptak-ptchak*—were, he thought, kin to the splashy gustatory sounds in a sty.

He did not understand Sindhi very well but occasionally he was able to grasp the gist of a sentence, the essence of their talk about him, and what he heard turned the food in his mouth into wads of thick fuzzy wool. It was a pity, the two men visitors said, clucking their tongues, that his uncle Vassanmal had sadly neglected the boy's upbringing. With the proper coaching in Sindhi reading and writing and a bit of fattening up, he would undoubtedly turn into as fine a specimen of young Hindu manhood as any young buck born and raised in India, and would command no less a handsome dowry in the Indian marriage mart.

He became aware of the three Indian salesmen teasing him with their eyes like black velvet swatches in the thin pasteboard of their faces. Across the table from him, his cousin Shewakram sniggered salaciously and ground a shoe on his foot under the table. He swung his leg in a vicious kick, stubbing his toe on the hard edge of the other's chair, and as he chafed at his futile retaliation, he saw Shewakram lifting the corners of his grease-coated lips in a grin of triumph.

The diners gorged themselves, and he saw a beatific expression like a brooding Buddha's spread over his uncle's face as he hoisted his mammoth pot-belly, shifted his weight on one buttock, and slowly, casually, matter-of-factly, broke wind. The others exhaled fat zestful belches and rose from the table.

At the lavatory he waited until everybody had finished washing their hands, rinsed their mouths, before he moved toward it. As he did so, he saw Shewa deliberately taking his own sweet time about soaping his hands. He stood to one side of Shewa, prepared to wait patiently for his turn and was indeed startled when Shewa, by inserting a finger in the tap nozzle, directed a taut squirt of water at him, catching him pointblank on the belly. Facing him, Shewa smiled wickedly, and hurrying past him, flicked the drops of water from his still wet hands into the boy's astonished face. As Rama washed his hands clean of their goaty smell, his thwarted anger stirred them to trembling, twitched his jaws in a quivery spasm.

"*Now!*" his mother said over his shoulder as he dried his hands on a towel hung on a nail above the washbowl. "There he goes into his room. Follow him, plant yourself squarely before him so he'll have no reason to ignore you. Tell him outright the things I told you to say. Catch his attention for he'll soon be sitting down at the card table and you know that once he's there, not even cannon shot can dislodge him. Make him understand, talk straight, and don't be a baby. Get results or you'd better take care when we return home. Better take care!" She left him then, for his aunt Jhamna was calling her to come to dinner.

He walked into the living room, saw that Krishinchand Lalchand and Sehwani Bhagwani were setting up the card table. Lhadu, the eldest of the three Indian salesmen, was mixing brandy and soda at the cellarette beside the cabinet radio, while the others were sprawled on chairs, leisurely picking their teeth. Shewakram, with one leg flung over the arm of his chair, was intent on the movie page of the newspaper, now and then rooting into the inner corner of his thigh where apparently the soft plump worm of his sex was snagged upon the crotch of his tight trousers. The boy waited until he was sure no one was paying him the least attention and then, swiftly crossing the living room, entered his uncle Vassanmal's room.

As he paused on the threshold, he felt his stomach tighten. His uncle Vassanmal, like a gross idol, was sitting on his bed, one leg bent and raised upon a knee. Slowly, his uncle leaned forward and unlaced a shoe which dropped on the floor. He raised his other foot and in the same laborious manner unlaced and shucked the shoe off, thumping it on the floor. He then emitted a faint belch after which he rested his hands on his hammy thighs as he worked his toes up and down inside their brown silk socks. It was then his uncle noticed him leaning there by the doorjamb and his uncle spoke across the room to him in a natural perfunctory tone: "*Aré*, Rama, how're you?"

With marked diffidence, the boy walked into the room, stopped by a chair beside the round table with the crocheted lace tablecloth, watched his uncle wheeze as his enormous potbelly pressed on the edge of the bed while he leaned over to peel off his socks, then tenderly rub his bunions. He was of middle height but enormously fat so that his bloated torso and mammoth potbelly were in grotesque contrast to his rather small-calved spindly legs. Still discernible on his swarthy face were the ravages of smallpox he once had many years ago, the pockmarks no longer distinct but shallow and blurred by time. His black slick hair, austerely brushed down, hugged his head in the round clasp of a skullcap and fringed the edge of his narrow brow with a tiny fluted curl. His face was broad, his mouth wide, and the high ridge of his nose dominated the landscape of his face like a mountain peak.

As he watched his uncle wipe his toes with his socks, he felt the desire to speak erupt within him like a shooting geyser. He must have sputtered an involuntary mumble, for his uncle looked up at him and said, still quite perfunctorily: "You go to school?"

The boy's tenseness, like boiling liquid when the heat is lessened, ebbed a little and he was glad for this release of tension, for this brief respite from the fear that his uncle, as he had habitually done in the past, would leave to him the sole burden of their conversation while maintaining, as he struggled and suffered the damnation of the chronic stutterer, a cold stoic silence. His fear of meeting his uncle had stemmed from those excruciating moments in the past when he had stood before him mute and tongue-tied, a welter of words stillborn on the threshold of his lips, while the other regarded him with an impassive stare and did not by so much as a gesture, a look, a word, ease the torment that clotted in his belly like tangled twine. *Now* his uncle had spoken to him *first*, wanted to know if he went to school, was kind, was generous, was altogether not the hard, mean, avaricious bogeyman of his childhood fancy; oh, he'd been wrong, now all that would be *past*, his uncle would speak to him, would have sympathy, would above all understand how it was, how it is with a chronic stutterer who every waking moment of his day must strain and struggle and try to break away from the crippling tenacious strands of shyness, inferiority, self-consciousness that hamstrung him and made of him a suffering prisoner.

He managed a clumsy smile and when he replied, his voice, at first unsteady and quavering, became more natural, normal, even warm towards the end of his little speech. "No, Dada, we have no school. We are on vacation since March. School will open in June, next month. Then I'll . . . I'll be fourth year. I got 92 average. That is second highest. The first is 94. She's a girl. Teacher said maybe if I study more I can be first in class."

He watched his uncle wheeze again as he leaned over and tried to hunt for his slippers under the bed. "You find slippers, Rama, I think they go there . . . in corner, there!"

The boy was glad for this preoccupation. He had long wanted to move; standing there by the chair was making him feel absurd, only he didn't quite know how to manage any movement without attracting attention, without appearing awkward. He always felt glad whenever he could be of use to anybody even if it were only in doing the least little thing. If only people kept asking him to do something for them instead of, as often happened, staring at him and what was most intolerable, trying to make fun of him and speaking to him as if he were a dimwit or a child! He walked over to the bed, crouched on his hands and knees, and thrusting an arm under the bed, reached for the slippers that lay there against the wall. He dropped the sandals before his uncle's feet and shyly sat himself on the edge of the bed. Now that he was closer to his uncle, his fear was no longer as potent as before; in fact it had almost completely disappeared, and he was only hoping that their relation could stay forever thus, without terror, closer, more congenial.

His uncle rose from the bed and the sudden release of his
enormous weight shot the bedsprings upward into position
bouncing the boy on his back. He laughed, scrambling to his
feet, and quickly looked at his uncle to see if he had noticed
his momentary discomfiture. Apparently he hadn't for he was
at the moment standing before his clothes bureau rummaging in
its drawers. His uncle pulled out pyjama trousers and a house
shirt, slung these over one shoulder, started unbuckling his belt.
He dropped his trousers to the floor, shook loose the silk pyjamas
and stooped over to step into these. His uncle wore no under-
wear and the sight of his swollen half-nudity made the boy turn
away and study the linear pattern on the chenille bedspread.
When he looked up again his uncle was clad in wide loose silk
pyjamas over which his pin stripe silk house shirt hung to his
knees. He watched his uncle grunt and stoop over to pick up his
trousers and empty the pockets of balled dirty handkerchiefs,
keys, loose bills, coins, receipts, swatches of men's suiting, a but-
ton, string, a checkbook which he tossed on the lace-covered
round table.

The boy remained seated on the bed with his knees crossed,
swinging one foot in an attempt at nonchalance while deep
down, tiny licking tongues of panic swept inward from the outer
fringes of his well-being. Between his uncle and himself there
had been silence perhaps for the better part of five minutes, and
the thought that if he didn't quickly think of something to say
next, this silence would rise like a flood and submerge him completely into a vortex of speechlessness, tormented him because
he now knew as well as if the other had explicitly told him that
his uncle had nothing more to say to him, would not attempt
anything else to say to him, was in fact, as was his habit in the
past, ignoring him, snubbing him, as a Brahmin a pariah. The
simmer of anger in him clove his tongue to the roof of his
parched mouth. Words started seething inside him, clamoring
for release, for utterance, for spitting out against an injustice
he felt was being done him. He started taking deep breaths to
still his violently agitated heart and retain a measure of calm

with which to speak out his mind clearly, lay out his plea coherently, manfully. He was no longer a child. His aunt Jhamna had covered her head in his presence, the Messrs. Krishinchand Lalchand and Sehwani Bhagwani, including their wives, thought him mature enough to warrant speculations, his mother was now even more hysterically careful about his making acquaintances with girls; no, he was no longer a child. His uncle had better realize the fact here, now, at once.

He watched his uncle seated at the lace-covered round table appearing to balance the stubs in his checkbook. After several false starts in his mind, he managed to blurt out: "Dada, I . . . I . . . I've been sick. I've been sick with pneumonia. I stayed in hospital for three weeks. Doctor said my illness serious." He paused to lick his dry lips, and suddenly frightened at the lengthening silence, hurtled on, impelled with the notion to let the momentum of his excitement push out everything he had to say. "D-d-doctor said if I not careful I'll have p-p-pleurisy. I'm all right now but I take injections. We have n-n-not yet paid the doctor and the hospital. Mama already paid part but there's still a balance of ninety pesos. Mama said you please give me the money including the thirty pesos for tuition and books I need next month. So next month I no bother you again. That makes a total of one hundred twenty pesos in all. Mama said you please give me because doctor is waiting and she is ashamed."

Halfway in his speech his uncle looked up, turned to him, hitching his armpit over the back of his chair. "Aré, Rama," his uncle said in a voice only a little less loud than a shout. The tone made the boy wince for he did not wish the people in the living room to know the nature of his talk with his uncle. "I have idea for you . . . Nice idea I have for you. What grade you now, ha?"

"I just finished third year. Next month in June, I'll start the fourth year."

"No use going back school. I have better idea for you. You stop school. You work for me. I send you Zamboanga with Lhadu. I open branch there. You have nice house, nice food, nice clothes. You no more sick. I tell Lhadu give you small money for cinema, for ice cream. Luisa stay here. She can go here every month, get small money. What you say?"

All the food he had eaten turned into a grey blubbery lump that weighted him down, inclined him on the brink of nausea. He sat dumbfounded staring at his uncle who stared back at him, his mammoth potbelly resting between his thighs, looking now more than ever like a toad. When he was a child, he had regarded his uncle's belly with awe, remembering a remark heard from his mother that if you pierced his uncle's stomach and slashed a hole therein, the money his uncle had seized from his father when the latter died would come tumbling out like pennies from a slot machine.

"B-b-but I can't stop now. This is my last year. I have to finish high school to go to college."

"Study? Study? Why you always study? What you like? Become governor-general of Philippines?"

"I must go to college to study medicine. I-I-I want to be a doctor."

"Why you want to be doctor? That crazy idea. Always doctor, always lawyer. No attend to business. What I do with doctor? Many doctors poor people, no make money. Why you want be like that?"

The boy squirmed on the bed, cast his eyes down, toyed with his fingers, cracking them one by one.

"I no study," his uncle continued. "I finish only third grade in India. I make good business. I work hard. Why you no do the same? In Zamboanga you learn little Sindhi. Then later you go India. Learn some more reading, writing. Then you marry. I arrange for you. Maybe you get ten thousand, fifteen thousand rupees dowry. I keep money for you. Maybe I make you partner in business. What more you like? You own half store, half mine. You have money, you live nice. What more you want?"

He was sick, miserable, and it was a struggle to say this: "D-d-doctors also get to make a lot of money."

His uncle looked at him sharply. "Where you get money for

study?" His uncle's tone was low, packed with muffled thunder.

Inside the boy's head, his thoughts ran like frightened mice. He had a desperate time of it trying to collect them, to align them in one convincing rebuttal. "I-I-I get money from you. Bef-bef-fore, you promised you send me through school."

"*I* no have money." His uncle rose from the chair, lumbered toward the clothes bureau where he tossed the checkbook into a drawer. "What you think I am, millionaire?"

"But—but Dada, I need one hundred twenty pesos now for doctor and school——"

"I no have money. I give you twenty pesos, that enough. When you go home, you get from Jhamna. I tell her give you twenty pesos. *I* no millionaire."

From the living room the bland throaty voice of Mr. Krish-inchand Lalchand rose in a shout for his uncle, "*Aré*, Vassu,"—the boy caught the gist of the Sindhi words—"You hurry up if we are going to play. Also bring a new deck of cards, will you?"

Now panic gripped him. In a moment his uncle would waddle out of the room, leaving him and his plea for money washed dry like wreckage in the tide of their argument. He had to think fast, speak fast, try to hold his uncle's attention a little longer. Words hurled themselves against the gates of his mind, and he became frantic with worry, fear, panic, that he would never be able to use them, unleash them to assist him, avenge him. But his throat and mouth were again dry, and speech became an effort, strenuous and tiring.

"But—but—but Dada, I need the money b-b-badly. This is my last—last—last year in school. I have to finish that."

"You hard-headed," his uncle said, rummaging in his bureau drawers for a pack of cards. "Luisa spoil you. She teach you wrong things. *I* give you nice idea but you hard-headed. *I* no have money to give you. *I* have many expense. *I* pay house rent, store rent, *I* pay salary. Why *I* give you money? Why *I* always give you?"

"Be—beb—because—because——" His heart was thumping faster. He wondered whether he had the nerve to say what his

mother had coached him to say if his uncle proved difficult. "Be
—beb—because it's much more mine than it is yours. It's my
father's money!"

His uncle slowly turned and fixed him across the room with
a black flashing glare.

His audacity surprised him, and curiously enough, it gave him
a pervading sense of calm. As from afar he heard his voice say,
slowly, distinctly, with dreamy languor, "It's my . . . father's . . .
money . . . you . . . stole . . . it . . . when . . . he . . . died." An
impulse cranked him to say it, like a record needle caught in a
groove, softly, dreamily—"s-s-stole it . . . s-s-stole it . . . s-s-stole
it . . ."

The slap jarred his head back. His cheeks burned and his
head rang with the force of the blow.

His mind screamed: *You hog! You toad! You thief! It's true!
You took over Papa's store when he died, took his money, that's
why you promised the lawyer you'd support us . . . send me
through school . . .* But his mouth said: "Mh . . . mh . . . mh . . .
mh . . .," the whimpery syllables borne on shuddery gusts of
breath that escaped through locked teeth.

His uncle towered over him, hunched there on the bed, one
hand raised to his cheek now radiating heat like a flat iron. For
a minute his uncle looked at him with scorn, then turned and
walked away. Halfway across the room his uncle whirled, spat
an Indian obscenity at him, thrust a beefy hand toward him,
its fingers stretched apart, the thumb pointed downward—the
whole brown hand seemingly a fat obscene spider dangling in
the air. His uncle regarded him once more, then picking up a
deck of cards from the drawer, walked slowly out of the room.

Hunched there on the bed, he felt cold perspiration break
out on his brow, felt his blood roar and recede and scamper
innerwards to a cold leaden core somewhere in his belly. The
sensation was like a foot going to sleep, only this time, magnified
to the height and breadth of his whole body. The palms of his
hands itched and he felt a bowel movement coming on.

When his mother entered the room and confronted him

with her "Well, what did he say? What did he say?" he swung his stricken face to her and, as his bleary senses made out her sharp features thrust before him like a blade, there dropped out of his mouth, like the whir of an unraveled spring in a snapped mechanical toy, the dry gaspy splintered whine of idiot syllables.

BIENVENIDO N. SANTOS

The Day the Dancers Came

As soon as Fil woke up, he noticed a whiteness outside, quite unusual for a morning in November. That fall, Chicago was sandman's town, sleepy valley, drowsy gray, slumbrous mistiness from sun up till noon when the clouds drifted away in cauliflower clusters and suddenly it was evening. The lights shone on the avenues like soiled lamps centuries old and the skyscrapers became monsters with a thousand sore eyes. But now, there was a brightness in the air and Fil knew what it was and he shouted, "Snow! It's snowing!"

Tony, who slept in the adjoining room, was awakened.

"What's that?" he asked.

"It's snowing," Fil said, peering at the swirling flakes and smiling as if he had ordered this and was satisfied with the prompt delivery. "Oh, they'd love this, they'd love this," he repeated.

From the bedroom came the sound of shattered springs, a deaf, battered accordion of sagging coils.

"Who'd love what?" Tony's voice came after the battery.

When Fil did not answer, Tony asked again, his voice now raised in annoyance.

"The dancers, of course," Fil answered, facing the bedroom. "They're arriving today. Maybe they've already arrived. And they'll see this snow and walk in it. It will be their first snow, I'm sure. Now they have something to remember about Chicago."

"How do you know it didn't snow in New York while they were there?" Tony asked, his words coming through the squeak and creak of thoroughly punished springs.

255

"Snow in New York in early November?" Fil said. "Are you crazy?"

"Who's crazy?" Tony replied. "Ever since you heard of those dancers from the Philippines coming to Chicago, you've been acting nuts. Loco. As if they're coming here just for you."

Tony chuckled.

Hearing it, Fil blushed. Perhaps it was true that he had been acting too eager ever since he had learned that the dancers were coming to Chicago from New York, but he couldn't help feeling the way he did. Tony had said it—it felt that way, as if the dancers were coming to Chicago specially for him.

Filemon Acayan, Filipino, was fifty, a U.S. citizen. He was a corporal in the U.S. Army, training at San Luis Obispo, California, on the day he was discharged honorably, in 1945, and one of thousands like him for whom the war ended abruptly that day in August after Hiroshima and who never had the chance to fight for the homeland. Instead, a few months later, he got his citizenship papers. Thousands of them, smart and small in their uniform, stood at attention in drill formation, in the scalding sun, and pledged allegiance to the flag and the republic for which it stands, their voices like a prayer recited in unison during the Eucharist at the Luneta. Soon after, he got back to work. To a new citizen, work meant many places and many ways, factories, hospitals and hotels, tending a rose garden and a hundred-year-old veteran of a border war, waiter and cook, and several odd jobs that bore no names. Now he was a special policeman in the post office. He had had pictures taken of himself in uniform with the blouse a bit too loose and long, looking like a musician, a doorman, salvation army bugler, anything but special policeman.

He was a few years younger than Tony—Antonio Bataller, a retired Pullman porter—but he looked older in spite of the fact that Tony had been bedridden most of the time for the last two years, suffering from a kind of wasting disease that had intrigued doctors. All over Tony's body, a gradual peeling was taking place. At first he thought it was merely tinea flava, a skin disease common among adolescents in the Philippines. It had started around the neck and now affected his extremities. His face looked as if it was healing from severe burns. Nevertheless, it was a young face, much younger than Fil's, who had never looked young.

"I'm becoming a white man," Tony had said once, chuckling softly.

It was the same chuckle Fil seemed to have heard now, but this was derisive, insulting.

Fil said, "I know who's nuts. It's the sick guy with the sick thoughts. You don't care for nothing but your pain, your imaginary pain."

"You're the imagining fellow. I got the real thing," Tony shouted from the room. He believed he had something worse than the whiteness spreading on his skin. There was a pain in his insides, like dull scissors scraping his intestines. Cancer. Angrily, he added, "What for I got retired?"

"You're old, man, old, that's what, and sick, yes, but not cancer," Fil said, turning toward the snow-filled sky. He pressed his face against the glass window. There's about an inch now on the ground, he thought, maybe more.

Tony had come out of the room, looking as if he had not slept all night. "I know it is," he said, as if it were an honor and a privilege to die of cancer and Fil was trying to deprive him of it. "Never a pain like this. One day, I'm just gonna die."

"Naturally. Who says you won't?" Fil argued, thinking how wonderful it would be if he could join the company of dancers from the Philippines, show them around, walk with them in the snow, watch their eyes as they stared about them, answer their questions, tell them everything they wanted to know about the changing seasons in this strange land. They would pick up fistfuls of snow, crunch it in their fingers or shove it into their mouths, as he did himself the first time, long, long ago, remembering the grated ice the Chinese sold in the store near the town plaza where he played *tatching* with an elder brother who, later, drowned in a sudden squall. How his mother had grieved over that death, who had not cried too much when his father died, a broken man. Now they were all gone, after a storm and suddenly, or lingeringly, in a season of drought, all, all of them he had loved. He continued, "All of us will die. One day. A medium bomb marked Chicago and this whole dump is *tapús*, finish. Who'll escape then?"

"Maybe your dancers will," Tony answered, now watching the snow himself. "I don't know what makes you so crazy about them."

"Of course, they will," Fil retorted, his voice sounding like a big assurance that all the dancers would be safe in his care. "The bombs won't be falling on this night. And when the dancers are back in the Philippines . . ."

Suddenly, he paused, as if he was no longer sure of what he was going to say. "But maybe, even in the Philippines the bombs gonna fall, no?" he said, gazing sadly at the falling snow.

"What's that to you?" Tony replied. "You got no more folks ove'der, right? I know it's nothing to me. I'll be dead before that."

"Let's talk about something nice," Fil said, the sadness spreading on his face as he tried to smile. "Tell me, how will I talk, how am I gonna introduce myself?"

He would go ahead with his plans. He was going to introduce himself to the dancers and volunteer to take them sight-seeing. His car was clean and ready for his guests. He had soaped the ashtrays, dusted off the floor boards and thrown away the old mats, replacing them with new plastic throw rugs. He had got himself soaking wet as he sprayed the car, humming as he worked. Bit by bit, stray songs from the islands came back to him. The dancers would sing and dance to these songs. He could sing broken phrases, unfinished bars. There were stretches of the forgotten between one phrase and another. Besides, popular songs he had since learned in America kept crowding out the songs of his country.

Fil shook his head as he waited for Tony to say something.

"Gosh, I wish I had your looks, even with those white spots, then I could face everyone of them," he said, "but this mug . . ."

"That's the important thing, your mug. It's your calling card. It says, Filipino. Countryman," Tony said.

"You're not fooling me, friend," Fil said. "This mug says, Ugly Filipino. It says, old-timer, *muchacho*. It says, Pinoy, *bejo*."

For Fil, time was the villain. In the beginning, the words he often heard were: too young, too young; but all of a sudden, too young became too old, too late. What had happened in between? A weariness, a mist covering all things. You don't have to look at your face in a mirror to know that you are old, suddenly old, grown useless for a lot of things and too late for all the lovely and splendid dreams you had wrapped up well against a day of need. The faces of all those you know had blended with other faces less familiar, strange.

When Fil worked as a menial in a hospital in Cook County, all day he touched filth and gore. He came home smelling of surgical soap and disinfectant. In the hospital, he took care of a row of bottles on a shelf, each bottle containing a stage of the human embryo in preservatives, from the lizard-like foetus of a few days, through the newly born infant, with the position unchanged, cold and cowering and afraid. Sometimes in his sleep, Fil dreamed of preserving the stages after infancy, but somewhere he drew a blank like the many years between too young and too old.

"It also says sucker," Tony was saying. "What for you want to invite them? Here? Aren't you ashamed of this hole?"

They had occupied the same apartment on West Sheridan Road for the past ten years and there had been no changes done or any repair made as if there was a tacit contest among all the apartments in the building as to which one was going to survive longest, untouched.

Tony had the bedroom to himself while Fil slept in the living room in a convertible bed. The carpet had lost its true color as if dust had settled on it permanently and had become imbedded in it, textured into a kind of loom where broken lines now stood for the design of what was once perhaps a pattern of beauty. Everything in the apartment was old, including the newspapers and magazines from the Philippines with dates as far back as ten years ago. The walls were eggshell bare except for a tiny crucifix which dropped on the floor every time the door swung against it with some force, but one of them always put it back.

The kitchen looked like an open closet with all sorts of deodorizers in open bottles and sprays. As soon as he woke up, Fil reached for the nearest one and began spraying the air as if a creature of decay had spawned stillbirths of stink during the night and these had to be removed.

On the kitchen wall was a shopping reminder with pegs and holes opposite spaces marked *salt*, *bread*, or whatever they needed. The pegs continually changed as various needs arose, except one opposite an article which Tony had added, pasting a piece of paper marked *Ligaya* on top of *starch*, which they never used. Ligaya is a girl's name, but it also means happiness. The peg remained stuck in the hole opposite *Ligaya*. For some time, both of them thought it clever and amusing.

In the kitchen, Fil felt he had something on his friend who could not cook as well as he.

"It's not a palace, I know," he said. "But who wants a palace when they can have the most delicious *adobo* here and the best boneless chicken with stuffing . . . yum . . . yum . . . "

Tony was angry. "Yum, yum, you're nuts," he said, "plain and simple loco. What for you want to spend and spend? You've been living on loose change practically all your life and now on treasury warrant so small, all full of holes and practically nothing, and still you want to spend for these dancing kids who don't know you and won't even send you a card afterwards."

"Never mind the cards," Fil answered. "Who wants cards? But don't you see, they'll be happy; and then, you know what? I'm going to keep their voices, their words and their singing and their laughter in my magic sound mirror."

The first time Fil heard his own voice played back in the

tape recorder, he didn't believe it was his own, but as soon as he recognized it, the whole thing became to him pure magic. He bought a portable. Tony and he had fun making recordings to songs from the radio and listening to their own voices as they debated in English or in the dialect. It was evident, Fil showed more mastery. His style was florid, sentimental, poetic.

The machine was now several years old, but it still looked new. Fil had a stack of tape recordings, patiently labelled, songs and speeches. The songs were in English, but most of the speeches were in the dialect.

Without telling Tony, he had experimented on recording sounds, like the way a bed creaked, doors opening and closing, rain or sleet tapping on the glass window panes, footsteps through the corridor and on the threadbare rug. He played all the sounds back and tried to remember how it was on the day or night the sounds had been recorded. Did they bring back the moment? He was beginning to think that they did. He was learning to identify each of the sounds with a particular mood or fact. Sometimes, whimsically, he wished that there was a way of keeping a record of silence because it was to him the richest sound, like snow falling.

Now as he and Tony watched the snow blowing in the wind, he thought, what took care of that moment if memory didn't? Like time, memory was often a villain, a betrayer.

"As soon as they accept my invitation, I'll call you up," Fil said; adding hastily, "no, you don't have to do anything, but I'd want you to know so you'd be here to meet them."

"I'm going out myself," Tony said, "and I don't know what time I'm coming back." Then he added, "So you're not working today. Are you on leave?"

"For two days. While the dancers are here," Fil said.

"It still doesn't make sense to me," Tony said. "But, good luck, anyway."

"Aren't you going to see them tonight? That ticket I got you is a good seat, right in front," Fil said.

"I know. But I'm not sure I can come."

"What? You're not sure?" Fil could not believe it. The opportunity of a lifetime. Something must be wrong with Tony. He looked at him closely, saying nothing.

"I'd want to, but I'm sick, Fil. I tell you, I'm not feeling so good. My doctor will know today. He'll tell me," Tony said.

"What will he tell you?"

"How do I know?"

"I mean, what's he trying to find out?"

"If it's cancer," Tony said. Without saying another word, he went straight to his room.

Fil remembered those times, at night, when Tony kept him awake with his long-drawn out sighs of pain. When he called out to him, saying, "Tony! Tony, what's the matter?" the moaning ceased for a while. But afterwards, as if unable to hold the pain any longer, Tony screamed, deadening his cries with a pillow against his mouth. When Fil went to him then, Tony drove him away. Or he curled up in the bedsheets like a big infant suddenly hushed in its crying.

The next day, Tony looked all right. When Fil asked him about the night before, he replied, "I was dying," but it sounded more like disgust over a nameless annoyance. Fil had more misgivings over the whiteness spreading on Tony's skin. He had heard of leprosy. Every time he thought of that dreaded disease, he felt tears in his eyes. In all the years he had been in America, he had not had a friend until he met Tony whom he liked immediately and worshipped for all the things the man had and which Fil knew he himself lacked.

"Fil, I can't find my boots, may I wear yours?" Tony's voice sounded strong and healthy.

"Sure, sure!" Fil answered. He didn't need boots. He loved to walk in the snow. Tony needed them.

They had been wearing each other's things. At first, they marked with their initials what each owned, but later, neither paid attention to the distinguishing marks. They wore each other's socks, shorts, handkerchiefs, ties, shoes, jackets, etc. Still they continued to exchange gifts on Christmas. Nobody sent them Christmas presents. Once in a rare while, they got Christmas cards, one from the florist near their apartment house, another from an insurance company. But they made merry on Christmas and drank a lot. Then it did not embarrass them to admit that they were fast friends, indeed. They shook hands on that; they shook hands on practically anything they said. Christmas Day was Armistice Day. They kept shaking hands and admiring each other's gifts. Drink affected them differently: Fil became boisterous and recited poems in the dialect and praised himself. Tony fell to giggling and cursing all the railroad companies of America. When they woke up the next morning, they glared at each other and, without a word, they cleaned up the mess, each obviously avoiding the other. Then one or the other left, but the next day, everything was normal again.

Now as he was getting ready to leave the apartment, Fil said, "Well, I'll be seeing you. Try to be home on time. I shall invite the dancers for luncheon or dinner, maybe tomorrow. But tonight, let's go to the theater together, ha?"

"I'll try," Tony answered.

There was no eagerness in his voice. He had returned to bed as if the morning, that early, had already wearied him.

As he was about to shut the door, Fil heard Tony saying, "Good luck." The voice was faint.

The air outside felt good. Fil lifted his face to the sky and closed his eyes as the snow and a wet wind drenched his face. He stood that way for some time, crying, more, more, more! to himself, drunk with snow and coolness. His car was parked a block away. As he walked toward it, he pushed one foot into the snow and studied the scar he made, a hideous shape among perfect footmarks. He felt strong as his lungs filled with the cold air, as if just now it did not matter too much that he was the way he looked and his English was the way it was. But perhaps, he could talk to the dancers in his dialect. Why not?

A heavy frosting of snow covered his ear, and as he wiped

it off with his bare hands, he felt light and young, like a child at play, and once again, he raised his face to the sky and licked the flakes, cold and tasteless on his tongue.

When Fil arrived at the Hamilton, it seemed to him the Philippine dancers had taken over the hotel. They were all over the lobby, on the mezzanine, talking in groups animatedly, their teeth sparkling as they laughed, their eyes disappearing in mere slits of light. Some of the girls wore their black hair long. For a moment the sight seemed too much for him who had all but forgotten how beautiful Philippine girls were. He wanted to look away, but their loveliness held him. He must do something, close his eyes perhaps. As he did so, their laughter came to him like a breeze murmurous with sounds native to his land. It was happiness itself.

Later, he tried to relax, to appear inconspicuous. True, they were all very young, but there were a few elderly men and women who must be their chaperones or well-wishers like him. He smiled at everyone who happened to look toward him. Most of them smiled back, or rather seemed to smile, but it was quick, without recognition, and might not have been for him, but for someone else near or behind him.

His lips formed the words he was trying to phrase in his mind: *Ilocano ka? Bicol? Ano na, paisano? Comusta?* Or should he introduce himself? How? His lips trembled at the unfamiliar phrases, frightening him into deeper incoherence.

Suddenly he felt as if he had stumbled into company where he was not welcome. All the things he had been trying to hide now showed: the age in his face, his horny hands. He knew it the instant he wanted to shake hands with the first boy who had drawn close to him, smiling and friendly. Fil put his hands in his pocket. They were cold and damp.

Now he wished Tony were with him. Tony would know what to do. He would charm these young people with his smile and his learned words. Fil wanted to leave, but he seemed caught up in the tangle of moving bodies that merged and broke in a fluid strangle hold. Everybody was talking, mostly in English. Once in a while he heard exclamations in the dialect right out of the past, conjuring up playtime, long shadows of evening on the plaza, fiestas, *misa de gallo.*

There was music in their voices. This was home. This was homelessness. The paradox confused him, but that was how he felt, uncertain whether this feeling was not really regret over all the wasted years away from home. He loved them all—that was clearest in his mind, as he walked among the dancers, pretending he was not a stranger.

Time was passing and he had yet to talk to someone. Suppose he stood on a chair and addressed them in the manner of his flamboyant speeches, recorded in his magic sound mirror?

"Beloved countrymen, lovely children of the Pearl of the Orient Seas, listen to me. I'm Fil Acayan. I've come to volunteer my services. I'm yours to command. Your servant. Tell me where you want to go, what you want to see in Chicago. I know every foot of the lakeshore drive, all the gardens and the parks, the museums, the huge department stores, the planetarium. Let me be your guide. That's what I'm offering you, a free tour of Chicago, and finally, dinner at my apartment on West Sheridan Road—pork *adobo* and chicken *relleno,* name your dish. How about it, *paisanos?*"

No. That would be a foolish thing to do. They would laugh at him. He felt a dryness in his throat. He was sweating. As he wiped his face with a handkerchief, he bumped against a slim, short girl who quite gracefully stepped aside, and for a moment he thought he would swoon in the perfume that enveloped him. It was fragrance long forgotten, essence of *camia,* of *ilang-ilang,* and *dama de noche.*

Two boys with sleek, pomaded hair, were sitting near an empty chair. He sat down and said in the dialect, "May I invite you to my apartment?" The boys stood up, saying, "Excuse, please," and walked away. He mopped his brow, but instead of getting discouraged, as though he had moved another step beyond shamelessness, he grew bolder. Approaching another group, he repeated his invitation, and a girl with a mole on her upper lip, said, "Thank you, but we have no time." As he turned toward another group, he felt their eyes on his back. Once, a boy came toward him, but as soon as he began to speak, the boy said, "Pardon, please," and moved away.

They were always moving away. As if by common consent, they had decided to avoid him, ignore his presence. Perhaps it was not their fault. They must have been instructed to do so. Or was it his looks that kept them away? The thought was a sharpness inside him.

After a while, as he wandered about the mezzanine, among the dancers, but alone, he noticed that some were going down the stairs and others were crowding noisily into the two elevators, through the revolving door, out into the street. He followed the crowd going down the stairs. Beyond the glass doors, he saw them getting into a bus parked beside the subway entrance on Dearborn.

The snow had stopped falling; it was melting fast in the sun and turning into slush.

As he moved about aimlessly, he felt someone touch him on the sleeve. It was one of the dancers, a mere boy, tall and slim, who was saying, "Excuse, please." Fil realized he was in the way between another boy with a camera and a group posing in front of the hotel.

"Sorry," Fil said, jumping away.

The crowd burst out laughing. Then everything became a blur in his eyes, a moving picture out of focus, but gradually, the figures cleared, there was mud on the pavement on which the dancers stood posing, and the sun threw shadows at their feet.

Let them have fun, he said to himself, they're young and away from home. I have no business messing up their schedule, forcing myself on them.

He watched the dancers, till the last of them was on the bus. Their voices came to him, above the traffic sounds. They waved their hands and smiled toward him as the bus started. Fil raised his hand to wave back, but stopped suddenly, aborting the gesture. He turned to look behind him at whoever the dancers were waving their hands. There was no one there except his own reflection in the glass door, a double exposure of himself and a giant plant with its thorny branches around him like arms in a loving embrace.

Even before he opened the door to their apartment, Fil knew that Tony had not yet arrived. There were no boots outside on the landing. Somehow he felt relieved, for until then he did not know how he was going to explain his failure.

From the hotel, he had driven around, cruised by the lakeshore drive, beyond the city limits hoping he would see the dancers somewhere, in a park perhaps, taking pictures of the mist over the lake and the last gold on the trees now wet with melted snow, or on some picnic grounds, near a bubbling fountain, still taking pictures of themselves against a background of Chicago's gray and dirty skyscrapers. He slowed down every time he saw a crowd, but the dancers were nowhere along the way he took. Perhaps they had gone to the theater to rehearse. He turned back before reaching Evanston, wondering where the dancers could be then.

He felt weak but not hungry. Just the same, he ate, warming up some left-over food. The rice was cold, but the soup was hot and tasty. While he ate, he listened for footfalls.

Afterwards, he lay down on the sofa and a weariness came over him, but he tried hard not to sleep. As he stared at the ceiling, he felt like floating away in sleep, but he kept his eyes open, willing hard to remain awake.

He had stared at that ceiling so many years, he had memorized every part of it: a corner with stain and dirt, dried up after a long dampness, with lines curved like boundaries between countries where peace was permanent and no borders ever changed, and lines within like rivers touching the sea, estuaries and dots to mark a city, a cape or a peninsula; and cobwebs that grew in a thickening maze, color of rust and soot and age. Always as he gazed at *his* ceiling, he wondered whether the boundaries had changed in the night, what city had vanished after what compromises, whose was the loss, whose the cunning, that a spot called city was gone and other spots had come up, as yet nameless, until he had chosen for each an identity. It was a fascinating game which he could play all by himself and forget time passing.

He lay there wide-eyed till the cities and rivers and the boundaries were nothing now but dirt. He wanted to be awake when Tony arrived. But soon his eyes closed against a weary will, too tired and weak to fight back sleep—and then there were voices. Tony was in the room, eager, to tell his own bit of news.

"I've discovered a new way of keeping afloat," he was saying.

"Who wants to keep afloat?" Fil asked.

"Just in case. In a shipwreck, for example," Tony said.

"Never mind shipwreck. I must tell you about the dancers," Fil said.

"But this is important," Tony insisted. "With this method, you can keep floating indefinitely."

"What for indefinitely?" Fil asked.

"Say in a ship . . . I mean, in an emergency, you're stranded without help in the middle of the Pacific or the Atlantic, you must keep floating till help comes . . . if help comes," Tony explained.

"Better yet," Fil said, "find a way to reach shore before the sharks smell you. You discover that."

"I will," Tony said, without eagerness, as though certain that there was no such way, that, after all, his discovery was worthless.

"Now you listen to me," Fil said, sitting up abruptly. As he talked, in the dialect, Tony listened with increasing apathy.

"There they were," Fil began, his voice taking on the orator's pitch, "some of whom that could have been my children if I had not left home—or yours, Tony. They gazed around them with wonder, smiling at me, answering my questions, but grudgingly, edging away as if to be near me were wrong, a violation in their rule book. But it could be that every time I opened my mouth, I gave myself away. I talked to them in the dialect, Ilocano, Tagalog, Bicol, but no one listened. They avoided me. They had been briefed too well: Do not talk to strangers. Ignore their invitations. Be extra careful in the big cities like New York and Chicago, beware of the old-timers, the Pinoys. Most of them are bums. Keep away from them. Be on the safe side—stick together, entertain only those who have been introduced to you properly.

"I'm sure they had such instructions, safety measures, they must have called them. What then could I do, scream out my good intentions, prove my harmlessness and my love for them by beating my breast? Oh, but I loved them. You see, I was like them once. I, too, was nimble with my feet, graceful with my hands; and I had the tongue of a poet. Ask the village girls and the envious boys from the city—but first you have to find them. After these many years, it shall not be easy. You'll have to search every suffering face in the village gloom for a hint of youth and beauty or go where the graveyards are and the tombs under the lime trees. One such face . . . oh, God, what am I saying?

"All I wanted was to talk to them, guide them around Chicago, spend money on them so that they would have something special to remember about us here when they return to our country. They would tell their folks: We met a kind, old man, who took us to his apartment. It was not much of a place. It was old—like him. When we sat on the sofa in the living room, the bottom sank heavily, the broken springs touching the floor. But what a cook that man was! And how kind! We never thought that rice and *adobo* could be that delicious. And the chicken *relleno*! When someone asked what the stuffing was—we had never tasted anything like it—he smiled, saying. 'From heaven's supermarket,' touching his head and pressing his heart like a clown, as if heaven were there. He had this tape recorder, which he called magic sound mirror, and he had all of us record our voices. Say anything in the dialect, sing, if you please, our *kundiman*, please, he said, his eyes pleading, too. Oh, we had fun listening to the playback. When you're gone, the old man said, I shall listen to your voices with my eyes closed and you will be here again and I'll not be alone, not any more after this. We wanted to cry, but he looked very funny, so we laughed and he laughed with us.

"But, Tony, they would not come. They thanked me, but they said they had no time. Others said nothing. They looked through me. I didn't exist. Or worse, I was unclean. They were ashamed of me. How could I be Filipino?"

The memory, suddenly recalled, was a rock on his breast. He gasped for breath.

"Now, let me teach you how to keep afloat," Tony said, but it was not Tony's voice.

Fil was alone and crying for air. His eyes opened slowly till he began to breathe easily. The sky outside was gray. He looked at his watch—a quarter past five. The show would begin at eight. There was still time. Perhaps Tony would be home soon.

The apartment was warming up. The radiators sounded full of scampering rats. He had a recording of that in his sound mirror.

Fil smiled. He had an idea. He would take the sound mirror to the theater, go to his seat close to the stage, and make tape recordings of the singing and the dances.

Now he was wide awake and somehow pleased with himself. The more he thought of the idea of recording the dancers' performance, the better he felt. If Tony showed up now . . . He sat up, listening. The radiators were quiet. There were no footfalls, no sound of a key turning.

Late that night, back from the theater, Fil knew at once that Tony was back. The boots were outside the door. He, too, must be tired and should not be disturbed.

Fil had waited for him till the last possible moment and he had to drive fast. He didn't want too many people staring at him as he lugged the sound mirror to his seat out in front. He had hoped Tony would be there. Shortly before the lights went out,

Fil placed the tape recorder on the seat reserved for Tony, next to his. He leaned back and watched, as the show began, manipulating the microphone, controls and tape quite deftly, keeping his eyes on the dancers. He would remember. After this, all he had to do was dub his memory of this night on the sounds recorded on the tape, and the dancers would be there again, frail and graceful and young.

An electric bulb high against a brick wall in the alley across the south window of the living room lighted his way to the sofa on which he placed the sound mirror, careful not to make any noise. He turned on the floor lamp, thinking as he removed his jacket that perhaps Tony was awake and waiting for him. They would listen together to a playback of the dances and the songs Tony had missed. Then he would tell Tony what happened that day, repeating part of the dream.

As he tiptoed toward Tony's bedroom, he heard the regular breathing of a man sound asleep. In the half-darkness, Tony's head showed darkly, deep in a pillow, on its side, his knees bent, almost touching the clasped hands under his chin, an oversized foetus in the last bottle. Quietly, Fil shut the door between them and walked to the sofa. Opening the case of the recorder, he looked around for a socket, and, finding, one plugged the sound mirror, adjusted the tape, and turned the volume low. At first nothing but static and odd sounds came through, but soon after there was the patter of feet to the rhythms of a familiar melody.

All the beautiful boys and girls were in the room now, dancing and singing. A boy and a girl sat on the floor holding two bamboo poles on each end, flat on the floor, clapping them together, then apart, and pounding them on the boards, while dancers swayed and balanced their lithe forms, dipping their bare brown legs in and out the clapping bamboos, the pace gradually increasing into a fury of wood on wood, in a counterpoint of panic among the dancers in a harmonious flurry of toes and ankles escaping certain pain—crushed bones and bruised flesh, and humiliation. Other dances followed, accompanied by songs and live with the sounds of life and death in the old country: Igorots in G-strings, walking down a mountainside, peasants climbing up a hill on a rainy day; neighbors moving a house, their sturdy legs showing under a portable roof; lovers in Lent hiding their love among wild hedges, far from the stewing chapel; a distant gong sounding off a summons either to a feast or a wake. And finally, a prolonged ovation, thunderous, wave upon wave.

"Turn that thing off!" Tony's voice was distinct and sharp above the echoes of the shuddering gongs and the applause settling into silence.

Fil switched off the machine; in the sudden stillness, the voices turned into faces, familiar and near like gestures and touch, that stayed on even as the memory withdrew, bowing out, as it were, in a graceful exit, saying, thank you, thank you, before a ghostly audience that clapped hands in silence and stomped their feet in a sucking emptiness. He wanted to join the finale, such as it was, pretend that the curtain call included him, and attempt a shame-faced imitation of a graceful adieu, but he was stiff and old, incapable of grace; but he said, thank you, thank you, his voice sincere and contrite, grateful for the other voices and the sound of singing and the memory.

"Oh, my God . . . " the man in the other room cried, followed by a moan of such anguish that Fil fell on his knees, covering the sound mirror with his hands to muffle the sounds that had started again, it seemed to him, even after he had turned it off.

Then, quickly, he remembered.

"Tony, what did the doctor say? What did he say?" he shouted and listened breathless, no longer able to tell at the moment who had truly waited all day for the final sentence.

There was no answer. Meanwhile, under his hands, there was a flutter of wings, a shudder of gongs. What was Tony saying? Fil wanted to hear, he must know. His arms went around the dead machine as his head fell, resting on a loosened tape.

It was near morning then and sleep overpowered him like a wave that drew his body into a darkness where he floated on and on in a shoreless sea.

Jose Garcia Villa

Inviting a tiger for a weekend.
The gesture is not heroics but discipline.
The memoirs will be splendid.

Proceed to dazzlement, Augustine.
Banish little birds, graduate to tiger.
Proceed to dazzlement, Augustine.

Any tiger of whatever colour
The same as jewels any stone
Flames always essential morn.

The guest is luminous, peer of Blake.
The host is gallant, eye of Death.
If you will do this you will break

The little religions for my sake.
Invite a tiger for a weekend,
Proceed to dazzlement, Augustine.

My most. My most. O my lost!
O my bright, my ineradicable ghost.
At whose bright coast God seeks
Shelter and is lost is lost. O
Coast of Brightness. O cause of
Grief. O rose of purest grief.
O thou in my breast so stark and
Holy-bright. O thou melancholy
Light. Me. Me. My own perfidy.
O my most my most. O the bright
The beautiful the terrible Accost.

The,bright,Centipede,
Begins,his,stampede!
O,celestial,Engine,from,
What,celestial,province!
His,spiritual,might,
Golding,the,night—
His,spiritual,eyes,
Foretelling,my,Size;
His,spiritual,feet,
Stamping,in,heat,
The,radium,brain,
To,Spiritual,Imagination.

Much,beauty,is,less,than,the,face,of,
My,dark,hero. His,under,is,pure,
Lightning. His,under,is,the,socket,

Of,the,sun. Not,Christ,the,Fox,not
Christ,the,Lord,His,beauty,is,too,
Sly,too,meek. But,Christ,Oppositor,

Christ,Foeman: The,true,dark,Hero.
He,with,the,three-eyèd,thunders,he,
With,the,rigorous,terrors:this,

Man's,under,is,pure,lightning. This,
Man's,under,is,the,socket,of,the,
Sun. After,pure,eyes,have,peeled,

Off,skin,who,can,gaze,unburned? Who,
Can,stand,unbowed? Well,be,perceived,
And,well,perceive. Receive,be,received.

Ferns

So, then, will he, discoverer of ferns,
His eyes the compass of his searching hands,
Name right the single naming of a leaf.
Though, dark before the riot flood of trees,
Dark where the green tides overflow the land,
The plural drowning of the green on green
Provokes the errors of the mind to choose
The simple shape before the sudden scene:

When he, tender between the banks of moss,
Kneels low to extricate a mass of leaves
From the imagined leaf:

> The tall fish's verdant fins
> row upon pointed row
> or the shark's green teeth.

Landscape II

Sun in the knifed horizon bleeds the sky,
Spilling a peacock stain upon the sands,
Across some murdered rocks refused to die.
It is your absence touches my sad hands
Blinded like flags in the wreck of air.

And catacombs of cloud enshroud the cool
And calm involvement of the darkened plains,
The stunted mourners here: and here, a full
And universal tenderness which drains
The sucked and golden breath of sky comes bare.

Now, while the dark basins the void of space,
Some sudden crickets, ambushing me near,
Discover vowels of your whispered face
And subtly cry. I touch your absence here
Remembering the speeches of your hair.

Asylum Piece

When the first girl came hopping
Along the corridor carrying
A bull-frog and a legend
The other and the third girl screeched
Like busy crickets, planning brigandage.

It was her insect instinct
That told her before
She rounded off just one more corner
That stalkers stalked nearby
Which she must beware.

"Is it Thursday," she said,
"That they would dare?
This has not happened before!"

Then she went back hopping
Down the corridor to her room
Carrying bull-frog and legend.

She was never forgiven by the
Crickets.

The Eye

The eye, sprout in the mesa of the mind,
Must seek sanctuary in the soul of sun.
Not the steely brilliance, no, not the blind-
Ing fierceness of the sharp and silvered spun

That hurtles in a rain-ray down the sky
With felt and instant fury like a stun
Of jewels in the panic of an eye.
No. Not the splendor of the sudden sun,

But the core of the sun's intensity,
The burning center in the hearth of sky,
(Unseen by the eye of the blinded tree,
Sprout of a tree of the mind's choked cry),

The dazzling furnace of the sun's bright soul
Where tempered whole is kindness in the tray
Of fire. O, if it must survive at all,
Tendrils of faith be pushed against the day.

Alejandrino G. Hufana

Pygmy Reservation

Unclothing so the Zambal Bali Dag
May for her dead infanta deep be soft,
The black she-parent grieving on the crag
A lullaby invokes: "Arrow aloft,
Time for your sleep, piece-of-my-thigh,
The fletcher is not false, time for your dream,
Meat will be yours." But deer is famine-shy
And in the tough grass armor-wearers gleam,
Who cut off headmen of the tribe, then in
The place of thorns their barbed wire strains as far
As christenings and unctions, light of skin,
Succeeding through supplying men-of-war
Whose monuments outbear orangutan
And birds of paradise, breast-sucked man.

Farmer in a Wrong Career

Camilo del Piedad has traced his lineage to
A musketeer that saved Juan de Salcedo
From poisoned water in his North Luzon campaign—
The tattooed heathens speared Camilo del Piedad's
Ancestor who was dying then of what he drank,
At which Salcedo took the hint to run and dig
A well, eroded so Camilo's carabaos
Make it a wallow now. It is a part of tales
Told by the heirs of fathers of the Revolution
Who were by leaders rich betrayed, their lands affixed
To titled orchards one of which Camilo del Piedad
Has eked by marriage to a waning family
Whose brick house keeps, in every corner, burns
And smudges of the torch. Now that Camilo learns
His musketeer-ancestor had been savior of
A man who vested thence sinecures in the North,
He faces his wife's family with rank assurance
Though their backs still are turned to him while they
Reminisce on their knitting and embroideries
That spell *Recuerdo* in the damask middle,
And on their archive, on their albums, on their realm
Of fleece, not on him who must dine alone and go
Up to the chamber of the invalid, his wife,
Who tends her homing pigeons by the bed to while
His absence overseeing clay and seed. Tonight, however,
There is no soul to squeal to—his restlessness
And his found worth; the invalid, it seems, has pined
Away on what can be a swoon bold of relief.
The surface of the outdoors now peels like the bark
Of that crabtree that deigns to scratch its wraith
Upon the room, upon the whole brickhouse now palled
By one of those untaken Poro Point moonlights.

Keeper of the Lighthouse

Astride a coconut-shredder, the closest touch
Allowed her touchy thighs, Gerarda Galang
With passion finishes her job but cuts
A finger on the shredder's teeth, and when
The shredded coconut is squeezed the milk
Is smeared with blood. There is no man to do
The job for her, a comely middle-aged one
Entrusted with the lighthouse and its lamp,
Her father's heir officially confirmed
To have her buried father's job. She has
Been taught from childhood, almost like an oath,
That mariners must be warned of the reefs
And guided in their wake—storms often blurring
The land but not the turning, constant lamp;
Why, only four weeks back a skipper came
With roses aiding him in thanking her
For that good light without which he would have
Now been one of the corals. Gratitude like that
Does gratify Gerarda Galang and no man
In person can quite measure up to such
A feeling though he be an actor or be he
One with a string of titles. She just cooks
Rice cakes for kins; one year ago tonight
She has been in the watch against the harm
To mariners, and she is blithe that deaths
Have elsewhere happened, not within the span
Of light from her good lamp. Her kins arrive
But with a stranger—he who notices
The lamp's encasement shattered as he picks
Up by the tail an inland bird, a dove,
Alive and bleeding. An instinct, quite
Submerged below Gerarda Galang's blush,

Converts her into mothering the bird
As she remembers but the wind that blew
Her scarf last night into the cliff nearby—
A shadow caught a little on the light,
And in the engine's beat within the heart
Of her stone lighthouse seemed a tiny flutter
That calmed as soon as it was heard. She feels
The pulse ebb in the dove, and her eyes meet
The stranger's as they break a sweet rice cake.

Oscar de Zuñiga

Suns Have Gone

Beneath the arcade of flame trees,
My love walks alone,
A frail creature from whose eyes
The twelfth sun has gone.

As she goes by feeling her way
With a swaying bamboo cane,
A panel of kindly faces wears
A long tender look of pain.

Sitting on a familiar stone,
Where she held hands with me,
Tears of lost desires flow down
The stony bone of her memory.

Beneath the deflowered trees,
My love still walks alone,
A gray woman in whose enfeebled eyes
Suns have brightly shone.

The Ants and the Chandlers

No one saw the old man bring the bread
That morning when famine swept the town;
Men with lean faces, backs against the walls,
Watched the ants move up and down the streets.

That day was lost in the ghostly shadows of wooden crosses:
Mounds of dry clay were everywhere, and the voice of the wind
Was in the gaping mouths of the dead, whose eyelids were moist
With blood, whose bones were dissolved in the salt of night.

Now there's nothing here except the silence of the graves
And the fragrance of incense; the odor of burning grass.
The fattened ants have migrated to the hills across the city,
Where chandlers sell rice cakes instead of candles.

Manuel A. Viray

Morning of Ang Shiu, Chinese Storckeeper

Day begins with the knock at early morn
On my head and the door: "Ang Shiu, the bread ration
Is here!" but the head still spins, the warm sensation
Of Clara, secret, clear, intimately born,
Floats above the boiling coffee's aroma, the stale
Bed scents, and garbage can we forgot, in our hurry, to throw
Away.

     Always nocturnal wants, day's needs mingle and flow
In the warmed blood; embraces paid for conjoined wail.
Such necessities as flesh fiercely needs glaring days reft.
We shake our limbs of dead desires as refuse of dreams drift
By in the awakening traffic roar and incoming
Customers: jeep driver, streetcleaner, and servant-maid.

In this alien land, as in Chungshun, desires are paid
For in cash, but Clara like us is forever roaming
Midnights from store to store, partly to still the roar
Of blood's sickness, partly to appease a hunger
Beyond heart and head.
So unlike in skin, we share the same guilt
For fair and ugly, we're but made of the same sap and silt.

Off the Aleutian Islands

I have reaped the sickle edge of rain,
Rain harvests that had no grass:
In youth I let, instead, lusty mushrooms
Discover me.

Also have I known
The craving blade of rainwash, clean
To my clean bones. But overnight I rose
Upright in marsh ground, naked
Looming with rain.

Now, I do not cry; here; because I am bigger
Than a sea-gull. A sea-gull screams;
Ungently leaps into the wind
Following the concave shine of water.

Does it break, irrevocably,
The all-pathos of mirrors,
To look back at rain memories, unvexed?
A gull cries now to the other

Sea-gulls: follow me.

Follow me.

Sun Series

Cosmic elixir of Hermit Prince: Noon,
In the bottom of this celadon
Fish is fish and rice turns
Wine, subtler than salt or
Cane, embalmer, where none dies
The small death, sleep except
By his darkest win, Night.

Shadow and Light

Rat brush whiskering on cicada wing silk, rough
And tender art is your knife bruising my mango's skin
A kiss is the gasping more
And sated enough, both
Left and right, shadow and light Round Game
Where Love is, Death is not, or is Death
When turned about.

Night and Day

What did you do to Sister Rain?
What to Brother Thunder? Sister Lightning
    and Cloud Mother? Accept a lover who
Will fold your arms and anger to her black breast.
But for the Moon and Night, the skies will have
Only You and Day after Day after Day.

Sunset, Sunrise

Golden boat fleeing from ghostly pier,
It is onyx o'clock.
Burning boat thirsting towards Imperial Port,
It is phoenix o'clock.
And you have no time, Tetrarch,
To be born for this instant.

Order for Masks

To this harlequinade
I wear black tights and fool's cap
Billiken, make me three bright masks
For the three tasks in my life
Three faces to wear
One after the other
For the three men in my life.

When my Brother comes
Make me one opposite
If he is devil, a saint
With a staff to his fork
And for his horns, a crown.
I hope by contrast
To make nil
Our old resemblance to each other
And my twin will walk me out
Without a frown
Pretending I am another.

When my Father comes
Make me one so like
His child once eating his white bread in trance
Philomela before she was raped.
I hope by likeness
To make him believe this is the same kind
The chaste face he made
And my blind Lear will walk me out
Without a word
Fearing to peer behind.

If my lover comes
Yes, when my Seducer comes
Make for me the face
That will in colors race
The carnival stars
And change in shape
Under his grasping hands.

Make it bloody
When he needs it white
Make it wicked in the dark
Let him find no old mark
Make it stone to his suave touch.
This magician will walk me out,
Newly loved,
Not knowing why my tantalizing face
Is strangely like the mangled parts of a face
He once wiped out

Make me three masks.

Batik Maker

Tissue of no seam and skin
Of no scale she weaves this:
Dream of a huntsman pale
That in his antlered
Mangrove waits
Ensnared;

And I cannot touch him.

Lengths of the dumb and widths
Of the deaf are his hair
Where wild orchids thumb
Or his parted throat surprise
To elegiac screaming
Only birds of
Paradise;

And I cannot wake him.

Shades of the light and shapes
Of the rain on his palanquin
Stain what phantom panther
Sleeps in the cage of
His skin and immobile
Hands;

And I cannot bury him.

Sung

The greenglaze
    Of a Sung bowl held out in the light
Repeats a sea
      On which the haze
Sloping from hills hangs
    Like still breath. The shape
Glowing round within the hollow
      Of two hands
    Is an overflow
Of a silence that is bare and whole.
      O it is
A bright achieved silence that sustains
    The morning's
Amaze of light live
    Upon all wet and dark.
It holds
      An air's
Poise-upon-the-edges-of-things.
      A flawless
Silence it is can catch so roundly
    A gaze
From the thick of crowds
And survive
      Clamors of the wilderness and the loud
    Vanity
      Of open wounds.

The Hazards of Hearing an Explosion
in Broad Daylight

A loud thunder comes from far
    Away. Frames of windows frailly shake.
It is a sound much heard before, and the fear
    That overtakes the quiet mind
Reading philosophy or preparing to compose a letter
    Is hardly new.

The fear dissipates. Other sounds
    Steady the quivering filaments of the stunned
Room. In the streets citizens walk free,
    Pretending not to have heard . . . it is the sound
Of builders blasting for a new homesite, not
    The cannon's cold appeal.

It is not so much Asia's lush jungles
    Gray with gunmetal nor the swarm
Of hungry mouths, Asia's children's, chill
    The bone, as something striped in its long
Spell of captivity trying to break into
    A sudden air.

What the gunshaken air says is dark:
    The delicate scaffolds of persuasion
Must in the end come down. My dear, must light
    Be clenched into a fist until
It is clay? Must the lock that will not give in be
    Forced ruthlessly?

Nothing is more terrible to recall
    Than a doorknob rattling as it is turned
Again, again. Waiting alone in a room
    Full of books, locked up in one's own sweat
For a letter to write itself out could make the mind
    Crumple its quietness.

The least sound of rain splashing
    Upon the trees could cause the lyric
Cry to happen. From all the unread books
    Of the world ideas of order, joy,
And consummated love would give off a blinding
    Summary blaze.

Words in a letter likely to draw no
    Answer would rain down in lines of light.
Tearing down a row of condemned houses
    Is not as loud as the angels' impatience
And the emptiness of an idealist's swivel chair
    Turning in the wind.

EDITH L. TIEMPO

Green Hearts

Under the night sky his fields bristled.
Lopped of grains the stalks crawled,
A great gleaming hide in the dark, sprawled,
Still watchful, keen hair chiseled
Stiff against the warning wind;

Reaped fields were omens—rapt growth's spectral end.
Yesterday, haste left with the harvesters;
The heat of their races was gone around the hill,
Gutting yellow trails after the sun.
　　　　This remained, chill
Heaving on the fields, death ruffling his grey hairs.

A full measure of rice he strew on the stairs
Those Holy Saturdays; clenched his stripling hands
　　about the trees,
Shaking the plump boughs to fruit while the bells' tremors
Bounced across the air like gay meadows stung by bees;
Moons later, shaking down the mangoes, small hearts strung

Tender in the warm night; stones and sticks flung
Skyward, whipping the twigs till the green fruit rained . . .
(Shaking his sons, if their fond pained
Wisdoms clicked fast into place)
The fields were wide after the reapers' feast.

The creeping stubble was a long-dead beast—
He should not fear it. Fear only the wind
When it blew young in scorching quests; or fear the mind
That now saw that holy and joyous rice spilled prodigally,
Those shaken boughs skewed, the young spirits
    napped in his eager heat.

O the green hearts spewing their cracked, livid meat;
Fear the raw-running spattered truths—
        O wrath-born beauteous maiden,
O bleary sage: young joys be feared for what age
    knew of them.
Not death, but Memory is the beast; mercifully
    his hairs were gray,
The sickles had gleamed and his harvest put away.

The Fisherman

All day his floating face tangled with the net.
Each haul the meshes thrashed with angry tails,
The clustered eyes clamored and the slime and scales
And gills quivered with his own disgust. Yet,
Once, a boy fished where the fishes were more tame,
A stream where he dipped a small hand and the fishes came,
And when he gently chucked their bellies with a finger,
They slowly wagged their fins, roiling the water
Hardly. Man now, he seized a fish and peeled
Its scales alive and flung it in again;
The naked creature hit the reefs and reeled,
The water swirled—he jeered to see the little stain.
He stalked again, he flung the net into a school,
Drew in the catch, cursed each thrash and pull;
His hunger scooped the sea, he preyed and trapped
And tore the masks, and voiceless faces wept;
He grudged the clutching mollusk its involuted stores,
Pried, that the pearly oyster part its scrupulous doors.

Voyages

To exile I ride on the bountiful surf. And foam-flowers of her dreams gather to waylay my anchors.

Roots shall burst the shell. Burnt roots.

She wanders. Sunk in glaciers.

Plough. Siren-song.

And seeds flower sibylwise to wake the sleeping oracles of desire. Woven. Until nets swing against the rocks of her breast-hulls.

Weeds leagues-long, moored by tides and horned nightmares! She summons her wild albatross!

Yield to the sargasso of her murmurings.

A Fable for Innocents

I. *The Judge Speaks*

When the flood's edge rose to his teeth
    Cursed our old gawky Emperor,
Spitting on the gall-tinged foam:
    "Order, ordcr the Executioner!"

Squat the blue-bellied Emperor
    Weaving dry spider loins,
The acrobat Policeman up the tower's light
    Cried: "Lo, our scaffolding gone!"

Hobnailed boots rout the gallery,
    Plaza rebels kicked heels
Once they caught stars dazzling—
    Like pearls ground by wheels.

In the Capitol's court the trial
    Swung with fire and smoke,
Blasted the engine: "Torture—
    Hang all the dynasts to the rack!"

Quick the accusers hawked hurrah,
    Pawned his gold-teeth to the butchers;
The mystery of the sower's cudgel
    Stamped with blood the newspapers.

When the powerhouse broke the crooks
    Croaked hell to the Tarpeian cliff
Their bankbook innocence; phantom shades
    Shed temper to the knife.

The Executioner hurls the horned dice
    Down deep the oyster's guts;
In combat gathering spins
    And shrieks: "Guilty to the heart!"

Now our Emperor sweeps the pail-pot
    Till the hinds of the ape;
Long will he dream the apocalypse,
    Never his ghost grow meat-ripe.

II. *The Witness Speaks*

Crawl and creep into the gallery
    Where she stands nude, armless,
That you proud beast may embrace
    The wounds of her loveliness.

Like a ghost dug from dreams
    Where bones breathless blossomed,
She stands on trial for a fabulous crime
    Grown from her marble bosom.

Unquenchable sting that feeds nightlong
    Till you wake—what bloodshed
You commit! On crooked fingers
    Count the victims. Go, hide

And as you wander in shade and strand
    Her breast accuses you.
Plunge to limbo's deeps; assuage
    Skulls with the grace of dew.

Here she lies plucked out, a shape
    Of disasters and ruins sown
For the dogs! Your brain throbs, throbs—
    What four-legged form dims the dawn?

Share the agony and suffering
    The Elect exalts. Let blood
Burst the shackles, limbs be torn
    That her bruised caress may abide.

Ghost with glazed eyes, bronze smile;
    Ivory look that burns, bears
Fire that dazzles and lights your guilt—
    What scarecrow rides your nightmare?

Crawl, proud beast! From the dunghill
    Claim your corpse. Doves rise
From suckling sleep, and the living yields
    The palm and scent of praise.

III. *The Executioner Speaks*

In the gallery of rogues
    The dreamer's pulsebeat bore
Alarm until bastards ripped
    The veiled boudoir, shrieked: "Murder!"

The Judge flexing his snout, giggles
    Over exhibits of the camera-eye;
The Madame foams with wax-grin:
    "With grace tonight this dog will lie . . ."

Dawn spoiled her alibi
    For suckers plucked with dope;
The Law Unto Herself, the Madame
    Slings round the lover's neck the rope.

Owl's snore, rat's twitching gabble:
    Let the toes swing forever—
Ululations of next-of-kin
    Strike our senses as bizarre!

This dumbshow Mistress licks with spice
    Her transgression; in the holocaust
She shows the nude twist of a smile
    As the corpse pawed its ghost.

Aghast the public burnt her image
    At virgin-bride's spitting distance;
The killjoy martyr of ordeals
    Croaked: "Joy to our Spawn!"

Beloved Boss whose wisdom's the highest
    Vowed to kill her with a kick;
Trials of loins when she was hired
    Made her squeal a bit.

Tracked at her trade he pitched the fork
    Behind the scaffold; at cockcrow
She leaped from the roof—
    Who can love a shrunken head?

IV. *The Assassins Speak*

When we dead awaken from our sleep
    We'll strike a peacock dance,
Plume our bosoms with fire and roses
    As lovers kiss in a trance.

Hear the shriek from the slaughter-house—
    What scandal gathers breath?
"Toll the bell, ghost of my bitch mother,
    My accusers are awake."

The scaffold cracks at the beastly roar,
    Vultures in furor spring
On our skulls, we poor clod—
    They blast what the dawn brings.

Armed with fork and knife
    The priest screams command
From the pulpit; the police
    Rattle their teeth on the round.

Someone (they whisper) poisoned the stoup,
    Devoured the loaf of god!
Alas, drunkards with bloodshot eyes
    Squeezed the wine into their guts.

Someone with cadaverous mug
    Kicked from the tomb, struck
Our darling with balance and sword:
    The System decrees burning the sweatshop.

With sanguinary laugh the Exploiter
    Pushes the pawns to gutter's edge;
"Behold the man of destiny!" he claims—
    A scarecrow on the rampage.

When we dead awaken the axe will hurl
    Edge of vengeance on the neck
That even we bones may sacrifice
    Our dreams, so the living wake.

RICAREDO DEMETILLO

from
Barter in Panay

"I am myself a *datu*, head of tribes.
These others, too, are *datus*, each a chief,
Hereditary masters, usually
The first-born of a noble family.
Each has command of *maharlikas*—brave
Retainers and *timauàs*, those who own
Their land and yield to no man save their lord,
Whose sword they follow when the war drums call.

The place from which we come is called Brunei,
One of two cities in a distant land
Of inlets, bays and valleys by the sea.
Great forests brood along the mountain-sides.
The people there, divided into tribes,
Are loosely ruled by Makatunaw, king
And tyrant, too, for through his treachery,
Datus have lost their valued properties.

King Makatunaw in a palace lives.
The palace is many-turreted and set
Amid wide gardens. Leaf-fringed pools and parks
With noble trees and fragrant flowers delight
The brilliant princes and their princesses.
His armed guards, with their scimitars and pikes,
Surround the ruling king with awe and might;
For every word of his is absolute.

The palace and the nobles' houses, walled
By palisades of brick and wood are proof
Against the strongest siege of enemies,
And soldiers keep a sleepless watch to see
That thieves and pirates would not seize the fort
Or break the walls of caste that separate
The nobles from *timauàs* and the slaves,
Whose houses huddle just beyond the gates.

Within the palace, I was minister,
One of the trusted ones who had the right
To counsel majesty. My youth was spent
In arms and travel with king's embassies.
Once I was sent as envoy to the King
That rules Vijaya, city near the Straits
Of Golden Chersonese. This brilliant port
Commands the passage of all merchant ships

From India, Araby and Chin—great junks
Loaded with fabulous Hunan silks and brigs
From distant Samarcand and Hindustan.
Favored by royalty and Fortune, I
Became the confidant of viceroys
Who told me of the mightiness of kings
Far to the North and East, where mighty folks
Reared palaces of marble friezed with gold.

I met the wisest in the court of kings
And listened to their high disputes. I conned
With them the texts of various sacred books
(There gods would speak instructing noble men).
Learning intricacies of government
And handling delicate affairs with tact
For my king. I rose to the topmost height
And sat beside two kings as minister.

The merchants made Brunei chief artery
Of commerce on the land, and wealth flowed in;
For laws protected all and those in power
Laid no unjust taxation. *Datus* lived
In peace with one another, for the king
Respected their ancestral rights and brooked
No lawlessness from pirates or from thieves.
Brunei became a marvel of the land.

Not only merchants but the wisest men—
Philosophers from India and Cathay,
Arabian teachers, poets, artisans
Crowded the court and added to our fame.
Not even Bandjarmasin boasted so much wealth.
Temples were built, some from whole mountain sides.
Statues lined parks; shrines flocked with devotees;
And theaters cast new plays and puppet shows.

The conquests of our arms were also famed.
On the high seas, our ships sailed unopposed
By pirates, who had learned our stern reproofs.
The islands of the seas brought tributes, too—
Dyaks and Suluans, fierce and untamed.
My fame was high. I was the favorite
Of my king and my policies were his
That brought in treasures, triumphs, fame and peace.

But Makatunaw, settled on the throne,
Knew but one law, which is no law at all—
To seize what he could get and stamp his name
On what he seized in greed, then raze the fame
Of those before him by the fire and sword.

        .   .   .   .

Thus have we sailed the seas to this new land
A hope has led us and a dream beside.
A hope that here peace will be ours at last;
A dream that here we'll carve a destiny
Commensurate with our hope for righteousness;
And we have pledged in solemn unity
That we shall work to make all this come true.
Chief Marikudo, drink with me a pledge."

Slaves poured a wine prepared from sugarcane
That we had brought in casks from far Brunei:
A heady drink that warmed the very veins.
The Aetas pledged. Now, since the sun would sink
Soon on the rim of mountains, they prepared
To leave. Chief Marikudo and his wife
Carried their new-got wealth, especially
The *batyâ*, beads and *salakót* of gold

Before they left, Chief Marikudo said:
"Tomorrow, we shall leave the settlement
And you are free to live there. As for us,
We go hunt among the hills and find
A new place where to build a settlement."
Soon all the beach was quiet. Dusk had come
And with it, stars which beamed like constant hope.
That night, most happy dreams gilded our sleep.

Save that within the hearts of some of us,
Desires grew tangled in a thicketry.
Slim Kapinangan dreamed a finger played
Upon her pearls, and then snatched them away
But, strangely, with her own consent. When she woke,
Stirred by her dream, she felt Sumakwel's hand
Upon her bosom; she moved out of his reach.
But feeling guilty, she crept to his embrace.

Her movement woke Sumakwel. When he found
Her close, he hugged her tightly to his breast.
She yielded to his touch, and, now aroused,
She gave her body to her lord. But in
Her mind, she saw young Gurong-gurong's face;
And so she lay, clasped in Sumakwel's arms,
Until the taut need in her flesh was stilled;
But sleep was fitful and she tossed all night.

NICK JOAQUIN

A Portrait of the Artist as Filipino

> How but in custom and in ceremony
> Are innocence and beauty born?
> —YEATS

(An Elegy in Three Scenes)

THE SCENES——

FIRST SCENE: *The* sala *of the Marasigan house in Intramuros. An afternoon towards the beginning of October, 1941.*
SECOND SCENE: *The same. A week later. Late in the morning.*
THIRD SCENE: *The same. Two days later. Afternoon of the second Sunday of October.*

THE PEOPLE——

CANDIDA *and* PAULA MARASIGAN, *spinster daughters of Don Lorenzo*
PEPANG, *their elder married sister*
MANOLO, *their eldest brother*
BITOY CAMACHO, *a friend of the family*
TONY JAVIER, *a lodger at the Marasigan house*
SUSAN *and* VIOLET, *vaudeville artists*
DON PERICO, *a senator*
DON ALVARO *and* DOÑA UPENG,
    his wife
DON PEPE   } *friends of the Marasigans*
DON ARISTEO
TWO POLICEMEN

(As adapted for the Barangay Theater by Daisy Hontiveros-Avellana.)

311

THE FIRST SCENE

Blackout—music in—spot on BITOY *on top of wall and taped narration is played.*

BITOY: Intramuros! The old Manila. The original Manila. The Noble and Ever Loyal City . . .

To the early conquistadores she was a new Tyre and Sidon; to the early missionaries she was a new Rome. Within these walls was gathered the wealth of the Orient—silk from China; spices from Java; gold and ivory and precious stones from India. And within these walls the Champions of Christ assembled to conquer the Orient for the Cross. Through these old streets once crowded a marvelous multitude—viceroys and archbishops; mystics and merchants; pagan sorcerers and Christian martyrs; nuns and harlots and elegant marquesas; English pirates, Chinese mandarins, Portuguese traitors, Dutch spies, Moro sultans, and Yankee clipper captains. For three centuries this medieval town was a Babylon in its commerce and a New Jerusalem in its faith . . .

Now look: this is all that's left of it now. Weeds and rubble and scrap iron. A piece of wall, a fragment of stairway—and over there, the smashed gothic facade of old Santo Domingo . . . [*From this point, light slowly grows about* BITOY.]

Not so long ago, people were dying here—a horrible death —by sword and fire—their screams drowned out by the shriller screaming of the guns. Only silence now. Only silence, and the moonlight, and the tall grass thickening everywhere . . . This is the great Calle Real—the main street of the city, the main street of the land, the main street of our history. Through this street the viceroys made their formal entry into the city. And on this street the principal families had their town houses—splendid ancient structures with red-tiled roofs and wrought-iron balconies and fountains playing in the interior patios. When I was a little boy, some of those old houses were still standing—but, oh, they had come down in the world! No longer splendid, no longer the seats of the mighty; abandoned and forgotten; they stood decaying all along this street. Intramuros was dying, Intramuros was decaying even before the war; the noble and ever loyal city had become just another jungle of slums. But there was one house on this street that never became a slum. It finally took a global war to destroy that house and the three people who fought for it.

[*The lights go on inside the stage. Through the transparent curtain, the sala of the Marasigan house becomes visible. It is a large room, clean and polished, but—like the furniture—dismally shows its age. The paint has darkened and is peeling off the walls. The windowpanes are broken. The doorways are not quite square any more. The baroque elegance has tarnished.*

[*Rear wall opens out, through French windows, into two sagging balconies that overhang the street. At center, against the wall between the balconies, is a large sofa. Ordinarily grouped with this sofa are two rocking chairs, a round table, and two straight chairs. Right now, the table and the straight chairs have been moved in front of the balcony at right, its windows having been closed. The table is set for merienda. Through the open windows of the other balcony, late afternoon sunlight streams into the room, and you get a glimpse of the untidy tenements across the street.*

[*At left side of the room, downstage, is a portion of the bannisters and the head of the stairway, facing towards rear. In the middle of the left wall is a closed door. Against back wall, facing stairway, stands an old-fashioned combination hatrack and umbrella-stand with mirror.*

[*At right side of the room, downstage, against the walls, is a what-not filled with seashells, figurines, family albums, magazines and books. In the middle of the right wall is a large open doorway framed with curtains. Next to it, against right wall, stands an upright piano. Embroidered cushions decorate the chairs. Pedestals bearing potted plants flank the balconies and the door-*

way at right. On the walls above the sofa, the piano, and the what-not, are enlarged family photographs in ornate frames. A chandelier hangs from the ceiling. The painting entitled "A Portrait of the Artist as Filipino" is supposed to be hanging in the center of the invisible "fourth wall" between stage and audience. "Left" and "Right" in all the stage directions are according to the view from the audience.]

I remember coming here one day early in October back in 1941—just two months before the war broke out. I stood in the *sala* and looked around me. Outside, outside, the world was hurrying gaily towards destruction. In here, life went on as usual; unaltered, unchanged; everything in its proper place. [*A pause, while* BITOY *comes upstairs and stands smiling at the room. Enter* CANDIDA MARASIGAN *at right, bearing a chocolate-pot on tray. Seeing* BITOY, *she stops in the doorway and stares at him inquiringly.* CANDIDA *is forty-two, and is dressed in the style of the twenties. Her uncut hair, already graying, is coiled up and knotted in the old manner. Her body is straight, firm, and spare. Not conventionally pretty, she can, however, when among friends, grow radiant with girlish charm and innocence. When among strangers, she is apt, from shyness, to assume the severe forbidding expression of the crabbed old maid. She is staring very severely now at the grinning young man on the stairway.*]

Hello, Candida. [*He waits, smiling; but as her face remains severe, he walks towards her.*] Candida, surely you know me? [*As he approaches, her face quickens with recognition, and she advances to meet him.*]

CANDIDA: But of course, of course! You are Bitoy, the son of old Camacho! And shame on you, Bitoy Camacho—shame, shame on you for forgetting your old friends! [*They have met at center of stage.*]

BITOY: I have never forgotten my old friends, Candida.

CANDIDA: Then why have you never—— [*She speaks this with emphatic gesture that causes chocolate to splash from pot.* BITOY *backs away. She laughs.*] Oh, excuse me, Bitoy!

BITOY: Here, let me take that. [*He takes tray and places it on table. Her eyes follow him. He turns around and, smiling, submits to her gaze.*] Well?

CANDIDA [*approaching him*]: So thin, Bitoy? And so many lines in your face already? You cannot be more than twenty.

BITOY: I am twenty-five.

CANDIDA: Twenty-five! Imagine that! [*Calls.*] Paula . . . Paula! [*Offstage,* PAULA *is heard answering: "Coming!"* CANDIDA *approaches* BITOY *and takes both his hands in hers.*] Bitoy, how sweet of you to remember us. You make me feel very happy. You bring back memories of such happy days.

BITOY: Yes, I know. You bring them back to me, too—all those Friday evenings I spent here with my father.

CANDIDA [*releasing his hands*]: But how is it you remember? You were only a child.

BITOY: But I do, I do! Oh, those *"tertulias"*—how I remember them all! On Fridays, do you know, I still wake up sometimes, even now, thinking: Today is Friday; the *tertulia* will be at the Marasigan house in Intramuros; and Father and I will be going.

[*He pauses as* PAULA *appears in doorway, carrying a platter of biscuits.* PAULA *is forty, also slightly gray-haired already, and also wearing a funny old dress. She is smaller than* CANDIDA, *and looks more delicate, more timid; like* CANDIDA, *she is ambiguous —the bleakest of old maids, you would call her, until she smiles, when you discover, astonished, a humorous girl—still fresh, still charming—lurking under the gray hair.*]

CANDIDA: Well, Paula—do you see who has come to visit us after all these years?

PAULA [*as she hurries to table and sets down the platter*]: Why, Bitoy! Bitoy Camacho!

BITOY: Hello, Paula. [*She goes to* BITOY *and gives him both her hands.*]

PAULA: Holy Virgin, how he has grown! Can this be our baby, Candida? [*They laugh.*]

BITOY: At least there's one thing that hasn't changed—this

house. [*Walks about.*] It looks just the same . . . except . . . yes, of course. That painting. Is this the celebrated picture?

CANDIDA [*expressionless*]: Yes.

BITOY: When did your father paint it?

PAULA: About a year ago.

BITOY [*after a staring pause*]: What a strange picture!

CANDIDA: Do you know what he calls it?

BITOY: Yes.

CANDIDA: "RETRATO DEL ARTISTA COMO FILIPINO."

BITOY: Yes, I know. "A Portrait of the Artist as Filipino." But why, why? The scene is not Filipino . . . What did your father mean? [*He holds up a hand towards Portrait.*] A young man carrying an old man on his back . . . and behind them, a burning city . . .

PAULA: The old man is our father.

BITOY: Yes, I recognize the face . . .

CANDIDA: And the young man is our father also—our father when he was young.

BITOY [*excitedly*]: Why, yes, yes!

CANDIDA: He has painted himself as he is now—and as he used to be—in the past.

BITOY: The effect is rather frightening . . .

CANDIDA: Oh, do you feel it, too?

BITOY: I feel as if I were seeing double.

CANDIDA: I sometimes feel as if that figure up there were a monster—a man with two heads.

BITOY: But this is magnificent! This is a masterpiece! Do you know, a visiting Frenchman has written an enthusiastic article about this picture?

CANDIDA: Oh yes—he was very nice, that Frenchman. He said he had long been an admirer of my father. He was thoroughly acquainted with my father's work. He had seen them in Madrid and Barcelona. And he promised himself—— [*She pauses. BITOY has taken out a notebook and is jotting down what she is saying. She and PAULA exchange glances.*]

BITOY [*looking up expectantly*]: Yes? He promised himself what?

CANDIDA: Tell me something, Bitoy—are you a newspaper reporter?

BITOY [*after a moment's hesitation*]: Yes. Yes, I am.

CANDIDA [*smiling*]: And that is why you have come to visit us after all these years! [*Still smiling, she walks away.* BITOY *looks blankly after her. She goes to table and begins to beat the chocolate.* BITOY *turns to* PAULA.]

BITOY: Paula, what is the matter! What have I done?

PAULA: Oh, nothing, Bitoy. Only, when people come here now, it is not to visit us, but to see this picture.

BITOY: Well, you ought to be glad, you ought to be proud! People thought your father died a long time ago! Now, after all these years of silence and obscurity, everybody is talking about him! The whole country is agog to discover that Don Lorenzo Marasigan, one of the greatest painters of the Philippines and the friend and rival of Juan Luna, is not only alive but has actually painted another masterpiece in his old age!

PAULA [*gently*]: My father painted this picture only for us—for Candida and myself. He gave it to us as a present; and for a whole year it has hung here in peace. Then that Frenchman came and saw it and wrote about it. And since then we have had no peace. No day passes but we must face a reporter from the newspaper or a photographer from the magazines or a group of students from the universities. And we—[*Laying a hand on his shoulder.*]—we do not like it, Bitoy. [*She turns away and goes to table where she begins to prepare her father's* merienda *on a tray. Meanwhile,* BITOY *stands where she has left him, staring at Portrait. Then he pockets his notebook and goes toward table.*]

BITOY: Forgive me, Candida. Forgive me, Paula. [PAULA *goes on arranging tray;* CANDIDA *goes on beating chocolate.*] Well . . . I suppose I ought to go away.

CANDIDA [*not looking up*]: No; stay and have some *merienda*. Paula, get another cup.

BITOY [*as* PAULA *goes to doorway*]: Please do not bother, Paula. I really must be going.

PAULA [*pausing*]: Oh, Bitoy!

BITOY: There are some people waiting for me.

CANDIDA [*pours chocolate into cup, hands cup to* BITOY]: Sit down, Bitoy, and no more nonsense.

BITOY [*hesitates*]: Well——

CANDIDA: Here, Paula. Take father's chocolate to his room. And tell him that the son of his old friend Camacho has come to visit him.

PAULA: Yes, Candida. [*Exits with tray.*]

BITOY: And how is he—your father?

CANDIDA [*pouring a cup for herself*]: Oh, quite well.

BITOY: Is he too weak now to leave his room?

CANDIDA: Oh no.

BITOY: But something is the matter with him?

CANDIDA [*evasively*]: He had an accident.

BITOY: When?

CANDIDA: About a year ago.

BITOY: When he painted that picture?

CANDIDA: A short time after he finished painting it.

BITOY: What happened?

CANDIDA: We do not quite know. We think he must have been walking in his sleep. And he . . . he fell from the balcony of his room into the courtyard below.

BITOY: And how is he now?

CANDIDA: He can move about—but he prefers to stay in bed. Do you know, Bitoy—he has not once come out of his room for a whole year. [*She suddenly presses her knuckles to her forehead.*] Oh, we blame ourselves for what happened!

BITOY: But why should you? It was an accident.

CANDIDA [*after a pause*]: Yes . . . Yes, it was an accident. [*She picks up chocolate pot again and pours a cup for* PAULA. BITOY *watches her in silence.* PAULA *appears joyously in doorway.*]

PAULA: Come, Bitoy! Hurry! Papa is delighted! He begs you to come at once!

BITOY [*walking to doorway*]: Thank you, Paula.

CANDIDA: Bitoy——[*He stops and looks at her.*] You will be very careful? Remember: you are not a reporter, you are a friend. You have come not to interview him or take his photograph. You have only come to visit him.

BITOY: Yes, Candida.

[*Exeunt* PAULA *and* BITOY. CANDIDA *sits down and begins to eat. The day's mail is stacked on the table. She opens and glances through the letters as she eats.* PAULA *comes back.*]

PAULA [*sitting down and sipping her chocolate*]: Father was really delighted. He even got out of bed to shake hands with Bitoy. And they were talking very gaily when I left them. Oh, father is really getting better, Candida! Do you not think so? [CANDIDA *does not answer. She has propped an elbow on the table and is staring at a letter, her head leaning on her hand.* PAULA *leans sideways to look at letter.*] More bills, Candida?

CANDIDA [*picking up and dropping one by one the letters she has opened*]: The water bill. The gas bill. The doctor's bill . . . And this—[*Waving the letter she's holding.*]—this is the light bill. Listen. [*She reads.*] "We again warn you that unless these accounts are immediately settled, we shall be obliged to discontinue all further service." And this is the third warning they have sent.

PAULA: Have you told Manolo?

CANDIDA: I called up Manolo, I called up Pepang—and they said: Oh yes, yes—they would send the money right away. They have been saying that all this month, but they never send the money.

PAULA [*bitterly*]: Our own brother and sister!

CANDIDA: Our own brother and sister are determined that we give up this house.

PAULA: Well, they are not going to make us do it. You and I are going to stay right here. We were born here and we will die here!

CANDIDA: But what if they continue not to send us any money? What if they refuse to support us any longer? All these bills . . .

PAULA [*pensively*]: There must be something we can do!

CANDIDA [*leaning towards* PAULA]: Listen, I have some new ideas.

PAULA [*not paying attention*]: But what can we do? We are two useless old maids . . .

CANDIDA [*rising and looking about*]: Where is that newspaper?

PAULA: Oh, I lie awake night after night wondering how we can make money, money, money!

CANDIDA [*who has found newspaper and is standing by the table searching through the pages*]: Ah, here it is. Now listen, Paula. Listen to this. It says here——[*She stops.*]

[*Below, in the street, a car is heard stopping. The sisters listen; then glance at each other.* CANDIDA *sighs, folds newspaper, places it on table, and sits down.* PAULA *pours herself more chocolate. Footsteps are heard on the stairway. The sisters pick up their cups and sip their chocolate. Enter* TONY JAVIER, *carrying books and his coat in one hand. He glances towards the sisters, pushes the hat off his brow, and calls out: "Good afternoon, ladies." Then he opens the closed door at left and flings his coat, hat and books inside. He pulls the door shut again and, smiling confidently, walks into the sala.* TONY *is about twenty-seven, very masculine, and sardonic. His shirt and tie are blissfully resplendent; his charm, however, is more subtle—and he knows it.*]

TONY: Ah-ha, *merienda!*

CANDIDA [*very old-maidish*]: Will you have some chocolate, Mr. Javier?

TONY: Tch-tch. That's bad business, ladies. Remember: I'm just paying for room without board.

CANDIDA [*severely*]: Mr. Javier, anybody who lives under our roof is welcome to our table.

TONY: But are good manners good business?

CANDIDA: Mr. Javier, will you have some chocolate?

TONY [*picking up a biscuit and popping it into his mouth*]: Yes, thank you! [*He sees* BITOY's *cup.*] Oh, you had a visitor!

CANDIDA: An old friend of ours. Paula, get another cup.

TONY: Oh, what for? [*As* PAULA *rises, he reaches across the table and presses a hand on her shoulder. She starts and looks at him, not angry but wondering. He slowly withdraws his hand, their eyes interlocked.*] Please do not bother, Miss Paula. I can use this cup. I'm not particular.

CANDIDA [*grimly*]: Paula, get another cup.

TONY: Or perhaps you would like to offer me your cup, Miss Paula?

PAULA [*her eyes still innocently fascinated*]: My cup?

TONY [*picking up* PAULA's *cup*]: Do you still want this chocolate?

PAULA [*shaking her head*]: No.

TONY: Then, may I have it?

CANDIDA [*rising*]: Mr. Javier, I ask you to put down that cup at once!

TONY [*ignoring* CANDIDA]: Thank you, Miss Paula. [*He lifts the cup above his head.*] To better business! [*Then he throws his head back and slowly, deliberately drinks the chocolate, the sisters staring at his throat in horror and fascination. Then he sets the cup down and smacks his lips.*]

CANDIDA [*coming to life*]: Mr. Javier, it is outrageous——

TONY [*picking up and gobbling another biscuit*]: Oh, no—it was delicious!

CANDIDA: It is useless to treat you with decency!

TONY [*bowing*]: Permit me to remove my indecent person from your sight. [*He walks towards his room. The sisters exchange glances. He stops and looks back.*] Oh—and thanks a lot for the *merienda!*

CANDIDA: Mr. Javier, you will please come back here. There is something we have to ask you.

TONY [*walking back*]: Okay, shoot.

PAULA [*quickly picking up chocolate-pot*]: I must just take this out to the kitchen.

CANDIDA: Put that down, Paula. You will stay right here.

TONY: Well, what is it? Come on, hurry up, I haven't got much time. I'd like to lie down a moment before I go out again. [*He yawns and stretches his arms; his brows darken with momentary irritation.*] Boy, but am I tired! I never get any sleep! I never get any sleep at all! [*He goes to table and picks up another biscuit.*] Studying all day, working all night! Ambition—hah! Everybody has it! [*Nibbling the biscuit, he goes to a rocking chair and flops down.*] Look at me—a cheap little vaudeville piano-player. Not a pianist—oh no, no—certainly not a pianist! Hey, you know what's the difference between a pianist and a piano-player? I can tell you. A pianist is uh —A pianist is—well—highbrow stuff. Oh, you know. He had professors to teach him; he went to the right academies; and he gives concerts for the high society dames. Culture—that's a pianist! While a piano-player—oh, that's me! Nobody ever taught me how to play. I taught myself—and I know I stink! [*He rises and thrusts his hands into his pockets.*]

A cheap little vaudeville piano-player. Three shows a day in a stinking third-class theatre. The audience spits on your neck and the piano rattles like an old can. And you never know how long the job will last . . . [*A pause, while he stares at the floor. Then he sighs deeply and shrugs.*] So what do I do? So I get ambitious! So I tell myself I'm not going to be just a piano-player all my life. No, siree! I'm gonna be a lawyer—a big, rich, crooked lawyer! So I'm going to school —yes, siree! Go to school all day, play the piano all night. What a life! Oh well, it used to be worse . . . [*He suddenly turns to the sisters.*] Can you, ladies, have any idea what kind of a life I've had?

CANDIDA: We are not interested in your private life.

TONY [*looking her in the eye*]: Oh no? [*Her eyes falter; she looks away. He smiles.*]

CANDIDA: Mr. Javier, when we allowed you to rent a room in our house, it was with the condition that you would permit no gambling, no drinking, and no women in your room.

TONY: So what now?

CANDIDA: You have broken our rules.

TONY: But I don't do my gambling here.

CANDIDA: I was not referring to gambling.

TONY: Well, I bring home a beer now and then.

CANDIDA: Nor to drinking either.

TONY [*his eyes widening*]: Oh, you mean—— [*Grinning, he traces a woman's form in the air with his hands.*]

CANDIDA [*not smiling*]: Yes!

TONY: But when?

CANDIDA: Last night, Mr. Javier, my sister and I heard you arriving with a woman.

TONY: Holy cow, were you still awake when I arrived last night?

CANDIDA: We happened to be still awake.

TONY [*bashfully dropping his eyes*]: Were you . . . waiting up for me?

CANDIDA: Mr. Javier, did you or did you not bring a woman here last night!

TONY [*wide-eyed*]: My dear ladies, you must have been dreaming! That was a wonderful, wonderful dream you had last night —and I sure hate to spoil your fun. So, you ladies dream about me, eh?

CANDIDA: How can you have the nerve to lie! I distinctly heard a woman laughing—and so, I told my sister to get up and look out the window. Go on, Paula—tell him. Did you see a woman?

PAULA [*timidly*]: Well . . . it . . . it may have been a woman——

CANDIDA: May have been! I thought you said you were sure you saw one!

PAULA: Only because you said you were sure you heard one! But it was so dark really—and all I could see was something white. It may have been a woman's dress—or it may have been a man's shirt . . .

TONY: It was a man's shirt! And the man inside the shirt was— uh—Oh yes, he was the drummer in our band! And he came along with me last night because I had some of his music in my room. So he came up; and I gave him his music; and then he went away. And that's all there is to it!

CANDIDA: Are you telling us the truth?

TONY [*putting up his hand*]: The whole truth and nothing but the truth.

CANDIDA: I wonder!

PAULA: Oh Candida, if we have falsely accused Mr. Javier, the least we can do now is to apologize for having hurt his feelings!

TONY [*instantly pitying himself*]: Oh no—why apologize to me? I'm just an animal! Animals have no feelings! It is useless to treat them with decency!

CANDIDA [*stiffly*]: Mr. Javier, if we have made a mistake, we are sorry—and we apologize.

TONY [*ignoring her; laying on the misery*]: Just a pile of trash . . . Rotten trash.

CANDIDA: Mr. Javier, this is not funny at all!

TONY: You bet it's not funny![*He stands scowling at her.* BITOY *appears in doorway, carrying tray.* TONY's *expression changes into surprise.*]

TONY: Why, hello there, guy!

BITOY: Hi, Tony. Paula, where do I put this?

PAULA [*approaching*]: Give it to me. [*She takes tray and exits.*]

BITOY [*walking in*]: Well, well, Tony!

TONY: Hi, guy.

CANDIDA: Do you two know each other?

BITOY: We used to work together.

TONY: At the piers.

BITOY: What are you doing here?

TONY: I live here.

BITOY: No!

TONY: Yes! See that room over there? It's mine. For fifteen pesos a month.

BITOY: Candida, are you taking in boarders?

CANDIDA: Oh, you know how poor we are! Paula and I—we thought we would try running a boarding-house. But Mr. Javier is our first—and so far—our only customer. [*Offstage,* PAULA *is heard shouting* "Candida! Candida!" CANDIDA *raises her voice.*] Yes? What is it, Paula? [PAULA *appears in doorway, still carrying tray.*]

PAULA: Oh Candida, a rat! A rat in the kitchen!

CANDIDA [*with a shake of the head*]: Oh Paula, Paula!

PAULA [*pleadingly*]: And such a big, big rat, Candida!

CANDIDA: All right, I am coming [*To* BITOY *and* TONY.] Excuse
me. [*Exeunt* PAULA *and* CANDIDA.]

TONY [*contemptuously*]: A pair of crazy dames!

BITOY [*rather stiffly*]: They are old friends of my family, Tony.

TONY [*carelessly*]: Well, you better stay away from them. They're
man-hungry.

BITOY [*smiling in spite of himself*]: Why, have they been trying
to eat you up?

TONY: Ah, they're crazy. If I just look at them, they start shivering. When I talk to them, they get a fever. And if I touch
them——

BITOY: So, you make love to them!

TONY: Me? Make love to them? Pah! [*He spits.*] I'd sooner make
love to the Jones Bridge! Nah—it's them that's crazy, not me.

BITOY: It must be the poverty . . . I didn't know they had become so poor . . .

TONY: Poor? They're desperate!

BITOY: But they still have a married brother, and a married sister.

TONY: The brother and sister have been paying all the expenses
—but it looks like they don't want to anymore. They want
to sell this house and put the old man in a hospital.

BITOY: And what becomes of Paula and Candida?

TONY: Candida goes to live with the brother, Paula goes to live
with the sister.

BITOY: Poor Candida! Poor Paula!

TONY: Why, they could have some big money if only—— [*He
stops and looks towards Portrait.*]

BITOY: If only what?

TONY [*coming downstage*]: See this painting? Well, I know an
American who's willing to pay two thousand dollars for it.
Dollars, mind you—not pesos.

BITOY [*coming downstage, too*]: And Paula and Candida refuse
to sell?

TONY: They absolutely refuse to sell. Just think of it—two
grand! Oh, I've been trying and trying to make them sell—

BITOY: You, Tony?

TONY: Sure—me. This American, he hired me to put over the deal, see?

BITOY: And no dice.

TONY: Those dames are crazy!

BITOY: Maybe they love this picture too much.

TONY: Love it? They hate it!

BITOY: How do you know?

TONY: Oh, I just do. And I hate it myself!

BITOY: Oh, come, come, Tony! It's only a picture. It won't eat you up.

TONY: Who does he think he is? Who the hell does he think he is?

BITOY: Are you referring to the painting or to the painter?

TONY: You were in his room just now, weren't you?

BITOY: Are you speaking of Don Lorenzo?

TONY: Yes, yes! This Don Lorenzo Marasigan—this great Don Lorenzo who has so much damn pride in his head and nothing at all in his pockets. He had you in his room, didn't he? He talked to you, didn't he?

BITOY: He was very friendly.

TONY: I've been living here for months and he hasn't once asked me to his room!

BITOY: But he doesn't know you, Tony.

TONY: He doesn't want to know me! He thinks it's shameful I should be living here! He feels ashamed because his house has become a flop-house! And why should he feel ashamed, I'd like to know! What is he anyway, I'd like to know!

BITOY: Well, among other things, he's a scholar, an artist, and a patriot.

TONY: So he's a great man. So he's a great painter. So he fought in the Revolution. And so what? And what's that old Revolution of his to me? I went hungry and I got kicked about just the same in spite of that old Revolution he's so damn proud of! I don't owe him any thanks! And what the hell is he now? Just a beggar! That's what he is now—just a miserable old beggar! And he has the nerve to look down on me!

BITOY: How do you know he does?

TONY: Oh, I know. I've talked to him. I forced my way into his room once.

BITOY: And he threw you out?

TONY: Oh no, no! He was very courteous, very polite. I went there to tell him about this American wanting to buy this painting for two grand—and he listened very courteously, he listened very politely. And he said he was very sorry but it was none of his business. He said: "The picture belongs to my daughters, it does not belong to me. If anyone wants to buy it, they will have to talk to my daughters." And then he asked me to excuse him, he said he wanted to take a nap— and I found myself on my way out. Oh, he threw me out all right—but very courteously, very politely—the damn beggar—— But he's going to pay for it! Oh, I'll make him pay for it!

BITOY: Aren't you being rather silly, Tony?

TONY [*grinning at Portrait*]: And I know just where it will hurt him!

BITOY: What has the old man done to you?

TONY: Won't his damn heart break when his loving daughters sell off his picture!

BITOY: Oh, is that why you're so eager to make them sell?

TONY: Besides, this American has promised to pay me a very handsome commission, you know! [*Enter* CANDIDA *and* PAULA. TONY *turns away from the Portrait.*]

TONY: Well, did you ladies catch the rat?

PAULA [*proudly*]: Oh, of course! My sister never fails! [*She and* CANDIDA *begin to clear the table.*]

BITOY: Candida, Tony tells me there is an American who wanted to buy this new painting of your father's.

TONY: And he still wants to buy it.

CANDIDA: We have told Mr. Javier again and again: the picture is not for sale.

TONY: Two thousand dollars! That's not chicken-feed.

PAULA: We are sorry, Mr. Javier. Our father painted that picture very especially for us. We will never sell it.

[*A silence. They are all staring at* Portrait. *Unnoticed,* SUSAN *and* VIOLET *come up the stairs and pause on the landing, surprised at the mutely staring people in the* sala. *They glance at each other and giggle behind their hands.* SUSAN *and* VIOLET *are "old girls," plumpish, cute-mannered, and thickly painted. They are wearing tight-fitting sleeveless frocks; and they are both quite tipsy.*]

VIOLET [*leaning forward, cupping her mouth with a hand*]: Yoo-hoo! [*Everybody in the* sala *gives a nervous start.* SUSAN *and* VIOLET *giggle wildly.*]

CANDIDA: Who are you? And what are you doing here?

TONY [*rising*]: Holy cow!

SUSAN [*ignoring* TONY]: Excuse us for intruding.

VIOLET: Don't you people know us?

SUSAN: I'm Susan.

VIOLET: And I'm Violet.

SUSAN: We're artists at the Parisian Theatre. You know. [*Giggles.*] Vaudeville!

TONY [*approaching*]: Now look, Susan—you're dead drunk. And we've got a show in an hour. You go home—— [*He lays a hand on her arm.*]

SUSAN: I'll go home when I please! And take your hands off me!

TONY: What's eating you, anyway?

SUSAN: A lot you care!

TONY: Oh, it's something I did, is it?

SUSAN: Where were you last night? Where did you go after the show?

TONY: I had a head-ache. So I came straight home.

SUSAN: You never bothered to tell me, did you? You didn't even remember we had a date, did you?

TONY: Sorry, I forgot. But I had such a splitting head-ache——

SUSAN: Don't make me laugh!

TONY: Now listen, Susan—the show goes on in an hour. You've got to sober up. Violet, you take her home and give her a bath.

VIOLET: I'll do nothing of the sort. We came here to rehearse.

TONY: Rehearse what?

Violet [*singing and dancing*]: "A-tisket, a-tasket, a brown and yellow basket——" It's the new number we do. We were supposed to rehearse it last night after the show but we couldn't find you anywhere.

Susan: He had a head-ache, Violet. Hah!

Tony: I said, go home.

Violet: But why? Oh, are those your landladies, Tony? Well, why not introduce us?

Susan [*ambling forward; an arm akimbo*]: He's ashamed of us, Violet. He thinks we don't look decent. He thinks we're drunk.

Tony [*hurrying after her and grabbing her arm*]: I told you to get out of here!

Susan [*wrenching her arm loose*]: I'll go when I please! I've got as much right to stay here as anybody else! You think I don't know what kind of a house this is? Oh, I found out last night, dearie! I saw you and that Shanghai woman——

Tony [*raising a fist*]: Shut up! Shut up or I'll——

Susan [*backing off*]: Yes, I saw you! I saw you last night! And I saw you bring that woman in here! [*She turns to the sisters.*] Now, is that the kind of a house you run?

Tony [*grabbing her arm and dragging her off*]: You're getting out of here if I have to throw you out!

Susan [*screaming and struggling*]: Let me go! Let me go! Let me—AOUH! [*He has slapped her hard across the mouth. She cowers away, holding her mouth.*]

Tony: Now get out! GET OUT OF HERE!

Violet [*taking the sobbing Susan in her arms*]: Okay, big boy— keep your shirt on! We're going. Come on, Susan. [*She leads the sobbing Susan away. At stairway, she pauses and looks back.*] Hitting a woman when she's drunk—che!

[*Tony waits until they have gone down the stairs; then he strides off to his room, slamming the door behind him.*]

Bitoy: I think I'd better go. But may I come again?

Candida: Come whenever you like, Bitoy. We are always at home.

Bitoy: Thank you—and goodbye till then.

SISTERS: Goodbye, Bitoy.

[*Exit* BITOY. PAULA *and* CANDIDA *leave stairway and begin moving back the chairs and table to their proper place at center with the sofa. From this point, twilight starts and the stage dims very gradually.*]

PAULA [*as they shift the furniture*]: What are we going to do, Candida?

CANDIDA: About what?

PAULA [*nodding towards* TONY's *door*]: About him.

CANDIDA: We must order him to leave this house.

PAULA: Yes—certainly!

CANDIDA: Bringing a woman here——

PAULA: And then lying about it!

CANDIDA: Oh, we have been too lenient!

PAULA: Well, we needed the money.

CANDIDA: He can take his money somewhere else—and at once! He shall leave this house immediately!

[TONY's *door opens and he comes out, wearing his coat and carrying his hat. He now looks gentle and rather wistful. The sisters stiffen and assume their coldest expressions.* CANDIDA *raps on the table.*]

CANDIDA: Mr. Javier, please come over here. We have something to say to you.

TONY [*approaching; guiltily fingering his hat*]: Yes, I know. And there's something I would like to say to you too.

CANDIDA: There is nothing you can say that would interest us!

PAULA: We refuse to be flattered and deceived over and over again!

TONY: But look here—I'm not flattering you, I'm not deceiving you! Remember the first time I came here? As I came up those stairs I suddenly felt as if I was coming home at last. Everything looked so clean—this was the home I never had; the home that nobody ever gave me.

CANDIDA: Mr. Javier——

TONY: You were born in this house, you grew up in this house! Do you know where I was born? Do you know where I grew up? Listen: when you were going off to your fine convent-school in your fine clean clothes, I was wandering about in the streets—a little child dressed in rags, always dirty, always hungry. And you know where I found my food? In the garbage cans!

PAULA [*sinking weakly into a chair*]: Oh no!

TONY: Oh yes! And do you know what it's like to go begging in the streets when you're still just a baby? Do you know what it's like to have your own brute of a father driving you out to beg? Can you even imagine that kind of a childhood?

CANDIDA [*sinking down too, on the sofa*]: We know you have had a hard life——

TONY: You know nothing! [A *pause, while he scowls at the memory. Then the scowl fades into a bravado smile.*] Oh, I'm not crying over anything! I never cry! I haven't had a hard time really. I'm clever, and I learn fast. Besides, I'm very good-looking, you know—and I've got a lot of charm. Heck, I don't care if that sounds vain—it's the truth! Ever since I was a kid, people have been fascinated with me—they pick me up and give me the breaks. Nice people, too —people with class . . . Well, just to be completely honest, I'll admit that when they get to know me they drop me quicker than a hot brick! But what the heck—somebody else always comes along and picks me up again. I'm irresistible! All I have to do is smile and look sort of pathetic—you know; very young, very brave, and very broke. They always fall for that.

CANDIDA: Oh Paula, this is all just the same as usual. He is only making fun of us!

TONY: Oh no—honest, I'm not! [*Glancing at his watch.*] Wow! I'll be late for the show! I must rush! [*He claps his hat on and runs to stairway where he suddenly stops and turns around.*] Oh, I forgot—you ladies had something to say to me. [*He shrugs and looks pathetic.*] Well, you may as well say it now. [*The sisters look at him; then at one another; and then down at their hands. There is a moment's silence.*]

CANDIDA [*looking up, but not towards* TONY]: We merely wanted to say, Mr. Javier, that . . . that we do not accept the testimony of intoxicated persons.

TONY [*gravely*]: I see. [*A pause.*] And is that all?

CANDIDA [*now looking towards him*]: That is all, Mr. Javier.

PAULA: Good night, Mr. Javier.

TONY [*grinning and lifting his hat high above his head*]: Good night, ladies. Good night, sweet ladies. Good night, good night! [*He puts his hat on with a swagger and runs down the stairs whistling "A tisket, a tasket." The sisters burst into laughter.*]

PAULA: Oh, he is funny, is he not?

CANDIDA: It would have been unjust to ask him to leave on such doubtful evidence.

PAULA: And besides, we need the money.

CANDIDA [*rising*]: Oh, money, money, money! We must act, Paula—we must act at once. And I know just what we can do. [*She picks up newspaper.*]

PAULA: Your new plans?

CANDIDA: Yes. Listen to this. "Fifty centavos for every rat caught." Now, I wonder where this Bureau of Health and Science is? I shall go there and offer them my services. And, Paula—you will give lessons.

PAULA [*horrified*]: Lessons!

CANDIDA: Lessons in the piano, lessons in Spanish. We will put up a sign.

PAULA [*rising*]: Oh no, no!

CANDIDA: Now Paula, remember—we must be bold, we must become women of the world. We must show Manolo and Pepang that we can support ourselves, that we do not need their money.

PAULA: But lessons for whom—girls?

CANDIDA: Girls for the piano, and some men for Spanish. So many of these young students are eager to learn the language nowadays. And men have more money, you know.

PAULA: They would only laugh at me.

CANDIDA: Nonsense! Be bold! Drink a little wine before you face them. Talk in a loud voice. If they become impertinent, call a policeman. We could arrange to have a policeman nearby during the first days.

PAULA: You will not be here, Candida?

CANDIDA: I shall be working at this [*Glancing at newspaper.*] This Bureau of Health and Science. If they are so eager to pay fifty centavos for one rat, how they will welcome somebody who is willing to catch as many rats as they want. I shall be appointed to clear the entire city of rats. Of course, then, I would hardly have time to do the actual catching anymore. I shall be just a kind of director—with a desk, a map, and a staff of workers . . .

PAULA [*giggling*]: And they will all be calling you Miss Marasigan!

CANDIDA: And I shall make them all wear uniforms. [*She turns wistful.*] Still, from time to time, I should want to do some of the actual catching myself—but only in the more difficult cases, of course . . .

PAULA: And how much will you earn?

CANDIDA: I will consult Manolo on what salary to ask. Oh, they have a sea of money rolling about in the government!

PAULA: Yes indeed. Just look at the newspapers—always talking of those people who made millions!

CANDIDA: Oh, I have it all planned out. We will make money, Paula—we will make money! And we will show Manolo and Pepang that we can keep up this house with our own efforts.

PAULA [*rapturously*]: And they will not be able to turn us out of here anymore! We will not be afraid anymore! [*She sinks down on the rocking chair.*]

CANDIDA [*sitting down at the piano*]: We shall stay here till we die! You and I and papa. Yes—and papa! He will get well, he will come out of his room, we will be happy again—just the three of us. It will be like the old days again . . .

PAULA: Oh Candida, we were happy enough then—and we did not know it! We destroyed the happiness we had . . . Oh, why did we do it, Candida, why did we do it!

CANDIDA: Hush, Paula—— [*Pause.*] It is getting dark. Go and turn on the light. [PAULA *goes to light switch on left corner of the "fourth wall."*]

PAULA [*in voice of alarm*]: Candida, there is no light!

CANDIDA [*looking around*]: What! Try again!

PAULA: I have turned this switch a dozen times. There is no light!

CANDIDA [*rising quickly*]: Try the switch on the stairway—I will try this one in the corridor.

[PAULA *goes to stair-landing.* CANDIDA *steps just inside the doorway at right. After a moment, she comes in again and looks at* PAULA *across the room.*]

CANDIDA: No light either on the stairs?

PAULA: None! How about in the corridor?

CANDIDA: None. And I saw no light in father's room.

PAULA: Oh Candida, they have cut off our light!

CANDIDA: S-h-h! [*The sisters fearfully come to center of stage where they huddle together.*]

PAULA [*whispering*]: Shall we call up the company?

CANDIDA: It would be useless . . .

PAULA: Then call up Manolo, call up Pepang! Tell them what has happened to us! They must send us the money right away! Oh, how could they do this to us! How could they possibly allow us to suffer this horrible, horrible humiliation!

CANDIDA [*bitterly*]: And how shall I call them up, Paula? Am I to go down and use the telephone at the corner drugstore?

PAULA: But that is where we always telephone——

CANDIDA: But how, how can I go down to the street now! Think, Paula—everybody who lives on this street knows by now that we have no light, that the company has cut off our light!

PAULA [*in mounting horror*]: Oh Candida . . . Oh Candida! [*Trembling, they glance behind them at the open balcony.*]

CANDIDA: Go and shut those windows.

PAULA [*shivering*]: Oh no, no! They would see me! The neighbors, Candida—they will be all gathered at their windows, watching our house, pointing at our house—the only house without light in the whole street! Oh Candida—they are all there at the windows, pointing and laughing and jeering!

CANDIDA: We must close those windows. I will close them.

PAULA: No, Candida! They will see you!

CANDIDA: But perhaps no one has noticed yet that we have no light . . .

[*She cautiously tip-toes towards balcony, keeping herself out of street-range. As she closes the windows, she notices something odd in the street and peers out. Then, boldly, she steps right out onto the balcony and looks up and down the street. She turns around joyously and steps back into the room.*]

CANDIDA: Paula, there is no light anywhere!

PAULA: No light?

CANDIDA [*with exultant relief*]: All the houses are dark! All, all of them!

PAULA: What has happened?

CANDIDA: Oh, come and look! There is total darkness all over the city!

PAULA [*approaching balcony*]: Why, yes, yes! There is no light anywhere! [*Clasping her hands in gratitude.*] Oh, merciful, merciful God!

CANDIDA [*suddenly bursting into laughter as she moves downstage*]: But what fools we are! What ignorant fools we are!

PAULA [*following*]: What has happened?

CANDIDA [*laughing uncontrollably*]: Nothing has happened! Nothing has happened at all! Oh Paula, Paula—we must read the newspapers with more interest! It was all in the newspapers! Didn't you read it?

PAULA: What?

CANDIDA: Tonight, Paula—tonight is the night of the black-out —of the practice black-out! All the lights have been turned off!

PAULA: Why?

CANDIDA: It is part of all their preparations—they are preparing for war!

PAULA [*sighing with relief*]: Oh, is that all?

CANDIDA [*laughing hysterically*]: And we thought . . . Oh Paula, we thought . . . We thought our light had been cut off!

PAULA: Oh, thank God, thank God, thank God!

CANDIDA: And how frightened we were, Paula! We were almost trembling!

PAULA [*beginning to laugh, too*]: And we were afraid to close the windows! We were afraid to go down to the street!

CANDIDA [*gasping with laughter*]: And we . . . we were afraid that we could never . . . never show our . . . our faces again in the . . . in the street! Oh Paula—how funny! How funny we were! [*She goes off into another wild peal of laughter that ends in sudden sobs. She buries her face in her hands.*]

PAULA [*alarmed; approaching*]: Candida, Candida!

CANDIDA [*wracked with sobs*]: I can bear no more! I can bear no more!

PAULA: Candida, the neighbors will hear you!

CANDIDA [*holding out her hands before her face*]: All the humiliations, Paula . . . All the bitter, bitter humiliations we have suffered!

PAULA [*taking her sister in her arms*]: Hush, Candida! Compose yourself! [CANDIDA *sinks sobbing to the floor.* PAULA *kneels down and takes her sister again in her arms.*] Please, Candida! Please, please, Candida!

[CANDIDA *is still sobbing wildly while* PAULA *holds her tight and strokes her hair, whispering* "Candida, Candida," *as* BLACK-OUT.]

THE SECOND SCENE

BITOY [*offstage voice*]: After my father died—he died when I was about fifteen—I stopped going to the Marasigan house.

I had to leave school and go to work. [*Lights go on inside the stage, revealing the Marasigan sala in daylight.*] I had said goodbye to that house, goodbye to that world—the world of Don Lorenzo, the world of my father. I was bitter against it; it had deceived me. I told myself that Don Lorenzo and my father had taught me nothing but lies. My childhood was a lie; the nineteen-twenties were a lie; beauty and faith and courtesy and honor and innocence were all just lies.

[*Enter* PEPANG MARASIGAN *from doorway at right. She goes to table at center where her bag is. She opens bag, takes out her cigarettes and lights one.*]

The truth was fear—always fear—fear of the boss, of the landlord, of the police, of being late, of being sick, of losing one's job. The truth was no shoes, no money, no smoking, no loitering, no vacancy, no trespassing, and beware of the dog.

[PEPANG *glances around the room, her eyes stopping at Portrait. Looking at it, she comes forward and stands before it, with a half-wistful, half-mocking smile.*]

When the nineteen-forties came along, I had become a finished product of my age. I accepted it completely, and I believed in it. It was a hard world but it was the truth—and I wanted nothing but the truth.

[*Enter* MANOLO MARASIGAN *from doorway at right. He glances towards* PEPANG *as he goes to table and helps himself to her cigarettes. Having lighted one, he comes forward too, and stands beside her, gazing up at Portrait. They continue to stare at Portrait in silence, a moment longer.* PEPANG *and* MANOLO *have inherited their father's good looks; but in* PEPANG, *those fine features have grown hard; in* MANOLO, *they have gone flabby. She looks ambitious, he looks dissipated; she is cynical, he is shifty-eyed. They are both very stylish, and becoming stout.*]

PEPANG: The hero of our childhood, Manolo.

MANOLO: The most wonderful thing that can happen to any child is to have a genius for his father.

PEPANG: And the most cruel.

MANOLO: Yes.

PEPANG: Having to break one's childhood hero—to spurn one's childhood god . . .

MANOLO: Oh, he's still the same old hero up there—still the same old god!

PEPANG: And nobody to worship him anymore. [*She sits down on sofa.*]

MANOLO: He still has got Paula and Candida, hasn't he? [*He turns away too.*] And where can they be—those two? Haven't they shown up yet?

PEPANG: They've probably gone to market.

MANOLO: They get crazier every day.

PEPANG: We must talk to them, we must make them listen. Now remember, you promised to be firm. Where's the senator?

MANOLO: Still in father's room. And they're still talking away!

PEPANG [*glancing at her watch*]: That makes two hours of the good old days.

MANOLO: Oh, it's a regular reunion of the old boys in there.

PEPANG: With the senator around, we can make Candida and Paula listen to us. You know how they look up to him.

MANOLO: Because he's a senator?

PEPANG: Because he is a poet.

MANOLO: Was, Pepang—was! He stopped being a poet a long time ago.

PEPANG: Oh, but they still remember him the way he used to be —when he was still coming here to recite his verses—before he went into politics.

MANOLO: And forgot all about us—the old snob!

PEPANG: And besides, he is their godfather, you know.

MANOLO: Well, if the senator can persuade them to leave this house——

PEPANG: If anybody can do it, he can. And I've made a bargain with him. He says the government is very anxious to acquire that painting. I promised to help him persuade Candida and Paula to sell it if he will help us persuade them to leave this house.

MANOLO: I've got a buyer for the house.

PEPANG: I told you—I already have a buyer.

MANOLO: Now look—you leave all that business to me. After all, I'm the eldest son in this family.

PEPANG [*smoothly*]: That's just it—you are. And I have no confidence at all in the business ability of the men of this family.

MANOLO: Poor father! He ought to hear you!

PEPANG: We all have to grow up, you know.

MANOLO [*looking around*]: How about the furniture?

PEPANG [*rising*]: Well, let me see . . . I'll take that chandelier; I need it for my front hall. And I'll take the marble table in the study. You can have all the furniture here in the *sala*, Manolo—except the piano. I'll take that. And I'll take the dining room set. We can divide the plate and the silver.

MANOLO [*sarcastic*]: Why not take everything, Pepang?

PEPANG: Thank you. Maybe I will.

MANOLO [*raising his voice*]: Sure! Take everything! Take the floors and take the stairs and take the walls and take the roof——

PEPANG: Shh! The senator will hear you!

MANOLO [*lowering his voice*]: . . . and take the whole damned house! I'll cram it down your throat for you! [*Through the ensuing scene, they speak savagely but in controlled voices.*]

PEPANG: Are we going to fight over a few old chairs?

MANOLO: Excuse me—but you have already given me the few old chairs. Do I still have to fight for them? You have taken everything else!

PEPANG: You know that my Mila is getting married next year—and she will need furniture.

MANOLO: If your Mila is getting married next year, my Roddie is getting married this year—and he's going to have the furniture here in the *sala*, and all the furniture in the dining room, and all the furniture in three of the bedrooms, besides all the books and cabinets in the study, the big mirror downstairs, and the matrimonial bed!

PEPANG: Don't be funny!

MANOLO: I don't see you laughing!

PEPANG: I shall take the matrimonial bed for my Mila!

MANOLO: Let's see you move anything out of this house without my permission!

PEPANG: And why should I ask your permission? Who has been paying to keep up this house for the last ten years, I'd like to know!

MANOLO: Are you going to tell me I don't pay my share?

PEPANG: Yes—when you remember!

MANOLO: Now listen—just because I forget to send the money now and then——

PEPANG: Forget! I have to call you up and call you up, month after month, before I can squeeze any money out of you! Pay your share! You are the eldest son—this is your duty, not mine! But if I had left you alone to do it, father would have starved to death by now! And do you think it has been easy for me? Month after month I have to ask my husband for money to support my father and sisters. Do you think I enjoy that? Do you think I don't shrink with shame when he demands why it is not you who are supporting them?

MANOLO: Oh, so he asks that, eh?

PEPANG: You never have any money to send here—but, oh, you have plenty of money to throw away at the races, or to lavish on your *queridas!*

MANOLO: Well, you can tell that husband of yours——

PEPANG [*whispering; glancing towards stairway*]: Shut up!

MANOLO: Or, no—I shall tell him myself——

PEPANG: Shut up, I tell you! They're coming!

[MANOLO *sulkily throws himself into a chair.* PEPANG *sits down on the sofa.* PAULA *comes slowly up the stairs, carrying an umbrella and a basket full of the marketing. She looks rather bleak; but on seeing her brother and sisters, hurries to them—having deposited her umbrella at stand—with a show of animation.*]

PAULA: Oh, are you two here?

MANOLO [*affectionately*]: Hello there, Paulita.

PAULA [*approaching* PEPANG]: Have you been waiting long?

PEPANG: Only two hours.

PAULA: I walked all the way from Quiapo. [*She kisses* PEPANG *on the cheek.*]

PEPANG: Well, how are you? You look haggard.

PAULA: Oh Pepang, they cut off our light a week ago! We thought at first it was only the black-out—but we found afterwards that it really had been cut off!

MANOLO [*after a pause during which he and* PEPANG *look down at the floor*]: Yes, but you have light again now, haven't you? I went over to the company and fixed it up as soon as you called me. You have light again, no? Everything is all right now?

PAULA [*bitterly*]: Yes—everything is just fine! [MANOLO *and* PEPANG *unwillingly glance at each other.*]

MANOLO: We are sorry it happened, Paula.

PEPANG: And where is Candida?

PAULA [*evasively*]: She . . . she went somewhere.

PEPANG [*firmly*]: Where did she go?

PAULA: She is out looking for a job.

MANOLO: Where?

PAULA [*rather proudly*]: At the Bureau of Health and Science.

MANOLO: But whatever gave her the idea she could find a job there!

PEPANG: What does she think she is—a scientist?

PAULA: Why not? They published an advertisement, she has gone to answer it.

PEPANG: You two are becoming—oh, I don't know what! All these crazy ideas! And what are all those signs you have placed down there at the door? "Rooms For Rent." "Expert Lessons in Spanish." Who is giving all those "expert lessons"?

PAULA [*timidly*]: I am . . . I mean, I want to . . . I am willing— but . . .

MANOLO: But you have no pupils yet.

PAULA [*miserably*]: No—not one! Nobody has even come to enquire. And we have had those signs for a week! [*She feels herself at point of tears and quickly moves away, towards doorway.*] I must take this basket out to the kitchen.

PEPANG: Paula——

PAULA [*stopping but not turning around*]: Yes, Pepang?

PEPANG: Don Perico is here.

PAULA: Oh? Where?

PEPANG: In father's room.

PAULA: He has come to visit father?

PEPANG: And to talk to you and Candida.

PAULA: About what?

PEPANG: Well, he feels that being your godfather, and Candida's godfather too, he has a right to advise you two girls about your future. [*She waits; but* PAULA *says nothing.*] Paula, did you hear me?

PAULA: Yes, Pepang—but I must put these things away first. Excuse me. [*She goes out.*]

MANOLO [*rising moodily*]: Let's forget the whole thing.

PEPANG: There you go again, Manolo!

MANOLO: But if they want so desperately to stay here——

PEPANG: But how can they stay here? Be sensible! We simply can't afford to keep up this house any longer!

MANOLO: Oh, can't we?

PEPANG [*grimly*]: Whether we can or not, I don't want to! This house gets on my nerves!

MANOLO: Yes—it gets on my nerves too . . .

PEPANG: And I refuse to be sentimental over it anymore. It will have to be sold. And you will take Candida to live with you; I will take Paula.

MANOLO: So you can have someone to look after your house while you go off and play mah-jongg with your society friends!

PEPANG: And so your wife can have somebody to look after your house while she goes off to her clubs and committees!

MANOLO: Poor Candida! Poor Paula!

PEPANG: After all, we have been supporting them all these years. The least they can do now is to be useful to us. And it's about time they learned to be of some use. They're certainly old enough!

MANOLO: They're too old to change.

PEPANG: Oh, nonsense. The trouble with them is this house, this house! They're buried alive here. It will do them good to be pulled out of here. We are really doing it only for their own good.

MANOLO: And besides, good servants are so hard to get nowadays.

PEPANG: And they will learn to be happy, they will learn to live.

MANOLO: They are happy enough here, they have their own way of life.

PEPANG: What way of life? Hiding from the world in this old house; turning over the family albums; chattering over child-hood memories; worshipping at father's feet . . . Is that your idea of life, Manolo? [*She picks up her compact, snaps it open, and begins to do her mouth.*]

MANOLO: Well, what's yours—playing mah-jongg?

PEPANG: Now look here—don't you want Candida to live with you?

MANOLO: I suppose you want to take her too?

PEPANG: Your wife would never forgive me! Her need is greater than mine. She thinks her clubs and committees more im-portant than my mah-jongg.

MANOLO: Will you stop bringing my wife into this conversation!

PEPANG: Oh, is this a conversation?

MANOLO: And all those fool things you females do!

PEPANG: At least, we females always know what we do with our time—

PERICO [*off*]: Adiós, Lorenzo.

MANOLO: Shh! Here comes Don Perico.

PEPANG: (putting away her compact) But you men just sit around and groan at your watches.

PERICO [*entering*]: Pepang, has my wife arrived?

PEPANG: Is she coming here, Don Perico?

PERICO: I told her to pick me up here at ten o'clock. [*He pulls out his watch.*] It is almost eleven now. [*He groans.*]

MANOLO: Senator, the women always know what they do with their time.

PERICO: I never know what they are doing, most of the time. And I have to be at Malacañan at one o'clock. The President is expecting me. We have to discuss the present emergency. Oh, I hardly have time now even to eat!

PEPANG: Then come and sit down a moment, Don Perico. Paula has arrived. Manolo, do go and call her. [*Exit* MANOLO.] And how do you find our father, Don Perico?

PERICO [*sitting beside her on the sofa*]: He has gone to sleep now. [*He pauses, frowning.* DON PERICO *is in his early seventies, a big man with silver hair, handsome and still vigorous; dressed with expensive good taste; and gleaming with success, self-confidence, and that charming democratic friendliness with which the very rich and powerful delight to astonish their inferiors. Right now, however, his frown of concern is sincere; his complacency has been shaken.*]

PERICO: Pepang, what has happened to him?

PEPANG: What do you mean, Don Perico?

PERICO: Oh, I should have come to visit him before!

PEPANG: Has he changed very much?

PERICO: No—no, I would not say so. He still is the same Lorenzo I remember—very humorous, very charming. And how he can talk! Oh, no one can talk like your father, Pepang. Conversation is one of the lost arts—but your father is still a genius at it.

PEPANG: Yes, father was in fine form today—so gay, so amusing.

PERICO: And yet—something was missing . . .

PEPANG: But you must remember that he is not a young man anymore.

PERICO: About this accident that he had—it was nothing serious?

PEPANG: Oh, it was serious enough—God knows: Imagine a man of his age falling from that balcony in his room!

PERICO: And this happened a year ago?

PEPANG: Right after he finished painting that picture.

PERICO: But he suffered no serious injuries?

PEPANG: We called in the best doctors to examine him.

PERICO: Then why does he stay in bed?

PEPANG: We have been urging him to come out of his room.

PERICO: Pepang, what has happened to him?

PEPANG: Just what did you notice, Don Perico?

PERICO: He seems to have no will to live. [*Pepang is silent, staring at him. Enter* PAULA *and* MANOLO.]

PAULA [*approaching*]: Good morning, *ninong*. How are you?

PERICO [*rising*]: Is this Paula? [*She kisses his hand.*] *Caramba*, Paula—I hardly know you! You were only a little girl the last time I saw you.

PAULA: Yes, *ninong*—it is a long time since we have had the pleasure of your company.

PERICO: Oh Paula, Paula, you must forgive me. We people in the government—we cannot call our lives our own. Our days, hours, even our minutes—all, all belong to the nation!

PAULA: Let me congratulate you on your victory in the last elections.

PERICO: Thank you. As a senator, I find myself in a very good position to help you, Paula.

PAULA: Thank you, *ninong*—but we need no help.

PEPANG [*rising*]: Now, Paula—listen first!

PERICO: I have been told that your father has refused to apply for the pension to which he is entitled.

PAULA: My father will not accept any pension from the government.

PERICO: Of course, no one can force him to do so—and it is only a trifling sum anyway. But listen, Paula—you do desire your father's welfare, no?

PAULA: He will never take the money.

PERICO: No—and I quite respect his reasons, even while I deplore them. But he has served his country unselfishly; it is merely just that his country should not forget him in his old age.

PAULA: Ah, but his country has a poor memory!

PERICO: A poor memory—how true! We are always too excited

over the latest headlines and the newest fashions. But now there is this painting . . . [*He moves towards the Portrait, and the others follow.*] Yes, there is this painting . . . The whole country is talking about it. We can no longer afford to ignore your father. He has forced us all to remember him.

MANOLO: Do you think this a great painting, senator?

PERICO: My boy, it would be impossible for me to judge this picture objectively. It is too much a part of myself. Any opinion of mine would be merely affectionate and sentimental—for this is a picture of the world of my youth, a beautifully accurate picture.

[*A silence, during which they all look at Portrait. Unnoticed, Candida comes up the stairs. She glances disconsolately towards the group in front of Portrait; goes to the hatrack to leave her umbrella; and remains there, her head bowed, her back to the audience. Meanwhile, DON PERICO, who has been frowning at Portrait, turns resolutely towards Paula.*]

PERICO: Paula, your father tells me that this picture belongs to you and your sister. Now listen—would the two of you be willing to make a patriotic sacrifice? [*He waits; but PAULA is silent, CANDIDA turns her face around.*] Because if you were to be patriotic enough to give this picture, to donate this picture to the government—the government might, as a token of gratitude, be willing to set aside a fund—a fund to be administered by your sister and yourself—a fund sufficient to maintain your father and yourselves while he and you are alive. Your father would then have no objection to the money; it would not be offered to him but to you and your sister as a—well—as a kind of reward for your generosity. Paula, I am in a position to arrange all this. I ask you to have confidence in me. I ask you to be generous; give this picture to your country; give this picture to your people. [*PAULA is still silent, her head bowed. Upstage, CANDIDA has turned around.*] Oh, Paula, you would be making a noble and unselfish and heroic sacrifice. As you know, our country possesses not a single painting by your father. His great works are all abroad—in the museums of Spain and Italy. That is why the government is so anxious to acquire this picture. Surely, his own land is entitled to one of his masterpieces?

PEPANG: [*after a pause*]: Well, what do you say, Paula?

MANOLO: But of course, senator, Paula and Candida will want to discuss this first between themselves. They will want to think it over.

CANDIDA [*coming forward*]: We have no need to discuss it, we have no need to think it over!

PEPANG: Candida!

PERICO: Oh, is this Candida? How are you, my child? Do you remember me?

CANDIDA: I remember you, Don Perico, and I am very sorry— but you are only wasting your time. You can go back and tell the government that this picture is not to be had. Paula and I will never part with it!

PEPANG: Candida, be silent and listen!

CANDIDA: I have heard all I need to hear! [*She turns quickly, towards doorway.*]

MANOLO: Don Perico merely wants to help our father, Candida.

PERICO: I understand how you two girls feel about this picture. Your father has painted it for you as a last memento—and of course you find the thought of parting with it very painful. But if you really love your father, you will not think of your-selves—you will think of his welfare. Now listen, Paula; listen, Candida: I am not a doctor but I can see that there is some-thing wrong with your father. [PAULA *and* CANDIDA *look at each other.*] I ought to know; I have known him all his life. I have not seen him for a long time, and I blame myself. [*Pause.*] When I saw him again this morning, I could feel it. There is something wrong with your father.

CANDIDA [*dully*]: Yes.

PERICO: He is sick, and I agree with Pepang and Manolo: this old house is not the place for him. He needs light and fresh air and coolness and quiet. He should be under medical care; he ought to be placed in a hospital.

PAULA: There is no hospital that can cure him!

PEPANG: What do you mean, Paula?

CANDIDA: We mean that we cannot accept the offer.

PEPANG: Are you two out of your senses? Do you value this painting more than father's life?

PAULA: Father is not sick. And he wants to stay here.

CANDIDA: And we shall stay here with him.

MANOLO: But even if he is not sick, you cannot stay here, you should not stay here! Don't you know that a war may break out any day now? And Intramuros is the most dangerous place in the city! Oh, tell them, senator—tell them!

CANDIDA [*smiling; approaching*]: Yes, senator—tell us. What are we to do? Are we to abandon this house? Are we to abandon this house as you abandoned poetry? Go on, senator—tell us. Who could advise us better than you? I promise that we will do whatever you say. Do you agree, Paula?

PAULA: We will do whatever you think is best, *ninong*, I promise.

CANDIDA: There, we have both promised! Our lives are in your hands, senator. Think carefully, think very carefully! Oh, but what need have you to think? You made a similar decision yourself a long time ago. You yourself abandoned this house when you abandoned poetry, when you abandoned our poor little dying world of the past! Did you ever regret your decision, senator? But what a foolish question! One has only to look at you now. You are rich, you are successful, you are important——

MANOLO: Candida, be silent!

CANDIDA: I must talk. Someone must talk! The senator does not answer.

PERICO [*dully*]: Candida, Paula—I have no right to advise you——

CANDIDA: But why not?

PAULA: We listened to your poetry once; we will listen to you now.

CANDIDA: Surely a senator has more authority than a poet?

PERICO: I ask you to think in terms of reality, not in terms of poetry.

PAULA: Oh, poetry is not real?

PERICO: Poetry will not save you from the bombs.

PAULA: You did not always think so.

CANDIDA: And how fiercely you used to stand against the world! In what beautiful words, you used to pour out your scorn of its laws, your anger against its cruelty, your contempt for its malice.

PERICO: Poetry was the passing madness of my youth, a plaything of my childhood.

PAULA: But when you became a man you put away the things of a child.

PERICO: No man has a right to stand apart from the world as though he were a god.

CANDIDA: Then, what do you advise, senator? Shall we surrender—as you did?

PERICO [*after a staring pause*]: Why are you so bitter against me? What have I done? I saw my destiny and I followed it. I have no need to be ashamed of what I did! My whole life has been spent in the service of my country; that is more than your father can say for himself! Yes, I have grown rich, I am successful—is that a crime? What would you have wanted me to do? To go on scribbling pretty verses while my family starved? To bury myself alive as your father has buried himself alive? And what can he show for all those lost years? Nothing except this one picture? Look at yourselves, Paula and Candida—look at yourselves, and then tell me if this one picture is enough to justify what he has done to you! Oh, it is not against me that you are so bitter! It is not against me, I know! For what have I done to you?

CANDIDA: Nothing, senator. But what have you done to yourself?

PERICO [*recovering himself; embarrassed*]: I should not have said those things——

CANDIDA: You had to say them. I suppose you have long been wanting to say them?

PERICO: No, Candida—no! I do not resent your father, I admire him. He is a very happy man.

CANDIDA: Because he did what he has done?

PERICO: Because he always knew what he was doing.

CANDIDA: And you did not know what you were doing?

PERICO: Oh Candida, life is not so simple as it is in Art! We do not choose consciously, we do not choose deliberately— as we like to think we do. Our lives are shaped, our decisions are made by forces outside ourselves—by the world in which we live, by the people we love, by the events and fashions of our times—and by many, many other things we are hardly conscious of. Believe me: I never actually said to myself, "I do not wish to be a poet anymore because I will only starve. I shall become a politician because I want to get rich." Too often, one is only an innocent bystander at one's own fate . . .

CANDIDA [*approaching*]: Forgive me, *ninong*. [*She kisses his hand.*]

PERICO: It is you who must forgive me, Candida—if I have bitterly disappointed you. [*Shrugs.*] But I could not help it— and I cannot help you. [*He pauses, smiling, and looks at his watch again. Now his voice is tender, and rather sad.*] Paula —Candida—stand with your father! Stand with Lorenzo— *contra mundum!* [*Looks at watch.*] I must go. [*Turns to them.*] But remember—*contra mundum!* [*He leaves.*]

MANOLO [*sinking into a chair*]: Poor Don Perico!

PEPANG: The old doublecrosser!

CANDIDA [*smiling*]: We promised to do whatever he said, Pepang —and we will keep our promise.

PAULA [*parodying* DON PERICO]: We will stand with father— *contra mundum!*

PEPANG [*tartly*]: You can stand with him against anything you please—but not here, not in this house!

CANDIDA: This house will be our fortress!

PEPANG: Candida, I have a head-ache. Please do not make it worse.

PAULA: Perhaps you too would like an aspirin, Pepang?

PEPANG: What I would like is a little sense from the two of you! Have you no eyes, have you no feelings? Do you not see what a burden this house is for me and Manolo? Do you not see how unfair it is to our families to spend so much money here—money we ought to be spending on our own homes? Do you not know that I have to fight with my husband, month after month, to get the money to support you and this house?

CANDIDA: We are not asking you nor your husband nor Manolo to support us any longer!

PAULA: We will take care of ourselves!

PEPANG: And what will you do? Take in boarders? You are both completely useless!

MANOLO: Pepang, I think we can discuss this without losing our tempers.

CANDIDA: There is no need to discuss it at all!

PAULA: We will never change our minds!

PEPANG: We have pampered the two of you long enough!

MANOLO: Pepang, will you let me do the talking!

PAULA: Oh, you can both go on talking forever—it will make no difference!

PEPANG [raising her voice]: Oh, I know why they want to stay in this house! I know why they like it so much here! I know —and so does everybody! I have heard people whispering about it—behind my back!

MANOLO: Whispering about what?

PEPANG: About these two fine sisters of ours, Manolo! Oh, they have become quite a laughing stock—the talk of the town really—a regular scandal!

PAULA: Pepang, what are you saying! What have we done!

MANOLO: Just what is all this, Pepang? What the devil do you mean?

PEPANG: Surely you have heard the gossip?

MANOLO: I have more important things to do——

PEPANG: Oh, the shame I have suffered! Everybody knows, everybody is laughing at them!

MANOLO: WHY? WHY?

PEPANG: Because of this young man! This Tony Javier! According to what I hear, Candida and Paula are completely fascinated with him!

PAULA: PEPANG!

PEPANG: And he flirts with them! They allow him to flirt with them!

MANOLO: Pepang, that's enough!

PEPANG: And at their age! To be fooled at their age—and by a man of the lowest type!

MANOLO: Pepang, I told you to shut up!

PEPANG: And that is why they refuse to leave this house! They cannot bear to leave this young man! They cannot bear to be separated from him—— [*She turns away trembling. They are tensely silent for a moment, not looking at each other.* MANOLO *grimly confronts his youngster sisters.*]

MANOLO: Now, do you see why you cannot remain in this house?

CANDIDA: Do you believe this evil talk?

MANOLO: Do you think me stupid?

PAULA: Oh, there will be enough stupid people to believe it!

MANOLO: Exactly! And their tongues will go on wagging as long as you stay in this house!

CANDIDA: The wagging of all the evil tongues in the world cannot drive us away from here!

PAULA: They are not worth our contempt!

MANOLO: And how about the good name of our family? Is that worth nothing to you either? Is our name to go on furnishing entertainment for the malicious? And what about father? Have you considered how this would hurt him?

CANDIDA: Father knows nothing of this!

MANOLO: You deceive yourselves. Father always knows! Oh, I see now why he is ill!

CANDIDA: Father is not ill!

PAULA: Oh, tell them, Candida—tell them! Let them know! Why should we hide it any longer?

MANOLO: Then, there is something?

PAULA: Yes! Yes!

MANOLO: What have you been hiding from us? [*A pause. Then,* CANDIDA, *gripping herself together, turns around to face her brother and sister.*]

CANDIDA: Father tried to kill himself.

PEPANG [*sinking to a chair*]: Oh, my God.

MANOLO: To kill himself . . . When?

CANDIDA: When he had that accident. It was not an accident, Manolo. He did it on purpose.

PEPANG: But how do you know?

MANOLO: Why should he want to die?

PAULA: Because of us! Because of us!

CANDIDA: I was to blame, Paula. You merely followed me.

PAULA: Oh no, no—we were in this together. We faced him together, we accused him together!

PEPANG: Accused him of what?

PAULA: Of having ruined our lives!

MANOLO: Paula! Candida!

PAULA: And we blamed him for our wasted youth, we blamed him for our poverty, we blamed him for having squandered away mother's property, and we blamed him for the husbands we never had.

PEPANG [*shutting her eyes tight*]: Poor father! Poor, poor father!

MANOLO: And did you never ask him to forgive you?

CANDIDA: He kept away from us. He had begun to paint this picture; he was working on it night and day. And when it was finished, he called us to his room and showed us this picture. He said he had painted it very especially for us, that it was his final gift to us. We wanted to kneel down then and beg his forgiveness—but he pressed the picture on us, he waved us away. And when we were at the door he said: "Goodbye, Candida. Goodbye, Paula." And then that night . . . that very night, he fell from the balcony. [*A pause, as she chokes back her tears. When she speaks again her voice is flatter and more desolate.*] Do you see? Do you see now? It could not have been an accident . . .

MANOLO [*grimly*]: No, Candida—it was not an accident.

PAULA: And he will never, never forgive us!

PEPANG [*rising and swiftly approaching her sisters and putting an arm around each of them*]: Paula, Candida—do not say that! Of course he will forgive you! He is our father! You must go to him again——

CANDIDA: And that is why we cannot part with this picture. It is our punishment.

MANOLO [*rising*]: Well, one thing is definitely settled now. You cannot go on living together, the three of you—not with all this hatred and bitterness among you. This house must be sold. Father must be placed in a hospital.

PAULA: You cannot take him away from us now!

CANDIDA: You must give us time—time to atone for what we did!

PAULA: We must go on working for our forgiveness!

MANOLO: I want no more arguments! Oh, I did not dare sell this house as long as I thought that father wanted to stay here. But now I know he does not want to stay here, he does not want to stay with you! He will never get well until he has been completely separated from the two of you!

PAULA: Manolo!

CANDIDA: Oh, he has a right to be cruel. His conscience is clear!

PEPANG: Manolo, you must give them time.

MANOLO: They can stay until this house has been sold—but they must dismiss this boarder of theirs at once—and I shall arrange to have father transferred to a hospital as soon as possible. I expect to have this house disposed of before the end of this month. You will come to live with me, Candida. Paula, you will live with Pepang. And listen, all of you— this is absolutely the last talk we shall ever have on this matter. Pepang, are you ready to go now?

PEPANG [*going for her bag*]: Yes, Manolo. [*Kissing her sisters.*] Goodbye, Candida; goodbye, Paula.

MANOLO: Now, remember—you are to dismiss this boarder of yours immediately!

PAULA: Yes, Manolo.

MANOLO: Candida, did you hear me?

CANDIDA: Yes, Manolo.

MANOLO: And take away all those signs from the door.

SISTERS: Yes, Manolo.

MANOLO: Well, goodbye now. And be more sensible, both of you!

SISTERS: Goodbye, Manolo.

MANOLO: Tell father I shall be around again soon. [*Exeunt* PEPANG *and* MANOLO.]

PAULA [*after a pause*]: Candida, have you no news? Oh, tell me you have news—good news!

CANDIDA: We must go and do the cooking if we are to eat anything . . .

PAULA: Then, you did not go?

CANDIDA [*bitterly*]: Yes, I did!

PAULA: To this Bureau of Health and Science?

CANDIDA [*shuddering*]: Oh Paula, it was horrible!

PAULA: No place for you?

CANDIDA: They thought I was crazy.

PAULA: Oh Candida!

CANDIDA: They only made fun of me. They sent me from one department to another. Oh, I thought they were serious— I went into every office and told them that I wanted to catch rats, that I was an expert—and they listened attentively—I thought they were really interested—but they were only laughing at me, they were only making fun of me. And then they began to be afraid of me—they thought I was dangerous. They began running about excitedly and shouting and blowing whistles. A crowd began to gather. I had to run away! They chased me down to the street! I had to run and run!

PAULA [*taking her sister's hands*]: Oh, Candida!

CANDIDA: Pepang is right. There is no place for us anywhere in the world. We are completely useless. We must separate. You go and live with Pepang. I will go and live with Manolo.

PAULA: She will make me wear her old clothes and I must pretend to be grateful.

CANDIDA: And Manolo's wife will make me cut my hair and

paint my face. [*A car is heard stopping down in the street. They glance quickly at each other.* CANDIDA *shudders.*] Oh, I cannot talk to him now!

[*She hurries to doorway and* PAULA *follows.* TONY JAVIER *is heard running up the stairs and shouting: "Miss Candida! Miss Paula!" The sisters pause in the doorway.* TONY *appears on the landing, breathless.*]

TONY: Oh, there you are! Come here, both of you! Come and sit down! Oh Miss Paula, Miss Candida—I bring wonderful news! This is your salvation!

CANDIDA: Our salvation?

TONY: If you want to be saved—and I know you do!

PAULA: Mr. Javier, what is all this? Is it about that picture again?

TONY: And about the American who has long been wanting to buy it.

PAULA [*rising*]: Oh, Mr. Javier!

TONY: Sit down, Miss Paula—sit down and listen! [*Paula obeys.*] Now, about this American—he's going back to the States. He still wants this picture; he wants to take it back with him. Oh, he says he's crazy about it—and so, he's offering a crazy price for it. And, ladies, do you know how much he's offering now for that picture of yours? [*A pause, while he looks at the sisters.*] He is offering ten thousand dollars!

CANDIDA [*after a stunned pause*]: Ten thousand dollars!

TONY: And that's twenty thousand pesos.

PAULA: Twenty thousand pesos!

TONY: Oh, he wants it bad, and he wants it at once! He's leaving Friday. [*The sisters are silent, staring at Portrait.*] Well, what do you say now?

PAULA [*after a pause; rising*]: We . . . we are sorry, Mr. Javier. But we told you before that the picture is not for sale. Well . . . it is still . . . still not for sale.

TONY: WHAT?

PAULA: Come along, Candida. [CANDIDA *remains seated, staring at Portrait.*]

Tony: Wait, wait, WAIT! Think, ladies—think! This may never happen again! This is the chance of your lifetime!

Paula: We are very sorry.

Tony: But think of yourselves, think of yourselves! Miss Candida, just think what you'll be throwing away!

Paula: Candida, will you tell him he is only wasting his time?

Tony: Miss Candida, will you tell her what a chance you'll be wasting? [*Candida rises in silence and walks away.* Paula, *astonished, takes a step to follow her.*]

Tony [*grabbing* Paula's *arm*]: Oh, stay and listen! Listen to me—please!

Candida [*walking slowly towards doorway*]: I must go and do the cooking . . .

Paula: Oh Candida, do not leave me alone!

Candida [*whirling around; with sudden passion*]: Why? Are you afraid?

Paula [*startled*]: Afraid? [Tony *releases her arm.*]

Candida [*fiercely*]: Yes, yes—afraid! Afraid to stay! Afraid to find out that it is true after all! Everything they are saying, everything they are whispering and laughing about!

Paula: Candida! You know that is not true!

Candida: Then why are you afraid to stay? Why do you always need me at your side? Are you a baby, am I your nurse?

Paula [*grimly*]: I am not afraid to stay. I shall stay, Candida. I do not need you. [*They stare a moment at each other. Then* Candida *turns away quickly, towards doorway.* Paula *is motionless, looking at doorway.* Tony *shrugs.*]

Tony: I suppose you know what you're doing . . . But twenty thousand bucks. [*He whistles.*] Saying no to twenty grand! Saying no to a chance like that! If it was me! If it was only me! It's not fair! Why don't somebody come and offer to give me twenty grand—just like that? Oh baby, what I could do with twenty grand! Go to Paris, go to Vienna, go to New York . . . [Paula *comes and stands beside him. Absorbed in his dreams, he does not notice her.*]

PAULA [*in a sort of trance herself*]: Paris . . . ? Vienna . . . ? New York . . . ?

TONY [*not really noticing her*]: Yeah—and all those other glamorous places over there. Spain, Italy, South America . . .

PAULA: I used to dream of traveling myself . . .

TONY [*looking at her now*]: Huh?

PAULA [*smiling dreamily at Portrait*]: Europe . . . I've always wanted to go to Europe. Spain and France and Italy . . . Why are you smiling?

TONY [*turning his grin towards her*]: So, you want to travel, too—eh?

PAULA [*smiling again*]: When I was a girl.

TONY: How about now?

PAULA: And they were just dreams—just the foolish dreams of a young girl . . .

TONY: You could make your dreams come true.

PAULA [*with a sigh*]: Ah, it is too late now!

TONY [*softly, tenderly*]: Paula . . . too late?

PAULA [*beginning to shiver*]: Yes!

TONY: But why, Paula—why?

PAULA: I am not a young girl anymore!

TONY [*moving still closer*]: Paula, listen to me——

PAULA [*shivering; rooted to the floor; but keeping her face averted from his approaching face*]: No, no! It is too late now! I am not young anymore, I am not young anymore!

TONY: Paula, you do like me a little, don't you? [*She is tensely silent, her face averted.*] Won't you say you like me a little, Paula?

PAULA: Oh, you must not talk like that! What would people say?

TONY: Who cares what people say? Are you afraid of their big mouths?

PAULA [*with sudden spirit*]: I despise them!

TONY: You can leave them to their nasty talk! Pack up whenever you please, and go wherever you want!

PAULA: Far away?

TONY: Yes, Paula—as far away as you like. You can make your dreams come true.

PAULA [*faltering*]: My dreams are dead.

TONY: Dreams don't die.

PAULA: Mine did. A long time ago.

TONY: Suppose somebody came along and said the right words, do you think they would come alive again?

PAULA: I stopped waiting—a long time ago . . .

TONY: Paula, look at me. [*She keeps her face averted.*] Look at me, Paula—please!

PAULA: No!

TONY: You're still young, Paula, you've got a right to be happy. [*He moves towards her, his arms extended. She suddenly shudders away from his touch.*]

PAULA: No, no! Do not touch me! You must not touch me! Not— [*Glancing round the room.*]—not here . . . not in this house.

TONY [*with knowing smile*]: Okay, Paula—not here. [*He goes to stair-landing.*] Not in this house. Come, Paula. [*He waits, smiling. After a while, she walks to his side, her head bowed. He smiles down at her; she looks up at him, her face grave. Looking thus into each other's eyes, they descend the stairs. After a moment, his car is heard starting. Simultaneously, CANDIDA begins to shout "Paula! Paula!" inside.*]

CANDIDA [*appearing in doorway*]: Paula!

[*The car is heard moving away. She runs to balcony where she stands, looking up the street. Then she turns around, a hand pressed to her throat.*]

CANDIDA [*in shocked whisper*]: Paula!

[*Then, resolutely, she strides towards stairway. But she catches sight of Portrait and, with a terrified gasp, she cowers away. She stands shuddering, her eyes fixed on Portrait, her breath coming faster and faster as BLACKOUT.*]

THE THIRD SCENE

BITOY [*offstage voice*]: The next time I went to the Marasigan house was on a cold cloudy afternoon—the afternoon of the second Sunday of October. A typhoon wind was blowing; the skies above were dark—as dark as the weather in our hearts —for the rumors of war were thickening fast; panic was in the air.

But that afternoon, Intramuros was in a holiday mood. As though knowing that it was about to die, about to be obliterated forever, this old city was celebrating—celebrating for the last time. The streets were decorated, and filled with hurrying people. The bells rang out high and clear. It was the feast of La Naval de Manila. [A *faint faraway sound of bells and band-music.*]

As I walked down this street, I could hear my footsteps reverberating against the cobblestones; when I talked or laughed, my voice seemed to echo on and on. Aware of the doom hanging overhead, I looked about me with keener eyes; and everything I saw—even the slum-tenements—seemed suddenly very beautiful and very precious—because I might be seeing them for the last time.

[*The* sala *becomes visible.*]

I was seeing them for the last time. Two months later, the bombs began to fall. There is nothing left of it now—of the old Manila. It is dead, obliterated forever—except in my memory—where it lives; still young, still great, still the Noble and Ever Loyal City. And whenever I remember it, the skies about are dark; a typhoon wind is blowing; it is October; it is the feast of the Naval.

[*It is late in the afternoon, and the* sala *is rather dim. The doorway at right and the balconies have been decorated with festive curtains, which are blowing steadily in the wild wind.*]

[CANDIDA *comes slowly up the stairs, carrying prayer-book, rosary and umbrella. She goes to the stand to deposit her umbrella, and goes to table at center where she lays down her prayer-book and rosary. She takes off her veil and begins to fold it. She pauses, hearing a sound of distant bells and band-music. At table is a tray, with glasses and a bottle.*]

The bells begin to peal again and sound like silver coins showering in the fine air; at the rumor of drums and trumpets as bands march smartly down the cobblestones a pang of childhood happiness smites every heart. October in Manila! [CANDIDA *stands still, listening. The veil drops from her hands onto the table.* CANDIDA *is wearing her best dress—an archaic blue frock—and her jewels. She goes to the other balcony, on one side of which she stands, her face lifted, her eyes closed, the wind blowing her hair. She bows her head and covers her face with her hands. The distant rumor of bells and music fades out.* BITOY *steps into the room and places himself at stair-landing.*]

BITOY: Hello, Candida. [*She whirls around nervously.*]

CANDIDA [*with relief*]: Oh, it is you, Bitoy.

BITOY: I saw you and Paula in church.

CANDIDA: Yes, I came home ahead. There was such a crowd. I felt dizzy. Sit down, Bitoy. Paula will be coming in a moment.

BITOY [*remaining standing*]: And how is your father?

CANDIDA: Oh, just the same as usual. Do you want to see him? But he will——

TOGETHER: ——be having a nap just now.

BITOY [*laughing*]: I knew you would say that! [CANDIDA *smiles. Sound of bells pealing again. They listen, glancing towards the balconies.*]

CANDIDA: Have you come for the procession?

BITOY: October again, Candida!

CANDIDA: Yes . . . Oh Bitoy, the Octobers of our childhood! The dear, dear Octobers of our childhood!

BITOY: Remember how my family used to come here to watch the Naval procession from your balconies?

CANDIDA: And so did the families of all our friends.

BITOY: Year after year——

CANDIDA: And year after year our house stood open to all comers on this day, the feast of the Naval. It was always the biggest fiesta in this house. But now—— (CANDIDA *disconsolately turns away.* BITOY *straightens up.*]

BITOY: Is anything wrong, Candida?

CANDIDA [*bitterly*]: Yes! Everything!

BITOY: What?

CANDIDA: This is our last October here—in this house—where we were born, where we grew up!

BITOY: The last October?

CANDIDA: We are leaving this house.

BITOY: Why?

CANDIDA: Because to save one's life is to lose it!

BITOY: Candida, you would have had to leave this house anyway, sooner or later. It is too old——

CANDIDA: It is our youth.

BITOY: And when the war breaks out it will become very unsafe——

CANDIDA: There is no safety for us anymore, anywhere.

BITOY: And you must think of your father, you must think of this painting—— [*He looks towards the site of the Portrait and, suddenly, his eyes pop out, he gasps and steps forward, starting in amazement.*] Candida, the painting! It is gone!

CANDIDA [*not looking around*]: Yes.

BITOY: Where is it?

CANDIDA: I do not know.

BITOY: Has it been sold?

CANDIDA: No.

BITOY: Stolen?

CANDIDA: No, no!

BITOY: Then where is it!

CANDIDA: I tell you, I do not know!

BITOY: Oh Candida, what have you done with it!

CANDIDA: Paula took it down and put it away. She did not tell me where.

BITOY: But why did she take it down?

CANDIDA: She did not tell me that either.

BITOY: But how could you allow——

CANDIDA: Oh, stop asking, Bitoy! I know nothing, I know nothing at all! [*Sound of rapid knocking downstairs.* CANDIDA *starts nervously again, and presses a hand to her forehead.*] Bitoy, please see who that is. And remember: whoever it is, I am not at home, Paula is not at home, nobody is at home! [*She turns around quickly to leave the room but* SUSAN *and* VIOLET *have already appeared on the landing.*]

SUSAN: Oh yes—you are home all right! [SUSAN *and* VIOLET *advance into the room. They are sober this time, and look extremely determined. They have hurried right over from the Sunday matinee, and are still wearing their stage make-up and costumes; gaudy skirts and blouses.*]

VIOLET: Excuse us for coming right up.

SUSAN: And don't tell us to go away because we won't go away!

VIOLET: Not till we find out what we want to find out!

SUSAN [*earnestly*]: Look, we'll behave ourselves—honest!

VIOLET: You remember us, don't you? We're from the Parisian Theatre. We were here about a week ago.

SUSAN: And I'm sorry about how I acted that time—and about the things I said.

CANDIDA: What can I do for you?

SUSAN: We came to see Tony.

VIOLET: What's the matter with him?

SUSAN: Is he sick?

VIOLET: He hasn't shown up at the theatre for the last two days. And if he still doesn't show up tonight, the manager is going to fire him!

SUSAN: He'll lose his job!

VIOLET: We came right over from the show to tell him. It's important!

SUSAN: Where is he?

CANDIDA: I do not know. Mr. Javier hasn't come back here either for the last two days.

SUSAN: Oh, where did he go!

VIOLET: Did he take his clothes with him?

CANDIDA: No; his clothes and all his things are still here. Tell me—are you very good friends of his?

VIOLET: Yes, we are!

CANDIDA: Then, will you do me a favor? I have put his clothes and all his things together. They are downstairs.

VIOLET: In those two suitcases?

CANDIDA: Yes. Will you take them with you and give them to Mr. Javier when you find him?

SUSAN: So, you're throwing him out!

VIOLET: Couldn't he pay his rent?

CANDIDA: And please tell Mr. Javier that I beg him never, never to show himself here again.

VIOLET: What did he do?

BITOY: Now look, girls—that's strictly between Tony and Miss Marasigan. It's none of our business. You go and take his clothes with you. He's bound to show up sooner or later.

SUSAN: I won't go away until I find out what's happened to him!

BITOY: Nothing's happened to him. He's probably just out on a binge! [Sound of people coming up the stairs.]

CANDIDA: Oh God, who——

[She stops short as TWO POLICEMEN appear on the stairway. A silence, while the policemen fetch out their notebooks and glance around the room. Then, as nobody says anything, they move forward. One of them has a black-eye.]

1ST COP: We want to speak to Miss Marasigan.

CANDIDA [faintly]: I am Miss Marasigan.

2ND COP [glancing at his notebook]: Miss Candida Marasigan?

CANDIDA: What can I do for you?

2ND COP: Miss Marasigan, the day before yesterday, at around noontime, you telephoned us and reported that your sister had been abducted——

1ST COP: We have been unable to locate your sister but we have found the man who——

CANDIDA [quickly interrupting]: Please forgive me—but it was all, all a mistake!

1ST COP: What was a mistake?

CANDIDA: My telephoning you. Nothing had happened really.

2ND COP: Your sister was not abducted?

CANDIDA: No.

1ST COP: And she is not missing?

CANDIDA: I only thought she was. [*The* COPS *glance wearily at each other and shrug.*]

1ST COP: Then, why did you not call again to tell us?

CANDIDA: I am sorry. I forgot.

2ND COP: You are withdrawing your charges?

CANDIDA: It was all a mistake.

2ND COP [*pocketing his notebook*]: Miss Marasigan, you see this black-eye? I got this because of your mistake. Be more careful next time, will you?

1ST COP: Could we use your telephone?

CANDIDA: We have no telephone.

1ST COP [*to his companion*]: You go down and call up the station. Tell them to release this fellow.

BITOY [*as* 2ND COP *exits*]· Which fellow, officer?

1ST COP: The fellow she said had run away with her sister. We picked him up this morning.

SUSAN [*approaching*]: Is his name Tony Javier?

1ST COP: That's right.

VIOLET: Where did you find him?

1ST COP: In a bar—trying to break all the furniture.

BITOY: Drunk?

1ST COP: And violent. He gave my companion the black-eye.

SUSAN: But they're going to release him now?

1ST COP: Oh, sure—after he pays a fine.

SUSAN [*turning on* CANDIDA]: You see! Now I hope you and that sister of yours are satisfied!

1ST COP: Just what actually happened, Miss Marasigan?

CANDIDA: Nothing at all really. My sister simply went off for a drive—and forgot to tell me she was going.

1ST COP: And this was at around twelve o'clock noon, the day before yesterday?

CANDIDA [*desperately*]: But she came back right away!

SUSAN: I bet she didn't!

BITOY: Will you shut up!

SUSAN: Why should I? They get poor Tony in jail, they make him lose his job—and then they laugh and say: "Oh, excuse us please! It was all a mistake!" And then they try to get everybody to hush up! Oh, they think they can keep it all safe and quiet, do they? Well, you don't, Miss Marasigan! I'll take care of that!

VIOLET: We'll shout your name all over town!

SUSAN: We'll see everybody knows about this fine ride your sister had with Tony!

VIOLET: You bet we will!

SUSAN: So, she came back right away, did she? [*Laughs derisively.*]

CANDIDA [*going to pieces*]: NO! NO!, she did not come back right away! I lied, I was lying, I speak nothing now but lies! No, she did not come back right away; she came back at three in the morning. I was standing right here. I was waiting for her. No, she did not come back right away . . . I was lying . . .

BITOY: Candida!

CANDIDA: I was standing right there, waiting for her to come back. And I was going to throw her out. Oh, I felt righteous! I was horrified with what she had done. And then, she came slowly up those stairs . . . she stood there, not saying anything . . . And her face, her face! How can I ever forget her face!

BITOY: Candida, stop it!

CANDIDA [*wildly*]: You know where she was, you know what she did, you know what happened to her—but: I am the guilty one. It was I who let her go—who made her go! I knew it was going to happen—and I let it happen—I wanted it to happen! And do you know why? Because of ten thousand dollars! Oh, I was thinking of my own future safety, my own future security! And no more poverty, no more bickering over money, no more haggling at the market, and no more hiding here in the darkness, the light cut off, the water stopped, the bill-collectors pounding and pounding at the door!

BITOY [*grasping her by the arms*]: Candida!

CANDIDA: Oh, I was thinking of ten thousand dollars in the bank! And so I let her go! And so I let her perish! I have destroyed my father—and now I have destroyed my sister! I am evil, evil, evil——

BITOY [*shaking her*]: Candida! Candida!

CANDIDA [*subsiding*]: And now you all know . . . Now you have found out . . . [*She turns away from* BITOY's *grasp and passes a hand over her brow.*] You must excuse me . . . I . . . I do not feel well . . .

[SUSAN *and* VIOLET *look at each other, then go off slowly. The* COP *shrugs, pockets his notebook and, looking embarrassed, leaves too. There is a pause; then* BITOY *approaches* CANDIDA.]

BITOY: Candida——

CANDIDA [*dully*]: Go to her, Bitoy. Please go to her.

BITOY: To Paula?

CANDIDA: She is in the church. Go and look for her. Tell her to hurry home. I must speak to her. Oh Bitoy, we have not spoken to each other since she came back! There has been only silence, silence between us. But now I can break that silence. Now, I can look in her face and speak.

BITOY: Candida, you must not blame yourself.

CANDIDA: Will you go to Paula?

BITOY: What shall I tell her?

CANDIDA: Tell her . . . tell her that we are together again!

BITOY: Only that?

CANDIDA: She has been waiting and waiting to hear me say that!

BITOY: Very well, Candida.

[*Exit* BITOY. CANDIDA *stands still a moment; then she turns away, towards table. The bells peal out again; she pauses and listens, gazing wistfully at the blowing curtains. Then she goes to table, intending to take out the untouched tray of drinks. She takes hold of the tray but does not lift it, remaining thus: stooped over the table, her back to the stairway.* TONY JAVIER *comes up the stairs and pauses on the landing. He is hatless, uncombed, unshaved, untidy, and unsteady. He sports a black-eye, and looks physically—and spiritually—ravaged. He is still wearing the same clothes as in preceding scene; the clothes being very soiled and rumpled now, the loosening tie still dangling around the unbuttoned shirt-collar. From this point, twilight starts and the stage dims very gradually.*]

TONY [*at stairway; curtly*]: Where is she? Where is Paula? CANDIDA *straightens up but does not look around nor reply.* TONY *raises his voice.*] Where is she?

CANDIDA [*still not looking around*]: She is not here. [TONY *has turned his face towards site of Portrait; his eyes blaze.*]

TONY: And where is it? Where is the picture?

CANDIDA [*moving away; wearily*]: I do not know. [TONY *grabs her by the arm and whirls her around.*]

TONY: I said—WHERE IS THE PICTURE!

CANDIDA [*moaning*]: Go away . . . Please, please go away . . .

TONY: Oh, I'll go away—don't you worry. I'll go as far away from here as I can get! But not till you give me that picture!

CANDIDA [*with a toss of the head*]: I will never give it to you!

TONY [*sneering*]: Well! You have changed your mind, haven't you? Oh I could see you were willing enough to sell the last time, Candida!

CANDIDA: And you were right!

TONY [*with a leer*]: And you were willing to let me persuade your sister to sell too!

CANDIDA: Oh yes—yes indeed!

TONY: You were even willing to let me take her out and convince her! You didn't care how I did it—as long as it was effective!

CANDIDA [*mockingly*]: And was it?

TONY: You bet it was! I chose the most effective way in the world to convince her!

CANDIDA [*smiling contemptuously*]: Ah—but did you?

TONY [*flushing furiously and giving her a shake*]: You know I did! You know I did!

CANDIDA: All I know is that she came back alone! All I know is that she got away from you!

TONY: Well, she can't back out now! And you can't either! I've got the both of you in my hands! Oh, don't worry—I won't doublecross you! You'll get your ten grand; all I want is my commission.

CANDIDA [*jerking her arm loose*]: Your commission! And that is all you ever wanted, wasn't it?

TONY: Remember, Candida—I had your permission! When you walked out of this room that day, you left her completely in my hands!

CANDIDA [*trembling; her fists clenched*]: Please go! I beg you to go at once!

[*Unnoticed, PAULA has come up the stairs, carrying prayer-book, rosary and umbrella; her church-veil draped around her shoulders. She pauses and glances at the two people in the dim room. PAULA, too, is wearing her best dress—an archaic blue frock— and her jewels; and she looks very young, happy and tranquil. She has fought, she has conquered; now she comes back radiant— merciless as a child; ruthless as innocence; terrible as an army with banners.*]

TONY: I'm waiting for that picture. The American is waiting for that picture. Give it to me and we'll all get what we want. He gets his picture, you get your ten grand, I get my commission. Yes, Candida—that was all I ever really wanted! I wouldn't take you or your sister with me if the both of you had a million dollars! What do you take me for—a nut? [*PAULA goes to set her umbrella in stand.*]

CANDIDA: Will you go—or shall I call the police?

TONY: Will you give me that picture—or shall I go in and tell your father?

PAULA: My father knows, Tony.

TONY [*whirling around*]: PAULA!

PAULA [*moving calmly forward*]: My father always knows.

TONY [*hurrying to meet her; agonized*]: Why did you run away, Paula? Why did you leave me?

PAULA [*passing him by as she goes to table and lays down her prayer-book and rosary*]: Because there was something I had to do. Something very important.

TONY [*in anguish*]: Oh Paula, I could kill myself! I could kill myself for having touched you!

PAULA [*smiling at him*]: How vain you are!

TONY [*approaching*]: Do you know what I did when I found you gone? I went out and got drunk! I got roaring drunk! I wanted to kill myself! I wanted to kill everybody!

PAULA: Poor Tony! And all he wanted was his commission!

TONY: I don't want it anymore! All I want is ... that you forgive me!

PAULA: You will never forgive me, Tony, for what I have done to you.

TONY: Oh Paula, don't hate me!

PAULA: Why should I?

TONY: Then listen to me! Believe me!

PAULA: I listened to you before, Tony, and I believed you—remember?

TONY: I deceived you that time, Paula, but now I speak to you from the heart! I'm on the level now—as I've never been in all my life!

PAULA: I believe you. But—do you—love me?

TONY: I will learn to love you, Paula—I promise! All we need is to get away from here. All we need is the money so we can run away and be free. Where is the picture, Paula? The American is waiting.

PAULA: Then, you must go and tell him to stop waiting. [*She turns her face towards the site of the Portrait.*] The picture is no more.

TONY [*his eyes widening*]: What have you done with it?

PAULA: I have destroyed it. [*A pause, while* TONY *and* CANDIDA *stare at her. She is gazing down at her hands.*]

TONY [*stunned*]: OH NO! OH NO, NO!

PAULA [*turning towards* CANDIDA]: Did you hear what I said, Candida?

TONY [*feverishly*]: Say it's not true, Paula! Say it's not true!

PAULA: I have destroyed our picture, Candida.

TONY: No! No! It's not true! It's not true!

PAULA [*exultant*]: I slashed it up and I smashed it up and I tore it up and then I burned it! There is nothing left of it now! Nothing, nothing, nothing at all!

TONY [*bursting into sobs*]: Oh, you are mad, mad!

PAULA: Are you angry, Candida?

CANDIDA [*approaching*]: No, Paula. [*She embraces her sister. TONY has sunk to his knees.*]

PAULA: Candida, are you crying?

CANDIDA: Oh no—look at me!

PAULA [*looking around the dim room*]: But someone is crying. I hear someone crying.

CANDIDA [*indicating TONY*]: It's only Mr. Javier.

PAULA [*approaching the sobbing TONY*]: Oh yes . . . Poor Tony! He has found his tears. He has learned to cry.

TONY: Oh, why did you do it, Paula? Why did you do it!

PAULA: I told you, didn't I, that you would never forgive me for what I had done to you.

TONY: You could have saved me——

PAULA: But I have saved you, Tony. Oh, you do not know now——

TONY: You could have saved me but you didn't want to! Okay, now I'm going to the devil! [*He begins to move backward, towards stairway.*] I'm through with struggling and trying to be good! I'm going back to where I came from—back to the gutter! back to the life you could have saved me from!

PAULA: You will not go back, Tony. You cannot go back anymore. You will never be the same again. It is the price you pay. And you will not go back.

TONY [*sobbing again; moving backwards*]: Yes, I will! Yes, I will! I'm going back—back to the gutter! I'm through with fighting! I just want to rot! You could have saved me but you didn't want to! And I could have saved you, Paula. Well, now you're going to rot here! You're all going to rot in this house, the three of you, and be afraid to look in each other's faces! You're all going to sit here hating each other till you die! [*He is already at stairway and stops, overcome with sobs. He brushes his nose with his fist, fighting to control himself.*] Oh, I'll be rotting myself—but I'll be happy to rot, I want to go to the devil! I'll enjoy it, I'll have the time of my life, I'll simply love—Oh, damn you, damn you! [*He stops again, choked by sobs. Furiously he draws himself up to his full height and makes a final attempt at bravado.*] So, you think I've got to pay, do you? So, you think I won't ever be the same again, do you? You flatter yourself, Paula! Look at me! I'm still Tony! I'm still the same old Tony! And believe me, girls, I'm going to—— [*He breaks down completely; he doubles over, sobbing hoarsely, his face in his hands.*] Oh, why did you do it, Paula? Why did you do it? Why did you do it! [*He staggers down the stairs.*]

PAULA [*sinking down beside her*]: Candida, tell me you have no regrets!

CANDIDA: About the picture?

PAULA: What would you have done?

CANDIDA [*spiritedly*]: Just what you did! I would have destroyed it!

PAULA: Be careful, Candida! Have you considered to what we commit ourselves?

CANDIDA: To the darkness and the bill-collectors and the wagging tongues!

PAULA: And now they will say we have lost our senses. Remember: we have destroyed a piece of property worth ten thousand dollars. That is something they will never understand. They will say we are mad, they will say we are dangerous! And Candida—they may be right after all—eventually . . .

CANDIDA: I am willing to take the risk.

PAULA: We are free again! We are together again—you and I and father. Yes—and father too! Don't you see, Candida? This is the sign he has been waiting for—ever since he gave us that picture, ever since he offered us our release—the sign that we had found our faith again, that we had found our courage again! Oh, he was waiting for us to take this step, to make this gesture—this final, absolute, magnificent, unmistakable gesture!

CANDIDA: And now we have done it!

PAULA: And we will stand with him?

CANDIDA: *Contra mundum!*

PAULA: Oh Candida, let us drink to it! [*She pours out drinks.*]

CANDIDA: Yes—we have been born again—not of his flesh, but of his—spirit!

PAULA: Then let us drink to our birthday! Happy birthday, Candida!

CANDIDA: Happy birthday, Paula! [*They touch glasses. They drink; then burst into laughter. The bells peal out again, and continue pealing to end of the scene. From the distance a rumor of drums.*]

PAULA: Candida, the procession!

CANDIDA: And why are we standing in darkness?

PAULA: Let us turn on the chandelier!

CANDIDA: Let us turn on all the lights!

PAULA: It is a Holiday!

CANDIDA: It is the birthday of our lives! [*They fly apart—*PAULA *to the left;* CANDIDA *to the right—and turn on all the lights as* BITOY *appears on the stair-landing.*]

PAULA: Halt! Who goes there!

BITOY [*blinking*]: Why, Paula!

PAULA: Are you friend or foe?

BITOY: Friend!

PAULA: Advance, friend, and be recognized!

BITOY [*walking in*]: I have been looking for you everywhere.

CANDIDA: I sent him to look for you, Paula.

PAULA [*clasping her hands to her breast*]: My hero! And at last you have found me—in this enchanted castle!

BITOY [*laughing*]: What on earth has happened?

PAULA [*whispering*]: The evil spell has been broken!

CANDIDA: The enchantment has dissolved!

PAULA: The princesses will now return to their kingdoms——

CANDIDA: And live happily ever after!

BITOY: Don't I get half of the kingdom?

PAULA: Beware, Bitoy! Our kingdom is a barren land; and the king, our father, an old man.

CANDIDA: Bitoy Camacho, I am delighted with you!

PAULA: Oh Candida, they are gathering now! They are coming!

BITOY: Who?

CANDIDA [*giggling*]: Oh, what shall we do, Paula? Where shall we hide!

BITOY: What is all this?

PAULA: Hide! Quickly! [*They listen, looking towards stairway. Enter* DON ALVARO *and* DOÑA UPENG.]

UPENG: *Ave Maria Purísima!* I told you they always leave the door open in this house.

ALVARO: A holy and good evening to everyone in this house!

SISTERS [*hurrying to meet visitors; fingers on lips*]: Shhh! Shhh!

ALVARO: Is your father sick?

PAULA: Oh no, no, Don Alvero!

CANDIDA: He is in the best of health!

PAULA [*hurrying visitors into the room*]: Come over here, Doña Upeng! Come over here, Don Alvero! Oh, we are so glad you have come! Candida, some brandy for our guests!

CANDIDA: And of course you remember Bitoy Camacho. He was a regular member of our old *tertulias.*

BITOY: Good evening, Doña Upeng. Good evening, Don Alvaro.

PAULA: He, too, has come to celebrate the Naval with us!

ALVARO: You do well, my boy, to honor an old tradition before it disappears.

CANDIDA [*as she offers glasses*]: Disappears?

ALVARO: Yes—there is all this talk of war, war, war!

UPENG: And that is why we have come tonight. We wanted to salute the Virgin again from your balconies—as we used to do in the old days. Oh Paula, Candida—this may be the last time! [*Enter* DON PEPE.]

PEPE: Yes, Upeng—this may well be the last time!

UPENG: Pepe! Pepe, you old carabao—where have you come from?

PEPE: Practically from the graveyard, Upeng. But I felt I had to come tonight——

PAULA [*hurrying to meet him*]: Shhh! Come over here, Don Pepe!

PEPE [*as he is hurried into the room*]: My dear Paula, what is happening?

ALVARO: Yes—just what is wrong, *niñas?*

PAULA: Listen—we are in trouble—Candida and I.

CANDIDA: We need your help!

PEPE: Candida, Paula, we will do anything for you!

CANDIDA: Oh, thank God, you have come tonight!

PAULA: We need our old friends tonight!

PEPE: Here we are—gathered again—relics of the old dispensation . . .

[A *pause, while they watch the blowing curtains of the balconies and listen to the sound of bells and approaching drums. The visitors are all very old, very frail and very faded—but still talk and carry themselves with an air of grandeur, being impoverished gentlefolk. They are poorly but neatly dressed—canes and the "Americana Cerrada" for the men; fans and the starchy "saya" with train for Doña Upeng, an old shawl, draped under her panuelo.*]

ALVARO: And what memories, eh? Personal memories, ancestral memories . . . That wind, those bells, this feast . . . La Naval de Manila! How the words ache in one's heart!

PEPE: Ah, but you speak only for ourselves, Alvaro.

ALVARO: Yes, in this, we are the last of the generations.

PEPE: Already, for our children, these things awaken no special emotion, no memories, no filial pieties . . .

UPENG: The old traditions are dying . . . [*Enter* DON ARISTEO.]

ARISTEO: Who is dying?

VISITORS: Aristeo!

ARISTEO: *Caramba,* you are all here!

VISITORS: Shhh!

PAULA [*approaching, whispering*]: Welcome again to our house, noble soldier!

ARISTEO [*in booming voice*]: Paula, I have dragged my dying bones up here to salute the Virgin for the last time!

VISITORS: Shhh!

ARISTEO: But what is the matter with all of you!

UPENG: Stop your shouting, Aristeo! Paula and Candida are in great peril!

ARISTEO: Is this true, *niñas*?

CANDIDA [*smiling*]: Will you defend us?

ARISTEO: Oh, I should have brought my pistol!

PAULA: We need only your presence, Noble Soldier! Candida, some brandy for our champion!

ARISTEO [*taking her hands*]: Wait a minute, Paula—let me look at you. *Caramba*, your hands are cold!

PAULA: Oh, truly?

ARISTEO [*looking her in the eye*]: Paula, all this is not . . . just a joke?

PAULA: Oh no, no!

ARISTEO: You are actually in grave danger?

PAULA [*bending her face towards him*]: Surely you can feel the floor trembling beneath us?

ARISTEO: I can feel your hands trembling, yes. [*She withdraws her hands, still smiling.*] What is it, *niña*?

PAULA: This may be the last time, the last night, we shall stand here—Candida and I—in our own house.

ARISTEO: I see.

CANDIDA [*offering him a glass*]: But of course we mean to be stubborn!

PAULA: And listen—I am not afraid.

ARISTEO: Why should you be? Am I not here?

ALVARO: Yes! And though terrified by rumors of the war, we have all come running here as to a rock! Like those great warriors of Thermopylae——

UPENG: *Basta, basta!* We are in no mood for orations! [*They laugh gaily.*]

ARISTEO: Candida, pass the brandy! *Animo, amigos! Sursum corda!* We all have no money in our pockets—but we are not dead yet! We can still drink!

CANDIDA [*laughing*]: Don Aristeo is always right! Come everybody—more brandy!

PAULA: Yes, let us all drink and be merry!

UPENG: And to whom shall we drink?

CANDIDA: To the Virgin! To the Virgin, of course!

ARISTEO: *Amigos,* let us drink to the Virgin. We are gathered here in her honor.

ALVARO: And this is our feast——

PEPE: And the feast of our fathers!

ARISTEO: And they still live—our fathers. Something of them is left; something of them survives, and will survive, as long as we live and remember—we who have known and loved and cherished these things . . .

PEPE: And we will live for a long time yet!

EVERYBODY: VIVA! VIVA!

PAULA [*raising her glass*]: Don Aristeo?

ARISTEO: *Amigos y paisanos!* [*He raises his glass.*] A *la gran Señora de Filipinas en la gloriosa fiesta de su Naval!*

EVERYBODY: VIVA LA VIRGEN!

[*They drink. Enter* PEPANG *and* MANOLO, *and advance grimly into the room.* PAULA *and* CANDIDA *are standing side by side at center. The visitors are grouped solidly behind them.* BITOY *is standing a little apart at left, a worried on-looker.*]

PAULA [*gaily*]: Pepang! Manolo!

CANDIDA: Have you also come to salute the Virgin?

MANOLO [*grimly*]: You know very well why we have come!

PEPANG: Oh, this shameful, shameful scandal!

MANOLO: Go and get your clothes! You are both leaving this house at once!

CANDIDA: Where are your manners, Manolo? Do you not see we have visitors?

PEPANG: How can you have the nerve? You should be hiding your face—if you have any shame left!

MANOLO: Tell these people to go away! [*The procession is now approaching; and the drums rumble ever closer, ever louder.*]

ARISTEO [*coming forward*]: *Caramba,* it is Manolito! I hardly recognized you, my boy—you have grown so!

MANOLO: Don Aristeo, I am sorry but I must ask you to leave. My sisters and I have family matters to discuss.

ARISTEO: And is this Pepita?

MANOLO: Don Aristeo, did you hear what I said!

ARISTEO: Aie, Pepita—what an exquisite child you were; so tender, so affectionate!

PEPANG: Don Aristeo, we have not time to——

ARISTEO: No time, no time! Always no time, always in a hurry! Relax, both of you! Here, sit down—have a drink—and let us talk about the old days!

MANOLO: Candida, will you send these people away!

ARISTEO: Tch, tch! And you used to be such a quiet boy—very thin, very dreamy——

MANOLO: Don Aristeo——

ARISTEO: Upeng, do you remember how you used to scold him for being bashful?

UPENG [*laughing*]: Oh, he was always blushing—especially in the presence of the fair sex! [*Pats his cheek.*] Manolito!

MANOLITO: I ask you politely—all of you—for the last time——

ALVARO: And always reading, always off in a corner with a book——

PEPE: Or playing his violin down there in the patio——

UPENG: Or directing a *zarzuela,* with Pepita here as the prima donna——

MANOLO [*shouting*]: Will you let me speak!

ARISTEO: Oh, they were the most intellectual children I have ever known!

MANOLO: Don Aristeo, I beg you——

PEPANG: Oh, why do you waste your time, Manolo! It is useless to talk to them!

UPENG: And, Pepita, I will never forget how you used to recite the "Ultimo Adiós" when you were hardly seven! *Adiós, Patria Adorada—region del sol——*

PEPE: It was I who taught her that poem!

UPENG: And it was I who taught you to dance, Manolo, on the night of your fifteenth birthday—remember?—right in this very room!

ALVARO: What gay memories this house holds for all of us!

ARISTEO: And how Manolo and Pepang must love this old scene of their childhood!

PAULA: Alas, no!

ARISTEO: They do not love it?

CANDIDA: They want it sold!

VISITORS: SOLD!

UPENG: *Qué horror!* But why?

PAULA: That is something they refuse to confess, even to themselves!

ARISTEO: But, perhaps, they cannot afford this house any longer.

PAULA: Oh, it is not the expense!

CANDIDA: Although that is the reason they give!

PAULA: But they deceive themselves!

PEPANG: Paula! Candida!

PAULA: It is not the expense. Why, they throw money away right and left, night and day, at the gambling tables, and think nothing about it!

PEPANG: Manolo, are you going to stand there and let these——

PAULA: No, it is not the expense! They simply cannot stand this house, they cannot bear it!

CANDIDA: It haunts them, it spoils their fun!

PAULA: It is always rising before their eyes at the most inconvenient moments——

CANDIDA: When they are gossiping with their friends——

PAULA: Or playing mah-jongg——

CANDIDA: Or having a nice time at the races or at the Jai-Alai——

PAULA: Or when they cannot sleep——

CANDIDA: Suddenly—*cataplum!*—the shadow of this house falls upon them!

PAULA: And then their hands falter——

CANDIDA: Their blood turns cold!

ARISTEO: You mean, they are afraid of this house?

CANDIDA: And they want it destroyed!

ALVARO: But why?

PAULA: Because it is their conscience!

MANOLO & PEPANG: PAULA! [*The drums are now rumbling right under the balconies.*]

PAULA [*advancing slowly*]: Yes, Manolo! Yes, Pepang! This house is your conscience—and that is why you hate it, that is why you fear it, that is why you have been craving so long and so desperately to destroy it! No, you can not afford it! You cannot afford to have a conscience! Because you know you will have no——

MANOLO [*stepping back*]: SHUT UP! SHUT UP!

PAULA [*standing still*]: You know you will have no peace as long as this house stands here to rebuke you!

MANOLO [*raising his fists*]: SHUT UP—or, by God, I'm going to—— [*The balconies light up dazzlingly as the procession passes below.*]

PAULA: And you will not rest—no—you will never rest until you have laid waste this house; until you have stripped it naked, and torn down its walls, and uprooted its very foundations!

MANOLO: They are leaving this house this very moment!

PEPE: Oh no, Manolito—nobody can leave now!

UPENG [*waving towards balconies*]: Look! The procession!

ALVARO: The streets are closed!

ARISTEO: The Holy Virgin herself has come to save them!

MANOLO [*advancing*]: They are leaving this house right now if I have to throw them down the stairs!

ARISTEO: Then, you will first have to throw me down those stairs, Manolito!

PEPE [*stepping forward*]: And me!

UPENG [*stepping forward*]: And me!

ALVARO [*stepping forward*]: And me! [MANOLO *stands still, staring.*]

ARISTEO: Well, my boy—what do you say now?

CANDIDA: And that is not all, Manolo. There is father as well. Are you prepared to throw him also down those stairs?

PEPANG: Father hates you!

PAULA: Father stands with us!

CANDIDA: *Contra mundum!*

UPENG: *Señores, la Virgen!* [*Leads prayers.*]

PEPANG [*staring; gripping* MANOLO's *arm*]: Manolo, look! It's father! He's coming out of his room!

[*Chorus of "Lorenzo" and "Here comes Lorenzo" and "Hola, Lorenzo!" from the visitors as they all gaze, amazed, towards doorway.* CANDIDA *and* PAULA, *who have their back to the doorway, turn around slowly and fearfully. But, suddenly, their faces light up and lift up; they gasp, they smile; they clasp their hands to their breast.*]

PAULA & CANDIDA [*in ringing, rising, radiant exultation*]: OH PAPA! PAPA! PAPA!

[*From the street comes a flourish of trumpets as the band breaks into the strains of the Gavotta Marcha Procesional; and as* BITOY CAMACHO *steps forward to his usual place at left front of stage, everyone inside remains frozen. The lights die out on stage; the sound of bells and music fades. The ruins stand out distinctly.*]

BITOY: It is gone now—that house—the house of Don Lorenzo el Magnifico. This piece of wall, this heap of stones, are all that's left of it. It finally took a global war to destroy this house and the three people who fought for it. They are dead now—Don Lorenzo, Candida, Paula—they are all dead now—a horrible death—by sword and fire . . . They died with their house and they died with their city—and maybe it's just as well they did. They could never have survived the death of the old Manila. And yet—listen!—it is not dead; it has not perished! Listen, Paula! Listen, Candida! Your city—my city —the city of our fathers—still lives! Something of it is left; something of it survives, and will survive, as long as I live and remember—I who have known and loved and cherished these things! [*He stoops down on one knee and makes a gesture of scooping earth.*]

Oh Paula, Candida—listen to me! By your dust and by the dust of all the generations, I promise to continue, I promise to preserve! The jungle may advance, the bombs may fall again—but while I live, you live—and this dear city of our affections shall rise again—if only in my song! To remember and to sing; that is my vocation . . . [*The lights die out on* BITOY. *All you can see now are the stark ruins, gleaming in the silent moonlight.*]

Notes on Contributors

CARLOS A. ANGELES (1921———) was Manila bureau chief of International News Service from 1950 until 1958, the year that he won a Smith-Mundt "leader" grant. After serving briefly as press assistant to the Garcia administration, in 1959 he became public relations manager for Pan American. *A Stun of Jewels* won both the Republic Cultural Heritage Award for 1964 and the first Palanca award for poetry.

MANUEL ARGUILLA (1911–44), champion dancer and swimmer, was also winner in 1940 of the first Commonwealth prize for short stories. He was executed by the Japanese as an underground agent.

GREGORIO BRILLANTES (1932———), member of the *Philippines Free Press* editorial staff, previously was press officer for an advertising firm, staff writer for a news agency, and instructor at two universities. His stories have consistently won prizes since his first in 1953.

ANDRES CRISTOBAL CRUZ (1929———), former confidential assistant to Mayor Villegas of Manila, lectures at the Lyceum while he continues as managing editor of the distinguished poetry series, *Filipino Signatures*. As author of several novels in Pilipino as well as stories in English, he was considered one of 1962's Ten Outstanding Young Men and in 1964 received the Republic Cultural Heritage Award.

AMADOR T. DAGUIO (1912———) translated the Kalingas' epic harvest songs while at Stanford. Since then he has served as public relations officer for President Magsaysay's Huk resettlement commission, assistant to the director of the Bureau of the Budget, chief editor for the Philippine House of Representatives, and university lecturer-at-large.

RICAREDO DEMETILLO (1920———), an M.F.A. from the state University of Iowa, joined the humanities program at the University of the Philippines after having taught at Silliman in the Visayas. He has been the recipient of a Rockefeller grant, the U.P. Golden Jubilee Award for poetry, the Art Association of the Philippines award for art criticism, and the Jose Rizal Centennial Award in the essay.

N. V. M. GONZALEZ (1915———) has received all of the major Philippine awards: the Commonwealth Literary Award (1941), the Republic Award of Merit (1954), the Republic Cultural Heritage Award (1960), and the Rizal Pro Patria Award (1961). Rockefeller grants have taken him to three continents—to observe, to lecture, and to write. In addition to teaching at the University of the Philippines, where he has served President Romulo as special assistant, he edits the *Diliman Review*, *Philippine Writing*, and other periodicals.

ALEJANDRINO G. HUFANA (1926———) attended Berkeley under the auspices of the Smith-Mundt program and, later, the Rockefeller Foundation. Besides serving as editor of *Signatures, Comment,* and *Panorama,* he has recently joined the creative writing faculty of the University of the Philippines. In 1965, he received the Republic Cultural Heritage Award for poetry.

Nick Joaquin (1917——) writes for the *Philippines Free Press* under the anagram, "Quijano de Manila." He joined the magazine in 1950, after three years in Hong Kong, at the Dominican order's Albert College. His only novel, which won the first Stonehill Fellowship in 1960 and the Republic Cultural Heritage Award in 1961, was written in "Madrid-Mallorca-Manhattan-Mexico-Manila," on an extended Rockefeller grant.

Virginia Moreno (1925——) attended the University of Kansas in the early 1950's on a Smith-Mundt award and later observed the New York Theater under Rockefeller auspices. As teacher and projects director of the U.P. Listening Center, she has influenced most of the younger campus poets. She has staged her own extravaganzas, *Jasmin* and *Mariang Maya,* in Quezon City, as well as a cultural review in New York City, in 1965.

Anthony Morli (1927——), son of a British Indian and a Filipina, was christened Anthony Morli Dharam. He toured the U.S. in 1959 on a Smith-Mundt "specialist" grant in theater and music. Later, when he resumed his work as cultural commentator for the *Manila Times,* he also wrote a libretto for the operatic version of Rizal's *Fili* and Joaquin's "May Day Eve." He has converted his own musical, *Lenny,* into a motion picture scenario.

Wilfrido D. Nolledo (1933——) left a government office to join the *Philippines Free Press* staff a few years after graduating from the school of journalism at the University of Sto. Tomas. Not only his stories but also his one-act plays have been consistent award-winners since 1959.

Carlos P. Romulo (1901——), editor and publisher of a chain of prewar Manila newspapers, won a 1941 Pulitzer Prize for his articles on the Far Eastern crisis. Later he was selected to be General MacArthur's aide-de-camp and a member of President Quezon's War Cabinet in exile; first chief of the Philippine delegation to the U.N. General Assembly; president of the Assembly's fourth session (1949); and ambassador to the United States. In 1962, he became president of a revitalized University of the Philippines, and, in 1966, secretary of education. In addition to more than thirty honorary degrees and innumerable service decorations, he received the first Philippine Congressional Medal of Honor, in 1965. President Romulo is the author of such historic commentaries as *I Saw the Fall of the Philippines, Mother America, Crusade in Asia, The Meaning of Bandung,* and *I Walked with Heroes.*

Arturo B. Rotor (1907——) is a practicing physician and former director of the U.P. Post-Graduate School of Medicine. Selected articles from his *Manila Times* column were published in 1965 as *Confidentially, Doctor.* His collected stories, *The Wound and the Scar,* were the first publication of the Philippine Book Guild; they came out shortly after he had served as physician at the Iwahig Penal Colony. Later he was President Quezon's executive secretary in exile.

EPIFANIO SAN JUAN (1938———) attended Harvard as a university fellow and Rockefeller grantee. After receiving his doctorate in 1965, he joined the faculty of the University of California at Davis. He has written critical prefaces for the Tagalog writers, Amado Hernandez and A. G. Abadilla, and plans to do textural/historical studies of literature in the vernacular.

BIENVENIDO SANTOS (1911———) lectured widely on Philippine fortitude when the war caught him in America. On his return, he rose to the presidency of Legazpi Colleges, only to desert the position in 1957 in order to write novels at the State University of Iowa, with Rockefeller and Guggenheim support. In 1965, he received the Republic Cultural Heritage Award for fiction.

EDITH L. TIEMPO (1919———), of the Silliman University faculty in Dumaguete, was a classmate of her husband, Edilberto Tiempo, at the State University of Iowa and the University of Denver (where she took her doctorate) and his colleague at Western Michigan University and Wartburg College. In addition to the novel, A Blade of Fern, once serialized in Manila, she has completed at least one other, tentatively titled "The Dear Resemblance."

EMMANUEL TORRES (1932———) became curator of Ateneo's art gallery after receiving his M.A. from the State University of Iowa in 1957. Chosen one of the Ten Outstanding Young Men in 1961; in 1962, he was given a "specialist" grant to observe American galleries and methods of art education; and in 1965, he became the first Asia Society Fellow for research in Philippine visual art as a key to national identity.

JOSE GARCIA VILLA (1906———) finished his B.A. in 1932 at the University of New Mexico; then went on to Greenwich Village and an M.A. at Columbia. He has been the recipient of a Guggenheim Fellowship, an American Academy of Arts and Letters award, and a Bollingen Fellowship. In 1961, Villa received the Pro Patria Award; and, the following year, the Republic Cultural Heritage Award. He has been on the faculties of the City College of New York and the New School.

MANUEL VIRAY (1917———) served as foreign affairs officer for ten years at the Philippine Embassy in Washington. In 1965, he was transferred to the embassy at Djakarta. A collection of his poems, After This Exile, is in press in Manila; and a volume of stories, Shawl from Kashmir, has been readied for publication.

OSCAR DE ZUÑIGA (1912———) held news desks on the prewar Sunday Tribune Magazine and Philippines Herald. After liberation, he joined the Manila Chronicle as a horse-racing expert. He acknowledges the influence of Latin-American poets.

Selected Bibliography

of Philippine Literature in English

Agcaoili, T. D. (ed.). *Philippine Writing*. Manila: Archipelago, 1953.

Alfon, Estrella D. *Magnificence and Other Stories*. Manila: Regal, 1960.

Angeles, Carlos A. *A Stun of Jewels*. Manila: Florentino, 1963.

Aprieto, Pacifico N. (with Andres Cristobal Cruz). *Tondo by Two*. Manila: Filipino Signatures, 1961.

Arcellana, Francisco. *Selected Stories*. Manila: Florentino, 1962.

———— (ed.). *P.E.N. Anthology of Short Stories*. Manila: Philippine Center of International P.E.N., 1963.

Arguilla, Manuel. *How My Brother Leon Brought Home a Wife and Other Stories*. Manila: Philippine Book Guild, 1940.

Ayala, Tita Lacambra. *Sunflower Poems*. Manila: Filipino Signatures, 1960.

Bernad, Miguel A., S.J. *Bamboo and the Greenwood Tree*. Manila: Bookmark, 1961.

————. *Philippine Literature: A Two Fold Renaissance*. Manila: Bookmark, 1963.

Brillantes, Gregorio C. *The Distance to Andromeda and Other Stories*. Manila: Benipayo, 1960.

Bulosan, Carlos (ed.). *Chorus for America: Six Philippine Poets*. Los Angeles: Wagon and Star, 1942.

————. *The Voice of Bataan*. New York: Coward, McCann, 1943.

————. *The Laughter of My Father*. New York: Harcourt, Brace, 1944.

————. *America Is in the Heart*. New York: Harcourt, Brace, 1946.

————. *Sound of Falling Light: Letters in Exile* (ed. Dolores Feria). Quezon City: [Feria], 1960.

Carbonell, Rolando A. *Beyond Forgetting*. Manila: Horizons, 1961.

————. *Echoes of the Heart*. Manila: Horizons, 1963.

———— et al. *Sing! While the Heart is Dancing*. Manila: Florentino, 1963.

Carunungan, Celso Al. *Like a Big Brave Man*. New York: Farrar, Straus, and Cudahy, 1960.

————. *Return to Gomora and Other Stories*. Manila: Florentino, 1963.

Casper, Linda Ty. *The Transparent Sun and Other Stories*. Manila: Florentino, 1963.

————. *The Peninsulars*. Manila: Bookmark, 1964.

Crisostomo, Isabelo T. *The Lonely Room and Other Selected Stories*. Manila: Horizons, 1964.

Cristobal, Adrian. *The Trial*. Manila: Ayuda, 1963.

Cruz, Andres Cristobal. *Estero Poems*. Manila: Filipino Signatures, 1960.

———— (with Pacifico N. Aprieto). *Tondo by Two*. Manila: Filipino Signatures, 1961.

————. *White Wall: Selected Tondo Stories*. Manila: Yeba, 1964.

Da Costa, R. Zulueta. *Like the Molave and Other Poems*. Manila: [Da Costa], 1940.

————. *Like the Molave and Collected Poems*. Manila: [Da Costa], 1952.

Dauz, Florentino. *Caligula*. Manila: Filipino Signatures, 1963.

Demetillo, Ricaredo. *No Certain Weather*. Quezon City: Guinhalinan, 1956.

————. *La Via: A Spiritual Journey*. Quezon City: University of the Philippines, 1958.

————. *Daedalus and Other Poems*. Quezon City: [Demetillo], 1961.

————. *Barter in Panay*. Quezon City: University of the Philippines, 1961.

————. *The Authentic Voice of Poetry*. Quezon City: University of the Philippines, 1962.

Dizon, D. Paulo. *Twilight of a Poet and Other Stories*. Manila: Regal, 1962.

Edades, Jean (ed.). *Short Plays of the Philippines*. Manila: Progressive Schoolbooks, 1st ed. 1940, 4th ed. 1950.

————. *More Short Plays of the Philippines*. Manila: Edades, 1957.

Enriquez, Emigdio. *The Devil Flower*. New York: Hill and Wang, 1959.

Espino, Federico Licsi, Jr. *In Three Tongues*, I & II. Quezon City: Bustamante, 1963–64.

————. *Apocalypse in Ward 19*. Quezon City: [Espino], 1965.

Estrada, Nina. *Heart of Clay*. Manila: Carmelo and Bauermann, 1959.

Fernando, Gilda Cordero. *The Butcher, the Baker, the Candlestick Maker*. Manila: Benipayo, 1962.

Florentino, Alberto S. *The World Is an Apple and Other Prize Plays*. Manila: Philippine Cultural Publishers, 1959.

————. (ed.). *Outstanding Filipino Plays*. Manila: Filipiniana, 1961.

————. *Midcentury Guide to Philippine Literature in English*. Manila: Filipiniana, 1963.

Gonzalez, N. V. M. *The Winds of April*. Manila: University of the Philippines, 1941.

————. *Seven Hills Away*. Denver: Swallow Press, 1947; Manila: Halcon House, 1947.

————. *Children of the Ash-Covered Loam and Other Stories*. Manila: Benipayo, 1954.

————. *A Season of Grace*. Manila: Benipayo, 1956.

————. *The Bamboo Dancers*. Quezon City: Diliman Review, 1959; Manila: Benipayo, 1960.

————. *Look, Stranger, On This Island Now*. Manila: Benipayo, 1963.

————. *Selected Stories*. Denver: Swallow, 1964.

Guerrero, Wilfrido Ma. *13 Plays*. Manila: University Publishing Co., 1947.

———. *8 Other Plays*. Manila: University Publishing Co., 1952.

———. *7 More Plays*. Manila: Bookmark, 1962.

Hufana, Alejandrino G. *13 Kalisud*. Quezon City: Collegian New Review, 1955.

———. *Sickle Season*. Quezon City: Kuwan, 1959.

———. *Poro Point: An Anthology of Lives*. Quezon City: University of the Philippines, 1961.

———. *Curtain-Raisers*. Quezon City: University of the Philippines, 1964.

Ilio, Dominador I. *The Diplomat and Other Poems*. Quezon City: Guinhalinan, 1955.

Javellana, Stevan. *Without Seeing the Dawn*. Boston: Little, Brown, 1947.

Joaquin, Nick. *Prose and Poems*. Manila: Graphic, 1952; 2d ed., w/o play, Manila: Florentino, 1963.

———. *The Woman Who Had Two Navels*. Manila: Regal, 1961.

———. *Selected Stories*. Manila: Florentino, 1962.

———. *La Naval de Manila*. Manila: Florentino, 1964.

Jose, F. Sionil. *The Pretenders and Eight Short Stories*. Manila: Regal, 1962.

Lanot, Serafin. *Songs of the Brown Man*. Manila: Tamaraw, 1960.

Lansang, Jose M., Jr. *55 Poems*. Manila: Filipino Signatures, 1961.

———. *LV/22/xiii*. [n.p.: Lansang], 1964.

Laya, Juan C. *His Native Soil*. Manila: University Publishing Co., 1941.

———. *This Barangay*. Manila: Inang Wika Publishing Co., 1950.

Lopez, Salvador P. *Literature and Society*. Manila: Philippine Book Guild, 1940; 2nd ed., Manila: University Publishing Co., 1941.

Maramba, Asuncion David (ed.). *Philippine Contemporary Literature*. Manila: Bookmark, 1962.

Montano, Severino. *3 One-Act Plays*. Manila: Colcol and Co., 1953.

———. *The Love of Leonor Rivera*. Manila: Colcol and Co., 1954.

——— (ed.). *Prize Winning Plays of the Arena Theater of the Philippines: 1956–1957*. Quezon City: Phoenix, 1958.

Nakpil, Carmen Guerrero. *Woman Enough and Other Essays*. Quezon City: Vibal, 1963.

Polotan, Kerima (ed.). *The Carlos Palanca Memorial Awards for Literature Prize Stories: 1950–1955*. Manila: La Tondeña, 1957.

———. *The Hand of the Enemy*. Manila: Regal, 1962.

Ramos, Maximo, and Florentino B. Valeros (eds.). *Philippine Cross-Section*. Manila: Bardavon, 1950; 3d ed., Quezon City: Phoenix, 1964.

——— and ——— (eds.). *Philippine Harvest*. Manila: David and Sons, 1953; 2nd ed., Quezon City: Phoenix, 1964.

Rivera, Aida L. *Now and At the Hour and Other Short Stories*. Manila: Benipayo, 1957.

Roces, Alejandro R. *Of Cocks and Kites and Other Short Stories.* Manila: Regal, 1959.

Romulo, Carlos P. *The United.* New York: Crown, 1951.

———— et al. *Literature and Society.* Manila: Florentino, 1964.

Rotor, Arturo B. *The Wound and the Scar.* Manila: Philippine Book Guild, 1937.

San Juan, Epifanio, Jr. *Godkissing Carrion.* Cambridge: Concord, 1964.

Sta-Elena, Antonio E. *A Voyage of Love,* [Manila?: Sta-Elena?], 1961.

Santos, Bienvenido N. *You Lovely People.* Manila: Benipayo, 1955.

————. *The Wounded Stag.* Quezon City: Capitol, 1956.

————. *Brother, My Brother.* Manila: Benipayo, 1960.

————. *Villa Magdalena.* Manila: Erehwon, 1965.

Sison, George F. *In Words, In Color.* Manila: Filipino Signatures, 1962.

————. *23 x 23.* Manila: Filipino Signatures, 1963.

Sison, Jose Ma. *Brothers.* Manila: Filipino Signatures, 1961.

Tiempo, Edilberto K. *Watch in the Night.* Manila: Archipelago, 1953.

————. *More Than Conquerors.* Manila: Ayuda, 1964.

Tiempo, Edith L. *Abide, Joshua and Other Stories.* Manila: Florentino, 1964.

Tonogbanua, Francisco G. *A Stone, A Leaf, A Door.* Manila: Filipiniana, 1962.

Tuvera, Juan, *et al. Katha I.* Manila: Philippine Writers Association, 1954.

Veloso, Homera Ch. *Swirls of Impasto.* Manila: Cabanos, 1950.

Villa, Jose Garcia (ed.). *Filipino Short Stories.* Manila: Philippines Free Press, 1929.

————. *Footnote to Youth: Tales of the Philippines and Others.* New York: Scribner's, 1933.

————. *Many Voices.* Manila: Philippine Book Guild, 1939.

————. *Poems by Doveglion.* Manila: Philippine Writers League, 1941.

————. *Have Come, Am Here.* New York: Viking, 1942.

————. *Volume Two.* New York: New Directions, 1949.

————. *Selected Poems and New.* New York: McDowell, Obolensky, 1958.

————. *Poems 55.* Manila: Florentino, 1962.

————. *Selected Stories.* Manila: Florentino, 1962.

————. (ed.). *A Doveglion Book of Philippine Poetry.* Manila: Salas and Florentino, 1962.

Viray, Manuel A. (ed.). *Heart of the Island.* Manila: University Publishing Co., 1947.

Yabes, Leopoldo Y. (ed.). *The Filipino Essay in English,* I. Quezon City: University of the Philippines, 1954.

Zuñiga, Oscar de. *Love Song and Other Poems.* Manila: Filipino Signatures, 1960.

————. *The Arid Year.* Manila: Filipino Signatures, 1962.

Checklist

of Philippine Literature Published in the
United States, 1930–65

KEY

BPJ   *Beloit Poetry Journal*, Philippine issue, XIV (Summer, 1964).

LE/W   *Literature East and West*, Philippine issue, guest ed. Leonard
         Casper (Winter, 1965).

LR   *The Literary Review*, Philippine issue, guest ed. Leonard Casper,
         III (Summer, 1960).

Mid   *Midland*, ed. Paul Engle. N.Y.: Random House, 1961.

MPSS   *Modern Philippine Short Stories*, ed. Leonard Casper. Albu-
         querque: University of New Mexico Press, 1962.

FICTION

Amansec, L[ilia] Pablo. "The Dream Tiger," *Short Story International*
(December, 1963), pp. 121–41.

Aprieto, Pacifico N. "The Case Against Marcelo Dungo, Watchman," LR,
pp. 519–26.

Arcellana, Francisco. "The Yellow Shawl," LR, pp. 487–96.

———. "Divide by Two," MPSS, pp. 208–17.

Arguilla, Manuel. "Midsummer," *Prairie Schooner*, IX (Winter, 1935),
225–31.

———. "How My Brother Leon Brought Home a Wife," *Story*, VIII
(February, 1936), 42–9; reprinted, MPSS, pp. 59–67.

———. "Heat," *Prairie Schooner*, X (Fall, 1936), 219–23.

———. "Epilogue to Revolt," MPSS, pp. 68–76.

Ayala, Jose V. "The Wheel," *Short Story International* (April, 1964),
pp. 67–80.

Brillantes, Gregorio C. "Faith, Love, Time, and Dr. Lazaro," LE/W, pp.
64–75.

Bulosan, Carlos. "The Laughter of My Father," *New Yorker*, XVIII (Dec.
19, 1942), 24–5.

———. "Father Goes to Church," *Town and Country*, XCVIII (Sept.,
1943), 99, 122.

———. "Marriage of My Father," *New Yorker*, XIX (Sept. 24, 1943),
40.

———. "Gift of My Father," *New Yorker*, XIX (Oct. 23, 1943), 66.

———. "My Father Goes to Court," *New Yorker*, XIX (Nov. 13, 1943),
47–8, 50.

———. "My Brother's Short Story." *Harper's Bazaar*, LVIII (March,
1944), 106, 163–64.

————. "My Uncle Runs for President," *Town and Country*, XCIX (March, 1944), 83, 132–33.

————. "My Family Goes to the Army," *Town and Country*, XCIX (June, 1944), 63, 91.

————. "My Brother Osong's Career in Politics," *New Yorker*, XX (July 22, 1944), 18–20; reprinted, *Best American Short Stories of 1945*, ed. Martha Foley (Boston: Houghton Mifflin, 1945), pp. 30–7.

————. "End of the War," *New Yorker*, XX (Sept. 2, 1944), 21–3.

————. "My First Day in America," *Town and Country*, XCIX (Dec., 1944), 84.

————. *The Laughter of My Father*. N.Y.: Harcourt, Brace, 1944; N.Y.: Bantam Books, 1946.

————. "A Virgin for Cousin Pedro," *Interim*, II (No. 2, 1946), 43–8.

————. "A Rich Man in the Family," *Arizona Quarterly*, II (Spring, 1946), 76–82.

————. "The Story of a Letter," *New Masses*, LIX (April 30, 1946), 11–3.

————. "My Cousin Vicente's Homecoming," *University of Kansas City Review*, XII (Summer, 1946), 293–96.

————. "The Champion Hog Stealer," *Arizona Quarterly*, II (Summer, 1946), 17–23.

————. "Amorous Ghost," *Mademoiselle*, XXIII (Oct., 1946), 186, 293–96.

————. "The Courtship of Uncle Ponso," *Arizona Quarterly*, II (Winter, 1946), 20–5.

————. "My Father and the White Horse," *Scholastic*, L (Feb. 17, 1947), 21ff.

————. "Andong, the Great Lover," *Arizona Quarterly*, III (Spring, 1947), 60–8.

————. "The Lovely Angel," *Arizona Quarterly*, IV (Summer, 1948), 140–47.

Carunungan, Celso Al. "Like a Big Brave Man," *New World Writing* (New York: New American Library, 1952), pp. 291–99.

————. "The Samurai Sword and the Music Box," *Southwest Review*, XXXIX (Summer, 1954), 196–203.

————. "Liberation," *Catholic World*, CLXXIX (June, 1954), 186–88.

————. "My Father's First Son," *Sign*, XXXIV (Nov., 1954), 40–3, 71–3.

————. "Hide-Out for a Hero," *Colliers* (Aug. 19, 1955), pp. 56, 58–61.

————. *Like a Big Brave Man*. New York: Farrar, Straus, and Cudahy, 1960.

Casper, Linda Ty. "The Longer Ritual." *Antioch Review*, XVIII (Summer, 1958), 229–35.

————. "Unleavened Flesh," *Southwest Review*, XLVI (Summer, 1961), 217–20.

————. "The Convert," *New Mexico Quarterly*, XXXV (Spring, 1965), 29–38.

Castillo, Irwin E. "Legend," *Short Story International* (Feb., 1964), pp. 61–8.

Crisostomo, Isabelo. "The Spider," *Arizona Quarterly*, XIII (Summer, 1957), 124–32.

Daguio, Amador. "Wedding Dance," *Stanford Short Stories 1953*, eds. Wallace Stegner and Richard Scowcroft (Stanford: Stanford University Press, 1953), pp. 13–21; reprinted, *MPSS*, pp. 5-14.

———. "The Dead," *MPSS*, pp. 15–20.

Diaz, Rony V. "The Centipede," *LR*, pp. 513–18.

———. "Death in a Sawmill," *MPSS*, pp. 168–78.

———. "Two Brothers," *MPSS*, pp. 179–90.

Enriquez, Emigdio. *The Devil Flower*. N.Y.: Hill and Wang, 1959.

Fernando, Gilda Cordero. "A Harvest of Humble Folk," *LE/W*, pp. 27–42.

Gonzalez, N. V. M. *Seven Hills Away*. Denver: Swallow Press, 1947.

———. "A Warm Hand." *Sewanee Review*, LVIII (Jan.-March, 1950), 118–29; reprinted, *MPSS*, pp. 154–65.

———. "The Blue Skull and the Dark Palms," *Hopkins Review*, III (Summer, 1950), 3–11.

———. "Morning Star," *Stanford Short Stories 1950*, ed. Wallace Stegner (Stanford: Stanford University Press, 1950), pp. 77–85.

———. "Where's My Baby Now?," *Hopkins Review*, IV (Spring, 1951), 20–7; reprinted, *MPSS*, pp. 102–12.

———. "Children of the Ash-Covered Loam," *Pacific Spectator*, VI (Summer, 1952), 300–10.

———. "On the Ferry," *LR*, pp. 478–85; reprinted, *Modern Stories from Many Lands*, eds. Clarence Decker and Charles Angoff (N.Y.: Manyland, 1963), pp. 217–26.

———. "Lupo and the River," *MPSS*, pp. 113–53.

———. *Selected Stories*. Denver: Swallow Press, 1964.

———. "Another Shore, A Rising Wind" (excerpt from a novel-in-progress), *LE/W*, pp. 79–82.

Hamada, Sinai. "Tanabata's Wife," *Story*, VIII (May, 1936), 28–36.

Javellana, Stevan. *Without Seeing the Dawn*. Boston: Little, Brown, 1947.

Joaquin, Nick. "Three Generations," *Wake 8* (1949), pp. 115–28; reprinted, *MPSS*, pp. 39–56.

———. "The Woman Who Had Two Navels," *Partisan Review*, XX (July–Aug., 1953), 397–409, 452–80.

———. "The Summer Solstice," *Hudson Review*, VIII (Autumn, 1955), 373–85; reprinted, *MPSS*, pp. 23–38.

———. "May Day Eve," *A Treasury of Modern Asian Stories*, eds. Daniel L. Milton and William Clifford (N.Y.: Mentor, 1961), pp. 156–65.

Jose, F. Sionil. "The God Stealer," *LE/W*, pp. 44–63.

Jubaira, Ibrahim A. "Uncle Syed Went to See the Mayor," *Arizona Quarterly*, XVIII (Autumn, 1962), 259–65.

Nolledo, Wilfrido D. "Canticle for Dark Lovers," *Short Story International* (August, 1964), pp. 21–36.

Nuyda, Hermel. "Pulse of the Land," *MPSS*, pp. 219–28.

Rivera, Aida L. "Love in the Cornhusks," *LR*, pp. 507–12; reprinted, *Modern Stories from Many Lands*, eds. Clarence Decker and Charles Angoff (N.Y.: Manyland, 1963), pp. 227–32.

Roces, Alejandro. "We Filipinos Are Mild Drinkers," *Arizona Quarterly*, III (Autumn, 1947), 261–65.

———. "Durian," *Southwest Review*, XXXIV (Winter, 1949), 81–2.

———. "My Brother's Peculiar Chicken," *Pacific Spectator*, IV (Autumn, 1950), 446–50.

Romulo, Carlos P. *The United*. N.Y.: Crown, 1951.

Santos, Bienvenido N. "Early Harvest," *Story*, XXVII (Sept.–Oct., 1945), 17–29.

———. "Accept the Homage," *LR*, pp. 497–506.

———. "The Transfer," *Mid*, pp. 250–60.

———. "The Common Theme," *MPSS*, pp. 79–89.

———. "Scent of Apples," *MPSS*, pp. 90–9.

———. "Without Heir" (excerpt from *Villa Magdalena*), *LE/W*, pp. 75–8.

Tiempo, Edilberto. *Cry Slaughter*. N.Y.: Avon, 1957.

Tiempo, Edith L. "The Chambers of the Sea," *MPSS*, pp. 193–205.

Villa, Jose Garcia. "Malakas," *New Mexico Quarterly*, I (May, 1931), 167–76.

———. "Untitled Story," *Clay* (Autumn, 1931), pp. 17–26; reprinted, *Best American Short Stories of 1932*, ed. Edward J. O'Brien (New York: Dodd, Mead, 1932), pp. 253–63.

———. "White Interlude," *Clay*, No. 2, pp. 25–31.

———. "Resurrection," *Clay*, No. 2, pp. 39–42.

———. "Walk at Midnight," *Clay*, No. 2, pp. 49–52.

———. "Given Woman," *Scribner's*, XC (Dec., 1931), 650–52.

———. "Daughter of Rizal," *Clay*, No. 3, pp. 24–7.

———. "Valse Triste," *Clay*, No. 3, pp. 33–6.

———. "Like My Boy," *Clay*, No. 3, pp. 48–51.

———. "Little Tales," *Clay*, No. 3, pp. 54–6.

———. "Footnote to Youth," *Frontier*, XII (Jan., 1932), 125ff.

———. "Kamya," *New Mexico Quarterly*, II (May, 1932), 112–18.

———. "The Man Who Looked Like Rizal," *Frontier*, XII (May, 1932), 330ff.

———. "The Fence," *Prairie Schooner*, VI (Summer, 1932), 203–9; reprinted, *Best American Short Stories of 1933*, ed. Edward J. O'Brien (Boston: Houghton Mifflin, 1933), pp. 314–20.

———. "Son of Rizal," *Prairie Schooner*, VI (Winter, 1932), 1–9.

———. "Story of My Country," *Prairie Schooner*, VII (Spring, 1933), 83-6.

———. *Footnote to Youth*. N.Y.: Scribner's, 1933.

Vinuya, Amado A. "Mahalia," *Short Story International* (Sept., 1964), pp. 15–21.

POETRY

Afable, Fernando. "Mirage in Galilee," *BPJ*, p. 6.

Angeles, Carlos. "The Least Miracle," "Storm Warning," "Explorers," "Rainy Day," "Badoc," "The Summer Trees," "Letters from a War Hero, Now Retired," "The Eye," "Gabu," *LR*, pp. 551–57.

Asis, R. Vinzons. "Gadaboutown," *Harper's* CXCVI (May, 1948), 412.

———. "Credendum," *Harper's*, CXCVI (June, 1948), 552.

Ayala, Tita Lacambra. "Credo," "Lesson for Judas," "From Underfoot, Thickly," "Wedding Song," "Detail Is Signpost," *LR*, pp. 558–60.

———. Poem for Eleanor," *BPJ*, p. 2.

Benesa, Leonidas V. "Parable of the Young Men," "Poet in the City Bisected," *LR*, p. 571.

———. "Cezanne in Search of a Painting or the poet in search of a poem," "The Stranger," *BPJ*, pp. 8–10.

Bulosan, Carlos. "The Foreigners": "Fear," "The Unknown City," "Address to the Nameless," "Above Empty Landscapes," "Song of Percival," *The Lyric*, XV (Spring, 1935), 159–60.

———. "The Unknown Quantity": "Without Ceremony," "Letter from America," "In Time of Drought," "Secret," "No Story," "Monuments," *Poetry*, XLVII (Feb., 1936), 263–67.

———. "Young Man Lost," "Biography," "Night Piece," "Needing No Time," "Phoenix," *Poetry*, L (Sept., 1937), 326–29.

———. "These Are Also Living," *Poetry*, LII (Aug., 1938), 259.

———. "Letter to Donald," "Address to Youth," *The Lyric*, XIX (Summer, 1939), 16–7.

———. "Chorus for America": "Beyond Lies America," "The Last Trip," "History of a Moment," *Voices*, No. 104 (Winter, 1940), pp. 13–5.

———. "Letter in Exile," "Sunset and Evening Star," "American History," *Poetry*, LX (April, 1942), 12–6.

——— (ed.). *Chorus for America: Six Philippine Poets.* Los Angeles: Wagon and Star, 1942.

———. *Letter from America.* Prairie City, Ill.: Decker Press, 1942.

———. *The Voice of Bataan.* N.Y.: Coward-McCann, 1943.

———. "Bataan," *Saturday Review of Literature*, XXVI (March 20, 1943), 20.

———. "Interlude: Song of the War," *Saturday Review of Literature*, XXVII (Feb. 12, 1944), 14.

———. "Now You Are Still," *Saturday Review of Literature*, XXVII (Oct. 14, 1944), 58.

————. *Dark People*. Los Angeles: Wagon and Star, 1944.

————. "For My People": "A Song of Freedom," "My People," "Praise and Warning"; "For My People: II": "The Blue Sky," "Dark Moment," "My People," "Love Song," *Voices*, No. 122 (Summer, 1945), pp. 26–8.

Cruz, Andres Cristobal. "A Song I Should Have Sung to You," "I: Revelation," "II: Requiem for a Christ-Bride," *LR*, pp. 561–62.

————. "Sea Scene," *BPJ*, p. 1

Cuenca, Alfredo, Jr. "Poem to Any Woman," *BPJ*, pp. 30–1.

Daguio, Amador. "Information," *Pacific Spectator*, VI (Summer, 1952), 291.

————. "Off the Aleutian Islands," *Beloit Poetry Journal*, III (Spring, 1953), 19.

————. "Bloom of Waters Call," "Thoughts on Art and the Blue Monkey," *LR*, pp. 568–70.

De Castro, F. D. "House Mouse," *BPJ*, p. 7.

Demetillo, Ricaredo. "The God My Father Chiseled with His Tongue," *Poetry*, LXXXIX (Feb., 1952), 271; reprinted, *Mid*, pp. 439–40.

————. "You Laugh Within the House of Me," *Mid*, p. 439.

————. "The Storm," *LR*, pp. 566–67.

Gerardo, Leopoldo T. "Spaces," "God," *BPJ*, pp. 12–3.

Hufana, Alejandrino G. "Blacksmith," "Strong Man," "Decadent," "Salidom-Ay, Dancer in the Death Dance," "Return of the Magi," "Adolf Hitler's First Attempt at Love," "Manila Motifs: Fountain in Sta. Mesa; High Walls in Malate," "Poro Point," *LR*, pp. 540–50.

————. "The Rain is Too Harsh, Love," "Coin of the Realm, Speaking," *BPJ*, pp. 14–5.

————. From "Memento Mori," *LE/W*, pp. 84–5.

Ilio, Dominador I. "Diplomat Listening to Speech of Another Diplomat," *Poetry*, LXXIX (Feb., 1952), 276; reprinted, *Mid*, p. 488.

Miraflor, Erlinda Ortiz. "Mantilla '63," *BPJ*, p. 11.

Moreno, Virginia R. "Trapper," "Order for Masks," "Batik Maker," *LR*, pp. 563–65.

————. "Lament of a Cathay Handmaiden in Marco Polo's Tent Pavilion," *Beloit Poetry Journal*, XIII (Winter, 1962–63), 56–7.

————. "Elements": "Earth," "Fire," "Air," "Sea Water," *LE/W*, p. 83.

Olaguer, Valdemar. "To a Shelleyan Poet," "The Albatross at Capricorn," "Bonbons for Miss Magpie," "Miss Magpie at the Bodleian," *New World Writing* 17 (N.Y.: Lippincott, 1960), pp. 113–17.

————. "On the Portrait of a Peeress by Sir Joshua Reynolds," "Genaro and Victoria," *BPJ*, pp. 27–9.

Romulo, Carlos P. "Voice of Liberty," *Saturday Review of Literature*, XXXIII (Jan. 14, 1950), 19.

San Juan, Epifanio, Jr. "The Dream of the Rose Window, or The Three Temptations," *Harvard Advocate*, CXLIV (Dec., 1960), 14.

————. "Topsy-Turvy Scene in a Theater," *South Carolina Quarterly* Summer, 1963), p. 32.

————. "Portrait of a Lady," "Testament of Lovers on an Antique Manuscript," "Dialogue in the Dark," "The Stature of the Native Man," *BPJ*, pp. 24–6.

————. *Godkissing Carrion*. Cambridge: Concord, 1964.

————. "Le Mot Juste," "Loyola's Composition of Place," "Aspects of Experience," *Descant*, IX (Fall, 1964), 32–3.

————. Translation: 7 Poems by Amado V. Hernandez, *Literature East and West*, VIII (Spring-Summer, 1964), 126–29.

————. "Ballad of the Honeysuckly Rose," *Lines* (March, 1965), pp. 11–2.

————. "Commitment," *Radix*, I (Summer, 1965), 12.

————. "To the Muse," *December*, VII (Dec., 1965), 189.

————. Translation: "The Blacksmith" by Amado V. Hernandez, *Books Abroad* (Fall, 1965), p. 399: in "Social Consciousness and Revolt in Modern Philippine Poetry."

Santos, Bienvenido N. "Sulucan," "The Junkman," "Father and Son," "The Gods We Worship Live Next Door," "Apostate," LR, pp. 529–31.

Tiempo, Edith L. "The Return," *Western Review*, XIV (Spring, 1950), 190.

————. "Lament for the Littlest Fellow," *Poetry*, LXXIX (Feb., 1952), 275; reprinted, *Mid*, p. 561

————. "Pestle," "Mid-morning for Sheba," *Poetry*, LXXXIX (Jan., 1957), 223–24.

————. "Cover of Crags," *Poetry*, XCII (May, 1958), 106–10.

————. "Tracks of Babylon," *Poetry*, XCVII (Dec., 1960), 168.

————. "Five Homes": "The Mason," "The Boy," "The Fisherman," "The Hunter," "The City Man," *BPJ*, pp. 3–5.

Tinio, Roland S. "Gentle My Song," *Mid*, pp. 562–63.

Torres, Emmanuel. "Women with Child," *Poetry*, LXXXVIII (Sept., 1956), 378–79.

————. "Three Poems": "Song for a Dry Season" (reprinted, *Mid*, p. 564), "A Highway Parable," "The Jungle," *New Campus Writing* #2, ed. Nolan Miller (N.Y.: Bantam, 1957), pp. 100–2.

————. "Li Po Discovers an Oriole," *Beloit Poetry Journal*, XIII (Spring, 1963), 14.

————. "Mu Ch'i's Persimmons: A Lecture for Six Students," "The Woman in the Window," *BPJ*, pp. 16–21.

Villa, Jose Garcia. "Evening Lover," *New Mexico Quarterly*, I (Nov., 1931), 330.

————. "Quiet Songs": "Communion," "Songs to Be Whispered," *Poetry*, XL (June, 1932), 136–37.

————. "Parliament of Giraffes," "Her Day-Rose Is Much Sweet," "I

Can No More Hear Love's Voice," *Poetry*, LVIII (June, 1941), 136–38.

————. "Bring the Pigeons Watermelons, Abelard," "In Picasso You See Blue, Rose, and the Virginity of Cubes," "Because Thy Smile Is Primavera," *Poetry*, LX (Sept., 1942), 308–9.

————. *Have Come, Am Here*. N.Y.: Viking, 1942.

————. "There Came You Wishing Me," "Be Beautiful, Noble, Like the Antique Ant," "God Said, 'I Made a Man,' " "Now, If You Will Look in My Brain," "My Mouth Is Very Quiet," "The Way My Ideas Think Me," "Saw God Dead But Laughing," "Mostly Are We Mostless," *Twentieth Century American Poetry*, ed. Conrad Aiken (N.Y.: Modern Library, 1944), pp. 366–71.

————. Be Beautiful, Noble, Like the Antique Ant," "God Said, 'I Made a Man!' " "Now, If You Will Look in My Brain," "My Mouth Is Very Quiet," "The Way My Ideas Think Me," "Saw God Dead But Laughing," *An Anthology of Famous English and American Poetry*, eds. William Rose Benet and Conrad Aiken (N.Y.: Modern Library, 1945), pp. 933–36.

————. "Parthenogenesis of Genius," *Harvard Wake*, I (June, 1945), 33.

————. "A Song": "So, beautiful, is, so," *Wake* 5 (Spring, 1946), 84.

————. "Radio Made of Seawater," *Scholastic*, L (Feb. 17, 1947), 15.

————. "Ten Poems": "am so very am and," "Hands kindle the hours of night," "her day-rose is much violet," "I think, yes, a leopard in Dufy blue world," "Bring the pigeons watermelons, Abelard," "To make icecream crysantheme," "I have observed pink monks eating blue raisins," "A radio made of seawater," "in blue without when blues dream bears," "Futurity's equivalence to Now," *Spearhead* (N.Y.: New Directions, 1947), pp. 310–14.

————. "Seven Poems": "The,bright,Centipede"; "Much,beauty,is,less, than,the,face,of"; "When,I,was,no,bigger,than,a,huge"; "My,whose-ness,is,to,me,what,I"; "Clean,like,idioform,between,the,tall"; "More, miracled,and"; "A,living,giant,all,in,little,pieces," *Wake* 6 (Spring, 1948), 57–62.

————. "Six Poems": "A Virginal," "A Song for Rosemarie," "Poem: David, fourteen,fifteen,a,little,pepper,and,fox," "Count Ten," "Sonnet in Polka Dots," "The Emperor's New Sonnet," *Wake* 7 (1948), 36–9.

————. *Volume Two*. N.Y.: New Directions, 1949.

————. Translation of Federico G. Lorca's "Gazelle of Unforeseen Love" and of Gabriela Mistral's "Ballad," *Wake* 9 (1950), 50–1.

————. "Two Poems": "A Valentine for Edith Sitwell," "(Up) (in) (the) (Tree)," *Wake* 10 (1951), 83–4.

————. "Theseus," *Poetry*, LXXXI (Oct., 1952), 82.

————. *Selected Poems and New*. N.Y.: McDowell, Obolensky, 1958.

Viray, Manuel A. "Vigil," *Talisman* (Summer, 1953), p. 6.

———. "Malgar, Hindu Watchman at His Ablutions," *Antioch Review*, XIII (Dec., 1953), 466.

———. "Autumn's Quick Dark," *LR*, pp. 538–39.

———. "The Blind Woman Next Door," *Beloit Poetry Journal*, XIII (Winter, 1962–63), 54–6.

———. "The Houses of the Fathers," *BPJ*, p. 22.

———. "Washington Morning," *LE/W*, p. 43.

Zuñiga, Oscar de. "Love Song," *Pacific Spectator*, VI (Summer, 1952), 311.

———. "Confusion at Sunrise," *California Quarterly*, III, No. 2 (1954), p. 45.

———. "Remembrances, for Vi," "Graveyard," "The Lost," "The Color of Death," "from Walk Through the City," "The Salt of Summer," *LR*, pp. 535–37.

———. "The Dogs," *Beloit Poetry Journal*, XIII (Winter, 1962–63), 57.

———. "The Purple Town," *BPJ*, p. 23.

DRAMA

Lapeña, Amelia L. *Sepang Loca*, LR, pp. 592–611.

Moreno, Virginia R. *Straw Patriot*, LR, pp. 573–91.

LITERARY CRITICISM

Bernad, Miguel A., S.J. "Philippine Literature: A Twofold Renaissance," *Thought*, XXXVII (Autumn, 1962), 427–48.

Viray, Manuel A. "Certain Influences in Filipino Writing," *Pacific Spectator*, VI (Summer, 1952), 292–99.

———. "Philippine Writing Today," *LR*, pp. 465–77.

Acknowledgments

"Asylum Piece": copyright 1948 by Far East Publishing Corporation; "Ferns": copyright 1949 by *This Week Magazine* of the *Manila Chronicle*; "Landscape II": copyright 1951 by *Weekly Women's Magazine*; "The Eye": copyright 1952 by the *Saturday Mirror Magazine*: reprinted by their permission and by permission of the author, Carlos A. Angeles.

"The Socialists". copyright 1940 by the Philippine Book Guild, and reprinted by their permission and by permission of Lyd Arguilla Salas, for the author, Manuel Arguilla.

"A Wind over the Earth": copyright 1954 by the *Philippines Free Press*, and reprinted by their permission and by permission of the author, Gregorio C. Brillantes.

"So": copyright 1961 by the author, Andres Cristobal Cruz, and reprinted by his permission.

"Off the Aleutian Islands": copyright 1953 by *Beloit Poetry Journal*, and reprinted by their permission and by permission of the author, Amador T. Daguio.

"Barter in Panay": copyright 1961 by the author, Ricaredo Demetillo, and reprinted by his permission.

"The Sea Beyond": copyright 1954 by the *Sunday Times Magazine*, and reprinted by their permission and by permission of the author, N. V. M. Gonzalez.

"Pygmy Reservation": copyright 1959 by the author; "Keeper of the Lighthouse" and "Farmer in a Wrong Career": copyright 1961 by the author, Alejandrino G. Hufana, and reprinted by his permission.

A Portrait of the Artist as Filipino: copyright 1952 by the author, Nick Joaquin, and reprinted by his permission.

"Batik Maker" and "Order for Masks": copyright 1960 by the *Literary Review*, and reprinted by their permission and by permission of the author, Virginia R. Moreno; "Sun Series": copyright 1965 by the author, and reprinted by her permission.

"Dada": copyright 1953 by T. D. Agcaoili for Archipelago Press, and reprinted by their permission and by permission of the author, Anthony Morli.

"Rice Wine": copyright 1961 by the *Philippines Free Press*, and reprinted by their permission and by permission of the author, Wilfrido Nolledo.

"The Impact of Literature on Philippine Society": copyright 1964 by the author, Carlos P. Romulo, and reprinted by his permission.

"Zita": copyright 1937 by Philippine Book Guild, and reprinted by their permission and by permission of the author, Arturo B. Rotor.

Portions of the critical text have appeared previously in modified form, in *College English, Literature East and West*, the *New Mexico Quarterly, Saturday Review*, and the 1964 monograph, *Writers the Other Side of the Horizon*, sponsored by the National Council of Teachers of English: to all of which I am grateful for permission to reprint.

Many of the analyses have benefited, beyond description, from discussions with USEF and USIS directors in Manila, and with student-faculty groups at the Bicol State Teachers' College, the Cebu City colleges, Mindanao Colleges, Silliman University, University of the East, University of the Philippines, and Zamboanga Normal School; and especially at the writers' seminars and forums conducted by the Ateneo de Manila University in 1962/63.

None of these discussions could have occurred, were it not for the sabbatical grant from Boston College which made practical my acceptance of a Fulbright/Smith-Mundt award in 1962. Since then, enlargement of my exploratory volumes, *The Wayward Horizon* and *The Wounded Diamond*, has been supported in essential areas by grants-in-aid from the American Council of Learned Societies and the Asia Society. In addition, the present study was assisted immeasurably by such personal kindness as that shown by Daisy Avellana who, in the midst of filming Joaquin's *Portrait* for the Venice Festival, found time to send me her own copy of the adaptation which she had made in 1953 and which I had seen staged in the Intramuros; and by Jock Netzorg of Cellar Book Shop in Detroit who trusted me, a "known stranger," with irreplaceable books from his private collection of Filipiniana.

None of these—individuals, institutions, societies—expected repayment. Nevertheless, perhaps this volume will be achievement enough to return to them all some part of that satisfaction which their unselfishness has permitted me.

L.C.

Glossary / Index